Invitation to Chemistry

IRA DUFRESNE GARARD was born and brought up in the hills of western Pennsylvania in the last decade of the last century. He spent his early years helping to make ends meet on the family farm and attending a one-room village school for about one-half of every year. Through a process of rote and the balanced application of the switch, he was able to pass the finishing examination in all subjects within ten years.

At the age of sixteen, although officially underage by two years, he received his first teaching assignment in a rural school of forty-five students for thirty-eight dollars a month. Since the term lasted only seven months, he was able to begin courses at the Southwestern State Normal School and still be home in time for the harvest. The next few years were spent in this way until he was called to the city high school in Coraopolis to teach science and economics, the latter a subject about which he knew nothing. In 1909, at the age of twenty-one, he had his first glimpse of higher education at the Grove City College. With a light teaching load and a heavy study schedule, he was able to graduate in 1911 with a B.Sc. *cum laude* in chemistry. He became a science teacher at the Grove City High School and remained there for four years.

In the summer of 1914, a friend persuaded Garard to attend the summer session at Columbia, one of the few universities that offered graduate credits in the summer. It was his first time east of the mountains and the start of the war in Europe—an extremely exciting time. He returned to Columbia the following summer and then, with the help of a wealthy uncle, stayed on to finish his Ph.D.—all except the dissertation—in 1917.

He taught for a term at Carnegie Tech while completing the thesis and was then drafted and sent overseas. He served in France at the front and in the Chemical Warfare Service in Paris.

Upon discharge he returned to a research assistantship at Columbia. In 1919 he was hired as the first permanent faculty member of the newly established New Jersey College for Women. He was now an associate professor of chemistry at a college of two buildings and fifty-four students. Just before the beginning of the term, he married Mabel Evelyn Baldwin, a graduate student and assistant to his former Columbia professor.

Ira Garard not only grew with the college—he helped make the college grow. Under the vigorous leadership of Dean Mabel Smith Douglass, for whom the college is now named, he became an indefatigable molder of curriculum and teaching and a gallant and effective spokesman for excellency in his department. When he was dissatisfied with the available textbooks, he wrote his own, *An Introduction to Organic Chemistry* (Wiley, 1932, rev. ed. 1940, 1948), and devised a set of laboratory experiments still in use today. He taught every course in the department at one time or another while continually active in administrative affairs. He was elected chairman of the North Jersey section of the American Chemical Society for 1947–48 and of the New York section of the Institute of Food Technologists in 1949.

In 1956, after thirty-six years on the faculty, Ira Dufresne Garard retired from the college and followed the sun to Florida. Now, prompted by the memories of students who couldn't see the forest for the trees and of laymen who asked simply what chemistry was all about, he has written a book—as he says, "to explain the whole thing."

Invitation to
CHEMISTRY

by IRA D. GARARD

Garden City, New York
DOUBLEDAY & COMPANY, INC.

QD
11
.G3

Preface

THIS BOOK has been written for the general reader who has taken only an elementary course in chemistry or none at all. It tries to tell what chemistry is and how it reached its present state. There are also included several examples of what chemists do and why they do it.

Those who are well informed in chemistry may also gain a perspective from the book that their courses have not provided since the historical approach to chemistry has been largely abandoned by the high schools and colleges. I have attempted to tell the nature of the research that led to the advances in the science and something of the personalities of the men whose efforts were the most effective.

I wish to express my indebtedness to the authors of the many books, journal articles and news notes that I have consulted to establish the accuracy of the facts in the book and to Dr. Mabel Baldwin for advice and for aid in preparing the manuscript for publication.

Lakeland, Florida

Contents

Invitation to Chemistry

CHAPTER ONE

The Ancient Days of the Chemical Arts

HUMAN CURIOSITY HAS NO LIMIT. Men have been curious about the heavens and their investigations became astronomy; others have been intrigued by the vegetation with its fruits and flowers—the beginnings of botany; the study of animals led to zoology. The nature of matter, the stuff of which everything is made, has received attention too and the result is chemistry. As the contemporary chemist puts it: chemistry is the science of the composition of matter and the changes in composition that occur either naturally or under imposed conditions. The Chinese definition of chemistry is much shorter: *hua hsueh*, the study of change.

No greater mystery has ever confronted the inquiring mind than the nature and composition of familiar things. Air, water, rocks, sand, vegetation and the animal body are all forms of matter that were known to ancient man—all of them stuff to excite his curiosity. Air had different odors at different times. Why? Some water was sweet and some was salty. Why? Some rocks were white, some were brown, and here or there was one that was green or blue or red. Why? These and similar questions have pestered the minds of countless men.

Many a detective has had a hand in the solution of these mysteries, thousands of years have been spent on them and many a false trail has had to be abandoned. But despite all the years that men have been curious about the nature of matter, the first real break in the solution of the puzzle came within the last two centuries. The science of chemistry got under way just about the time our forefathers were worrying about the declaration of independence from England.

The very beginning of chemistry is lost in the haze of the ancient past, but it must have begun with casual observations by the earliest men. Two forces not only gave chemistry its start but have kept it moving to the present day. These forces are man's innate curiosity and his desire to satisfy his material needs, comforts and luxuries.

We can easily imagine the beginnings of chemistry. They undoubtedly consisted of simple observations such as a child makes. It does not take the human animal long to observe the sights around him. Those who live near the ocean soon learn that sea water is salty and that when a pool of it dries up it leaves a white solid. Stop and consider for a moment how much chemistry you know from your own observation. By way of suggestion: gold is heavy and yellow and shiny; copper looks much like gold but is a bit redder. Silver, platinum, tin and chromium are all white metals, but they all have the same sheen that copper and gold have. In other words, they have a metallic luster, a shine, so to speak, which only metals possess. Salt, sugar and snow are all white, and the snow melts on a warm day, but the salt and sugar do not. Wood, coal and tobacco burn, but the smoke smells different in each case. Iron rusts when it is exposed to air and moisture. You undoubtedly know all this and a lot more from your own observations, and it probably did not take primitive man long to accumulate such information about the things around him.

If the facts mentioned in the previous paragraph do not

strike the reader as being chemistry, he should be reminded that the simplest and largest part of the science is what the chemist learnedly calls *descriptive chemistry*. This part of the science consists of descriptions of the different kinds of matter and the changes that occur in them. The hardest question a layman can ask a chemist starts with "What is?" What is aspirin? What is uranium? These questions tend to drive a chemist mad, because the only possible answer is a long description. For example, uranium is a metal, white like silver and very heavy. Correct, but not very informative, because lead, silver, platinum and several other metals are white and some are heavy; therefore, further description is called for. Uranium is radioactive. It melts around 1150 degrees centigrade and has the specific gravity 18.9. Now the chemist is getting too technical and is accused of showing off, but there is no other way to tell anyone what uranium is. If there be any skeptic about, let him try to tell an inquiring young mind what something is: say brass, a skunk, a pineapple, a limousine—anything.

If the aspirin question comes up, the chemist usually avoids the issue and says that aspirin is a drug used for headaches. He would tell an inquiring colleague that aspirin is acetylsalicylic acid, which places it in a familiar class, like saying that a jeep is an automobile. If that did not satisfy the inquirer, the chemist might open up and tell him how it is made, the chemical formula, and all its characteristics, that is, provided he knew all these things.

PROPERTIES

The characteristics that a chemist uses to describe matter he calls *properties*. Most of the properties that a particular sample of matter has when it is alone are *physical* properties. Such things as color, odor, taste, transparency, heaviness, melting point and boiling point are all physical properties. Some of these are purely qualitative and of very little value to the chemist for one reason or another. Color and taste are hard to describe. Colors have a few names, but only a few, and the blue of the sapphire is not the blue of the ocean. There are only four tastes: sweet, sour, salty and bitter. And even here, lemons and vinegar are both sour, but they do not taste alike. Aside from the help a chemist can get from these four tastes the best he can do is to say that something tastes like something else that he hopes is familiar—Brussels sprouts taste like cabbage, or bananas taste somewhat like pears. Unless a chemist is working with foods or beverages, he doesn't go around tasting things anyway. In the ancient days of chemistry several chemists killed themselves by indiscriminate tasting.

Some of the physical properties, however, may be expressed quantitatively and these are used by the chemist to identify substances. Melting and boiling points are temperatures and can be measured with a thermometer: ice melts at 0° C or 32° F. Chemists express heaviness in two different ways. *Density* is the weight of a unit volume; a cubic foot of water weighs 62.5 pounds; a cubic centimeter of water weighs 1 gram; a liter of oxygen weighs 1.42 grams. The other method used to express heaviness is called *specific gravity*, which is relative heaviness. When we say that the specific gravity of uranium is 18.9 we mean that any piece of the metal is 18.9 times as heavy as its volume of water, that is, a cubic inch of uranium is 18.9 times as heavy as a cubic inch of water. Relative gravity would probably be a better name for this property. Scientists, like parents, do not always come up with the best names.

The behavior of one material with another and its behavior under special conditions are called *chemical* properties.

Wood burns when it is heated in air. If limestone is heated hot enough, the gas carbon dioxide escapes and lime remains. In chemical language, heat decomposes limestone into lime and carbon dioxide. Again, if a current of electricity from a battery or a dynamo is passed through water, the water is split into two gases, hydrogen and oxygen. Also, if yeast is added to a solution of sugar in water, the sugar is converted to alcohol and carbon dioxide. These effects are chemical properties of wood, limestone, water and sugar, respectively.

The physical properties are usually enough to distinguish one substance from another, and the chemist uses them for that purpose. When iron rusts the rust is a brown powder, very different from the iron. This alone tells the chemist that the iron has changed to another substance. Ashes are very different from wood and coal. Alcohol is a liquid and sugar is a solid and the taste is very different. Alcohol has an odor and sugar doesn't. These are all examples of the use of physical properties to distinguish between substances.

Sometimes it is not easy to tell one substance from another and then the chemist must use chemical properties or measure some of the physical properties quantitatively. For example, wood alcohol and grain alcohol are both colorless liquids. They have similar odors and both mix with water in all proportions, but wood alcohol boils at $65°$ C and grain alcohol at $78°$ C. Consequently, the boiling temperature of the liquid tells the chemist which liquid it is. Likewise, chloroform and carbon tetrachloride are both colorless liquids that smell much alike, but chloroform boils at $61°$ C and has the specific gravity 1.489, whereas carbon tetrachloride boils at $77°$ C and has the specific gravity 1.595. Obviously, the measurement of either of these physical properties is a way to tell these liquids apart. The measurement of both these properties would probably distinguish one of these liquids from all others, for no two substances are likely to have the same quantitative values for two physical properties.

Examination of the chemical properties is often the easiest way to tell one substance from another. For example, grain alcohol burns, but carbon tetrachloride does not—a simpler test is hard to imagine if the choice were between these two liquids and no other. If a chemist has the problem of identifying an entirely unknown substance, he must decide which properties are most likely to be useful. Experience helps him to make the selection and also tells him what properties are the most easily and quickly determined.

EXPERIMENTATION

From the activities that enabled primitive man to survive, he learned a lot of the properties of the matter about him by simple observation. However, if the boy is typical of the primitive man, as we often claim, our early ancestors also performed experiments. When I was ten or twelve years old I lived in a region that provided a large variety of matter for observation. There were coal, oil, limestone, sandstone, clay, slate, mussel shells and a great variety of plant and animal life. I had carried many a bucket of coal and re- moved the resulting ashes. I had also seen farmers "burn" limestone to make lime. This latter activity aroused my curiosity as to what would happen if sandstone were heated instead of limestone. The question plainly called for experi- ment. It was a case of pure, or basic, research; I was just after information and not trying to do anything useful. I built a wood fire and when it became a fiery furnace, I tossed in a sandstone. I soon got results. The stone exploded and a piece hit me on the shin. This seemed to answer the question and I did not pursue the matter any further. A good chemist would have tried to find out why the stone exploded and whether all sandstones explode, but I was a beginner with no instructor and it was years before I learned that somebody else had found the answer. Some stones contain cavities filled with air or water and the expansion caused by the heat produces enough pressure to burst them.

Experiments of the above type appeal strongly to children. Several years after my experiment I met a boy in a doctor's office where he had gone for repairs after sealing water in a bottle and heating it. These experiments illustrate a fundamental principle of experimentation: if a chemist plans to try a totally new experiment he had better take some precautions for the safety of himself and the surrounding property.

The experimental method of getting information is not always hazardous, but it is generally slow and most of the knowledge a chemist has he got from his teachers or from the books and journals that make up his own special literature. Although knowledge of the earliest chemical information and how it came about is purely speculative, by the year 3500 B.C. men began to leave records. There are three sources of this information: artifacts, writing done when the information was acquired and articles about old processes written at a later date.

Archaeologists in pursuit of knowledge about early man and his doings come upon many artifacts—objects made by the hand of man. These scientists, in their mysterious ways, have methods of telling how old these artifacts are. Most of the archaeological information comes from Egypt or from Mesopotamia where two of the very ancient civilizations flourished. In Egypt, numerous objects of ancient handicraft have been recovered from royal tombs, but in Mesopotamia the archaeologists have to dig for their objects of enlightenment. In China, a third site of an ancient civilization, the archaeologists have not done so well. The climate of

China is moist and many objects do not last as long as they do in the dry climate of the Middle East. Moreover, the Chinese frown upon digging up the possessions of their ancestors. Our knowledge of chemistry in old China comes mainly from writings and legends; the latter are sometimes not very reliable.

THE ART OF WRITING

The best-informed scholars in such matters think that the earliest civilization was that of the Sumerians in the valleys of the Tigris and Euphrates rivers, the land now referred to as Mesopotamia. Literally, Mesopotamia means the land between the rivers, but the word is now commonly used to include the neighboring territory. There is plenty of clay in Mesopotamia that can be molded into various shapes and dried hard in the sun. The Sumerians soon learned to use this clay to make bricks for building houses. They didn't confine their use of clay to the making of bricks, however, but made jars, pots, furnaces, sickles to cut their grain and even tablets to write on, for they also invented writing, possibly as early as 5000 B.C.

The earliest writing was pictorial. Men drew pictures on the walls of caves, or anything else that came to hand, to record events in their lives that they thought worth while. If the same practice were followed today the artist might record a forest fire, an astronaut taking off, an automobile wreck or a baseball game which the home team won—anything important. That is the sort of thing the ancient artists did. They not only painted, but they also carved some of their pictures in stone. Many of the latter and the paintings that were protected from the weather have survived earthquakes, the target practice of Napoleon's soldiers and other destructive forces. Some of them are records of chemical processes.

Drawing pictures is a tedious business, and so the pictures soon became stylized into characters to represent facts or ideas rather than to picture them literally. This practice enabled the ingenious to invent characters for ideas that they couldn't draw at all. Chinese writing is still a huge collection of these pictographs and ideographs.

The Sumerians went beyond these ideographs and made characters to represent syllables of words, which reduced the number of required characters considerably. Their writing is called *cuneiform* because of the wedge shape of the characters. The Sumerians made clay tablets, impressed their writing in the soft clay and then baked the tablet. Archaeologists have unearthed thousands of such tablets and many of them have been translated. These tablets and the pictorial writing, which is found mainly in Egypt, are the chief sources of political, religious and scientific information about the doings of these ancient times.

The ideographs, or hieroglyphics, of Egypt were developed further than the cuneiform writing of the Sumerians. Instead of representing syllables, characters were devised to represent the sounds used in spoken words, which took fewer characters. These collections of characters are the alphabets, and the first one appeared about 1500 B.C. There are several of these alphabets because several different peoples around the Mediterranean made them. The Phoenicians were the leaders in this activity. The Greeks changed the Phoenician alphabet somewhat, the Latins changed the Greek alphabet considerably and England and the countries of western Europe adopted the Latin alphabet, also with a few changes. The Arabic, Hebrew, Russian, Greek and Latin alphabets are all different in the characters they use to represent sounds and also in some of the sounds they represent, but any of them is a great improvement over pictorial or cuneiform writing.

By the time alphabets were invented, chemists and others made new materials to write on. Parchment was made from animal hide and papyrus from the stem of the papyrus plant, which is related to the bullrushes and which grew abundantly in the Nile Valley. The manufacture of papyrus was as old as the alphabets but, because of the limited habitat of the plant, it was used mainly in Egypt. It was not until about A.D. 700 that paper replaced papyrus, which had been used for two thousand years. The ancient Chinese wrote on wood or bamboo until A.D. 105 when they invented paper.

All these modern writing materials, alas, are perishable; time, weather and fire destroy them. But they did make writing easier, and after the first century A.D. many writers described old times or old processes as well as current events. These writers' knowledge often came from manuscripts that no longer exist. Consequently, much of our chemical knowledge comes from writing done long after the experiments that first revealed it.

Whatever the source of our knowledge, whether artifacts, ancient writing or modern writing, any historical information obtained is simply the earliest date that we know a process to have been in use. We may know that a process was used in 3500 B.C., but it may have been used a thousand years earlier.

How did the ancients make their discoveries? Even in the case of a recent discovery the way in which it came about is seldom revealed and the manner in which ancient discoveries were made is a complete mystery. How or why did anyone invent a wheel? How was the glass-making process discovered? Since iron seldom occurs in the free state, how did anyone happen to get iron from its ore? These and all other questions of the kind must be left to the reader's imagination, but we do know that several commercial chemical processes were in use in very ancient times.

Our earliest information about chemical processes dates from about 3500 B.C. But language difficulties slow down the acquisition of historical information. The Akkadians conquered the Sumerians in 2500 B.C. and thereafter most of the tablets were written in the Akkadian language. Other languages followed the political vicissitudes of the region but, despite the difficulties, the linguists and the archaeologists have pieced together an amazing amount of information about the things that happened in the years between 3500 and 500 B.C.

THE REFINING OF SALT

One of the earliest known chemical processes was the refining of salt, a thriving industry by 1000 B.C. Salt is an essential in the diet as well as a flavoring, and so all the ancients were interested in improving the supply. It was also used to preserve meat just as it is today—a process that is well over three thousand years old. Salt occurs in several parts of the world in a solid form known as rock salt. It is also in ocean water, water from wells here and there and water from salt lakes around the world of which the Great Salt Lake in Utah and the Dead Sea in the Holy Land are the best-known examples.

Rock salt is nearly pure salt, but if ocean water is evaporated the remaining salt has a strong, bitter taste. Of every 3.5 pounds of ocean salt, 3 are the common sodium chloride and the other half-pound is a mixture of many different salts, which tastes bitter.

Common salt is refined by dissolving it in water, filtering the solution through cloth, straw, sand or something else to remove mud or other trash, and then evaporating the water.

Most of the impurities are more soluble than the salt and there is less of them in the solution; therefore, as the water evaporates the salt settles out in nearly pure form. The impurities remain in the brine, which is drained off before all the water is evaporated. The process is very old, but it is still in use.

Strange as it may seem, glass is one of the oldest manufactured products. It is made by melting together sodium carbonate, sand and either lime or limestone—sometimes oyster shells for the lime. Colored glass contains compounds of some of the metals: iron compounds make a green glass; manganese, purple; and cobalt, blue. When the essential materials from which glass is made are not pure, the glass is often colored. In fact, iron compounds are so common that the cheaper glasses on the market are pale green.

The conversion of these raw materials into glass requires thorough mixing and a very hot fire for several hours or even days. All these conditions seem impossible for early man to have discovered, but glass beads that date from 5000 B.C. were found at Ur. Sand, of course, is found nearly everywhere. Lime comes from heating limestone, marble, chalk, coral or the shells of mussels, snails, oysters or other mollusks. Wood ashes contain both sodium carbonate and the related potassium carbonate and also a little lime. Some observing ancient may have had a big fire on ground that contained both sand and lime and a trace of iron. Most any seaside beach would meet these requirements. What must have been his surprise to find bits of colored glass among the ashes. Their nice shiny beauty would encourage him to make some more. His curiosity would surely lead to experiment and to improvement of the process.

The excavators have uncovered furnaces capable of producing temperatures of 2000° F and dating from 3000 B.C. These furnaces could have made glass in considerable quantity for beads or other objects. By 1450 B.C. the Egyptians were making small objects of colored glass for the toilet table. After more than a thousand years glass dishes appeared in Alexandria—about 300 B.C. These dishes and other vessels were made by pressing the hot glass into molds.

Glass blowing was invented about 100 B.C. and that increased the number of shapes that could be made. During the time of the Roman Empire (27 B.C. to A.D. 475) glass dishes were common and the Romans had even begun to use glass in windows. Some of the window glass was clear and some was colored, but it was all expensive. It was another thousand years before the use of glass in windows became general practice.

CLAY AND CERAMICS

Wet clay has the interesting property of plasticity; what country boy has not made it into shapes to suit his fancy. The Sumerians, and, much later, the American Indians, learned to mold the clay into something more useful than mud pies. Bricks probably came first. The wet clay was molded into blocks and dried hard in the sun—for two years or even longer. These bricks were not entirely weather-resistant, but they were used to build houses in regions where there was very little rain, such as Mesopotamia and our Southwest. Then, either by accident or experiment, the Sumerians, Egyptians and Chinese all heated their clay objects with fire, probably on the theory that if a little heat makes a good brick, more heat would make a better one or make it sooner. Here we have all the requisites for a thriving ceramics industry in very ancient times. Clay was abundant nearly everywhere. It was easy to wet and mold into shape, and could then be made permanently hard by moderate furnace heat. That the ancients were quick to take advantage of these gifts can be seen in any museum of antiquities. Ancient civilizations had bricks to build with, stoves to cook on, pots to cook in and jars to hold water, oil and wine. There were images of the gods, ornaments, and dishes to hold their food.

Bricks of baked clay, or clay and sand, are quite porous and often have been used in cisterns to filter rain water. However, to prevent water passing through jars, vases, dishes and tiles the ceramicist applies a glaze to one or both surfaces. The glaze can be applied to products by spraying salt on the surface of the baked product and firing it again. The surface fuses to a smooth, glassy, waterproof texture. Ceramic washbowls, vases and dishes are given a finer glaze. The quality of the glaze is very important; consequently, in many cases, the ceramicist keeps the composition of the glaze a secret. The main idea is to add to the surface of the baked object something that will melt at the temperature of the furnace and fuse with the baked clay and fill up the pores. Feldspar, various oxides of metals and some other substances will fill the bill.

The Chinese were the leaders in the improvement of ceramic products; in fact, they made bricks and tile as early as 2500 B.C. They also learned how to make porcelain, which is a high-grade pottery that has been glazed and usually decorated. Decoration requires at least three firings: one to make the original form, one to fuse the glaze and one to fuse the decoration into the glaze. The design is painted on the glazed surface with a paste containing metallic gold, cobalt oxide (blue), manganese dioxide (purple) or the oxide of some other metal that will contribute a color to the glaze.

By the year 200 B.C. the Chinese had the porcelain business well under way, but it was not until the latter part of the fifteenth century A.D. that Western navigators began to get about and to establish a brisk trade with the Orient. In fact, Columbus was trying to improve the route to the Orient when the Americas got in his way. As a result of this Oriental trade Chinese porcelain became a common possession of the Europeans who could afford it. Both the body of the porcelain and the glaze were of such high quality that as late as 1700 the French, Germans and English were doing their best to duplicate the Chinese product. Finally, hard work paid off and now we have dishes and objects of art from nearly every industrialized country of the world. But we still call our best dishes "china" whether they come from China, England, France, Germany, Japan or New Jersey.

METALS

Gold was probably the first metal to be discovered and used, some artifacts of gold dating to before 3000 B.C. For some strange, unknown reason, the purity of gold alloys is expressed in carats, which are twenty-fourths. This means that 22 carat gold is $2\frac{2}{24}$ gold and $\frac{2}{24}$ some other metal. Sumerian artifacts varied from 7 to 22 carat gold; the other metal was either copper or silver. Nobody has ever improved on these metals for the purpose of making gold alloys and so your watchcase or your ring is likely to be $1\frac{4}{24}$ gold and $1\frac{0}{24}$ copper.

In case anybody wonders why chemists bother to make alloys, the answer is that the purpose is to get a metal that has different properties from any other, and that therefore will be more useful than any other. The ancients never knew more than seven metals and even today there are only about two dozen single metals that are of much use in the arts and industries. Bronze made from copper and tin is much harder than either metal used to make it. Gold is too soft and pliable to be used for jewelry; it would be easy to hammer it into any desired shape, but it would lose that shape to any small blow or pressure. Also, copper and silver are both cheaper than gold; consequently 14 carat gold is used to make rings, brooches, watchcases and hundreds of other forms because it is cheaper than pure gold, looks like gold, is hard enough to resist ordinary jolts and is still soft enough to be worked into shape.

Gold was the earliest metal used primarily because pieces of pure gold occur here and there mixed with sand and gravel. These free pieces of gold are called *nuggets* and some have been found that weighed several pounds. Very tiny ones are more common, however, and some are so small that the miners call them dust. The Sumerians would easily notice the gold among the gravel in the beds of small streams, but they also discovered its presence in solid rock and devised methods to crush the rock and recover the gold.

The Egyptians were not far behind the Sumerians in the use of gold. Tutankhamen was buried in a gold coffin in 1344 B.C.; the oldest known map in the world dates from his reign and is a map of an Egyptian gold field.

The knowledge of copper and its alloys, bronze and brass, is about as old as that of gold. All three of the ancient civilizations made objects of these three metals. King Solomon had a copper refinery. In fact, plumbing is not so new either; in Sahure's mortuary temple, built in Egypt about 2400 B.C., there were five basins lined with copper and fitted with lead plugs for the drains, which were copper pipes that led to an underground drainage system also of copper pipes.

Battle axes, various tools, ornaments and vessels of copper and bronze were all common objects to the ancients. Copper does not occur to any great extent in the free state as gold does. Its ores are blue, green or black rock, and so our enterprising ancestors had to learn how to smelt the ore, that is, how to get the free metal out of these rocks. They had to crush the rock and grind it very fine and then heat it with charcoal in a furnace of special design. This method obviously was not learned in a day; it probably developed over several centuries.

Many writers have imagined that bronze was first made by smelting ores that contained copper and either tin or zinc, but there is some evidence that the Sumerians deliberately added one or both of these metals to make their bronze. The Chinese made bronze and brass also, but probably a thousand years after the Sumerians, and so they may or may not have developed the process independently. As early as 200 B.C. the Chinese were making brass coins. In addition to gold, silver and copper, artisans were familiar with tin, lead and iron long before the Christian Era.

THE OTHER ANCIENT CHEMICAL PRODUCTS

The manufacture of glass and pottery, the smelting of ores and the working of metals all require special furnaces and high temperatures, but the ancient workers in the chemical arts did not restrict themselves to high-temperature operations. There were several processes that required only moderate heat or none at all. Some of these processes probably originated in the family kitchen. Before 1100 B.C. the Chinese were using the sap of a tree, closely related to our sumac, as a lacquer to cover objects of wood, metal or porcelain—a lacquer that is still famous. And soy sauce, so familiar to habitués of Chinese restaurants, was served on the table before 1100 B.C. The production of rice wine in China is legendary—an art older than the art of writing. Wine from grapes is much more recent, about 200 B.C. Since vinegar comes from the souring of wine, it too must also date from that far-distant past.

Chinese ink was glue and lampblack: the glue from the horns of animals, and the lampblack from burned tung oil. The Chinese first used the ink to write on wood or bamboo, but by 200 B.C. they were writing on finely woven silk. Three hundred years later, A.D. 105, paper from rags or the bark of trees was being made in much the same manner as the paper of today. The manufacture of paper spread from the East to the West, and by 1189 there was a paper factory in operation at Hérault in the Pyrenees.

Although the stamps were not rubber, the rubber-stamp idea seems to be as old as the hills. More than three thousand years ago the Chinese were making a red stamping ink by grinding vermilion, a red ore of mercury, into a vegetable oil. They had already learned how to get oil from various seeds by grinding them to a meal and then either pressing the meal or boiling it with water. The pressing gave a better yield of oil, but the boiling was easier. When the meal was heated with water the oil formed a layer on the surface of the water and was easily skimmed off. The tung oil made the best stamping ink. There were other oils and they were used for many purposes; the seed of one native Chinese tree supplied a fat that is hard like beef tallow and, in fact, is called vegetable tallow. The Chinese have always used it to make candles.

Linen, cotton, wool and silk have been woven into cloth since the beginning of civilization. By 3500 B.C. the Sumerians were bleaching and dyeing their cloth and their leather, for they had also learned how to tan the hides of animals. All the peoples in the world seem to have brightened their clothes by the use of dyes from vegetable sources. The beautiful blue of indigo, the red of safflower and turmeric and the yellow of saffron were among the better early dyes. The American Indians used both dyes and paints long before the Europeans arrived to tell them how.

Perfumes, medicines, soaps and cosmetics are all older than history. Every generation wonders how the preceding one managed to get along with what they had; no teen-ager can imagine how great-grandfather got along without an automobile. Man has always managed to provide for his safety, his health, his comfort and his pleasure. The airplane and automobile may be convenient, but neither is essential. People have always got about without them, even around the world. An electric oven is a great convenience, but it doesn't bake any better bread than a wood stove. Drugs are probably the only real advance in the past five thousand years.

We know nothing of the personal lives of the artisans who produced the artifacts that have been found. They were not chemists in the modern sense, but worked by trial and error, probably in their spare time, and each of them used the knowledge that had been passed down to him from those who had gone before. The artisans learned nothing about the composition of matter, because they cared nothing about such things, just as we moderns care nothing about the composition of an automobile as long as it looks nice and gets us there.

The practical-arts feature of chemistry is of prime importance in the first period in the history of the subject. But it is a feature that has never ended—all through the ages men have worked to make objects of utility and beauty. For many generations they worked without any special knowledge of matter, simply by trying out whatever came to hand and adopting or rejecting materials according to their success. Granite, marble, limestone, sandstone, alabaster, shells, jade, ivory, gold, silver and wood have all been used for carving and so have other less suitable materials. Various oils and pigments have been used for paints. Several metals have been used for countless purposes from dental fillings to cooking pots. The search for new materials, or new uses for old ones, still goes on.

The chemistry of the practical-arts period of the pre-Christian Era may be summed up quite briefly. The artisans recognized the properties of natural materials; produced entirely new materials such as glass, porcelain, leather and several alloys of the metals they knew; and adapted their natural and new materials to the manufacture of many an item for use in their domestic affairs or their industries.

CHAPTER TWO

The Tangled Threads of Alchemy

UNTIL ABOUT THE YEAR 300 B.C. the practical arts were the whole of chemistry. Then a series of events began to occur that later overshadowed the artisans and produced a new trend in the science—alchemy.

For the three centuries after 600 B.C. Greece was the center of learning in the Western world. Greek scholars were generally philosophers, abstract thinkers who sought truth, or at least the solution of problems through a process of logical reasoning. The philosophers were freemen and work was beneath their dignity; all manual work in ancient Greece was done by slaves. Consequently, the philosophers made no experiments to test the truth of their opinions or for any other purpose. They simply thought about the nature of matter.

THE FOUR ELEMENTS

The last of the famous Greek philosophers was Aristotle, who lived from 384 to 322 B.C. He thought that matter is composed of four elements: fire, air, water and earth. Aristotle stated that "the elementary qualities are four, and any four terms can be combined in six couples. Contraries, however, refuse to be coupled: for it is impossible for the same thing to be hot and cold or moist and dry. Hence it is evident that the coupling of the elementary qualities will be four;

hot with dry, and moist with hot, and again cold with dry
and cold with moist, and these four couples have attached
themselves to the apparently simple bodies (fire, air, water
and earth) in a manner consonant with theory. For fire is
hot and dry, whereas air is hot and moist, and water is cold
and moist, while earth is cold and dry." Such arguments went
on at great length and, of course, got nowhere, but they
dominated the thinking of chemists for two thousand years,
and they delayed any possible progress toward making a
science of chemistry.

The idea of these four elements of the Greeks apparently
came from the observation that matter is either solid (earth),
liquid (water), or gaseous (air), and, of course, fire was too
important to be ignored. Whether the idea was original with
the Greeks is not known; it may have originated in the
Orient. Years earlier the Chinese philosophers had reached
the conclusion that the elements were metal, wood, earth,
water and fire and that all other matter is some combination
of these.

Greece consisted of several city-states, and Alexander, generally known as Alexander the Great, was king of Macedon;
Aristotle was his tutor. Alexander set out with an army to
conquer the rest of Greece and, in fact, the rest of the
world. By 332 B.C. he had conquered Egypt and founded the
city of Alexandria. He then turned east and got as far as the
border of India when his soldiers got tired and refused to go
any farther. Thereupon, Alexander returned to Babylon,
where he died in 323 B.C. at the age of thirty-three. He had
encouraged his fellow Greeks to follow the army and settle
in the various cities that he conquered or founded, and many
of them settled in Alexandria. After Alexander's death his
generals divided up his vast empire and Ptolemy took Egypt
as his responsibility.

General Ptolemy became the first of a dynasty of Egyptian rulers and is known to history as Ptolemy I. He soon established at Alexandria an institution dedicated to the muses and therefore called a museum. It was not like a museum today, a depository for minerals, artifacts, furniture or anything else. It was more like one of our research institutions. Ptolemy appointed scholars to the museum staff and paid them. They did research in what we now call astronomy, mathematics, geography, anatomy, medicine, pharmacy, physics and related subjects. These scholars also taught a few students, but the museum was not primarily a school.

THE ALEXANDRIAN LIBRARY

Ptolemy I also established a library in Alexandria. Books of that day were written on long strips of papyrus of different widths and lengths. Because the papyri were rolled up, reading them was a tedious process, but despite its shortcomings the Alexandrian library was a vital aid to scholarship. Just how many books there were is not known, but estimates run to half a million. Ptolemy ruled that any book brought into Egypt must be copied and a copy placed in the library. Printing had not been invented and so copying old books and the publication of new ones employed many copyists; every book had to be handwritten and the copyists enabled the library to sell books. While the museum attempted to obtain new knowledge the library was making both old and new knowledge available to scholars, not only those from Egypt, but also those from other areas of the Middle East, Greece, and western Europe—the entire world.

For more than a century scholarship was at flood tide in Alexandria; Ptolemy I and his successors continued to support the museum and the library. But the support of these institutions was expensive and the later Ptolemies were less enthusiastic about learning than the founder of the dynasty. The fate of the library is uncertain; however, we know that during the conquest of Alexandria by Caesar in 48 B.C. it was partly burned. After that date Egypt was a Roman province and about A.D. 290 Diocletian ordered all books in the realm that had anything to do with metals and the making of gold to be destroyed—he did not wish anyone to become wealthy enough to give him any competition. This decree probably took a considerable part of the Alexandrian library. Moreover, the Romans were not famous for their support of scholarly activities and copying books by hand was expensive. Books, especially those written on papyrus, deteriorate and so deterioration and neglect may have been the main factors in the passing of that fine old library. The museum continued until 415 when it was completely destroyed in riots incited by the Christians in Alexandria. With the passing of these institutions, Alexandrian scholarship was dispersed over a wide area east and south of the Mediterranean.

In the days of the Alexandrian library only a few could read and these were mainly the priests of the various religions. In Europe, religion occupied the full time of the priests for over a thousand years, but in Egypt the priests were concerned with a wide scope of knowledge, for the famous library had made available to them all the written knowledge of Greece, India, the Hebrews and China.

ORIGINS OF ALCHEMY

Just where and when alchemy began is not known. The Chinese had their philosophers and, unlike the Greeks, they were not above doing experimental work. So alchemy may have started in China; at least, it is known to have existed there as early as 400 B.C.

The origin of the name and who first used it are also unknown. The prefix *al* is the Arabic word for "the," and the root *chem* may come from the Greek word *chemi* which means "black" and which also was the Greek name of Egypt because of the black soil of the Nile delta. Another possibility that has been suggested is that the name comes from the Greek word *cheo*, which means "I pour" and refers to the work of alchemists with molten metals and the liquid extracts of plants. The facts are that the origin of the word is lost and one guess is about as good as another. However, the derivation first mentioned above has support from the fact that our knowledge of alchemy did originate in Egypt and that alchemy has been called the black art.

Whether the Egyptians originated the ideas of alchemy independently or got them from China is debated by the historians of the science. The art as we know it certainly developed in the Alexandrian complex, for it consisted of the philosophy of the Greeks, the mysticism of the Orient and the practical work of the Sumerians and the Egyptians.

The art of writing is older than that of alchemy and so our knowledge of the subject comes from manuscripts that have been found, mostly in Egypt, and that were written in Greek on papyrus. Greek was the language of the educated Alexandrians and all the books were written in that language including the Christian Bible.

It was the custom in ancient Egypt to bury with a man those objects that he had owned and prized during his lifetime. As a result of this practice several manuscripts have been found in the ancient tombs. Among these papyri were some on the subjects of alchemy and of the chemical arts of the time. The oldest that has been found dates from 1550 B.C., and was discovered by the German Egyptologist Georg Ebers in 1872. The Ebers Papyrus is a list of drugs and remedies including how to prepare the drugs and how to apply them; it is sixty-eight feet long and contains over eight hundred remedies. Many of the drugs were obtained from plants, but there were also some mineral substances, sulfur, salt and saltpeter, among them. The wide range of these remedies is indicated by the use of cat's fat on garments to protect them from mice and the use of half an onion and the froth of beer as a remedy against death.

Diocletian's order of the year 290 seems to have about eliminated manuscripts on alchemy, but those that were buried escaped because nobody knew that they existed. About the year 1800 Johann d'Anastasy, the Swedish vice-consul in Alexandria, made a collection of papyri that were coming on the market from the excavations of ancient Egyptian tombs. He sold part of the collection to the Dutch government and these were deposited in the library of the University of Leyden. The remainder he took to Sweden where they eventually found their way to the library of the University of Uppsala after a long sojourn in Stockholm.

The first of these papyri dealing with alchemy was translated in 1885 and is called the Leyden Papyrus X. It seems to have been written about the year A.D. 300, but it is thought to be a copy of a manuscript written about two hundred years earlier. This papyrus is what a chemist now calls a laboratory manual, that is, a book of directions for laboratory work. It contains over seventy recipes for making alloys, coloring metal surfaces, soldering, imitating precious metals and testing the purity of metals. Fifteen recipes are for methods of writing on gold or silver. Eleven sets of directions are for dyeing cloth. The remaining eleven deal with drugs and their uses.

The other Anastasy manuscript that dealt with alchemy was not translated until 1906; it is known as the Stockholm

Papyrus. These two papyri had belonged to the same chemist and were probably copies made at the time of his death. They were apparently companion books. Of the 150 recipes in the Stockholm Papyrus, 70 are concerned with the production of artificial gems, 60 deal with the process of dyeing, 10 with the whitening of off-color pearls and 9 supplement the metal recipes of the Leyden Papyrus.

These handwritten papyri indicate the chief projects with which the alchemists of the first century of our era were concerned: mainly medicine and metals, and particularly how to make the precious metals from the cheaper ones. The alchemists were men with a purpose, or rather with two purposes: to transmute the cheaper metals into gold and to find the elixir of life. The Chinese alchemists were more concerned with the elixir, a drug that would cure all diseases and thus provide eternal life. To them the transmutation of metals was secondary, but to the Egyptians it came first.

PLINY

Gaius Plinius Secundus, a Roman gentleman of many activities, was born in A.D. 23 and died in Pompeii during the volcanic eruption in 79. Pliny, as we know him, was a voluminous writer and among other things he wrote the thirty-seven-volume *Natural History*, which he published about the year 77 and in which he describes plants, animals, minerals, agriculture, mining and metallurgy. He was apparently more writer than scientist for his book is a compilation of information from other writers with his own personal comments. He mentions some five hundred references of which many no longer exist—manuscripts long since lost or destroyed. The book is a comprehensive treatment of the science of the time.

Pliny's *Natural History* was written about the same time

as the Stockholm Papyrus, which gives several recipes for producing artificial gems, and Pliny remarks: "There are books, the authors of which I refrain from mentioning, which give instructions how to stain crystal in such a way as to imitate emeralds and other transparent stones . . . and there are no frauds which bring greater profits." Fraud seems to have entered into alchemy very early in its history.

Scholarship requires a proper atmosphere. The early Ptolemies with their support of the museum and the library provided that atmosphere in Alexandria. However, after Egypt became a Roman province the Romans were fully occupied with conquest, politics and religion—scholarship was no part of their scheme of things. These were troublesome times; imperial edicts from Rome, the decline of the Empire and, finally, Christian riots, which destroyed the museum and killed the last of the Alexandrian scholars in 415, finished the city as an education center, but in 642 the Arabs conquered Egypt and a new era began.

Alchemy took a new turn when the Egyptian priests began to work with metals, surrounded their activity with secrecy and introduced philosophy, mysticism and religion into the art. With the coming of the Arabs, alchemy was gradually taken over by them from the Egyptians and spread throughout the Middle East and west across the north of Africa and into Spain. The scholars followed the armies as they had followed Alexander a thousand years before. The language of alchemy changed from Greek to Arabic and the literature was not translated into Latin for Europeans to read until about the year 1100.

ALCHEMISTIC THEORY

What was alchemy? To describe it in detail would take a big book and several have been written on the subject. To evaluate it with confidence is impossible. I have already mentioned its experimental objectives—the transmutation of cheap metals such as lead and mercury into gold or silver and to discover the elixir of life. The alchemists did some other experimental work also, as is established by the Stockholm and Leyden papyri, the books of Pliny and other writings of later date.

In addition to the experimental features of alchemy there was a system of philosophy, or a combination of several systems. Alchemy aimed to penetrate the mysteries of the universe and so astrology became part of the alchemists' scheme along with philosophy, religion and mysticism. The alchemists hoped to learn the effect of the sun, moon, planets and stars on human affairs, particularly their own. They accepted the four elements of Aristotle, which made transmutation seem plausible. If everything is composed of fire, air, earth and water or some combination of these four elements, then why shouldn't it be possible to change the combination and get a new substance? The metals were much alike to begin with; therefore it shouldn't take much of a change to convert one into another. Lead was nearly as heavy as gold, and copper was much the same color; a slight change in composition should change one or the other of these metals into gold, or so they reasoned. The idea was just as likely as some of the changes they did make. For instance, the alchemists converted a mixture of sand, lime and soda into glass and that was a much greater change in properties than the difference between lead and gold. In spite of the soundness of the reasoning, they never succeeded in changing lead, or any other metal, into gold or silver. The trouble was not with their logic but with the assumption that fire, air, earth and water are the basic substances from which all others are made. The results of logic are never any better than the facts on which the argument is based.

THE PHILOSOPHER'S STONE

Alchemical theory centered around the *philosopher's stone*, a magic stone that would give its possessor the power to transmute metals or to find or make the elixir. Nobody knows where or when the idea of the philosopher's stone originated, but it appears in alchemical literature very early and was probably a contribution of the Egyptian priests. Magic was widely practiced in Egypt and the idea of a magical stone would be in accord with their general beliefs. Some alchemists even tried to describe the stone, although it was a bit difficult to describe something that nobody had ever seen, and, in fact, never did see.

The idea of the philosopher's stone persisted until the end of alchemy—for more than a thousand years. Pages and pages were written about it; what it was like, where it could be found and what it could do. Since it was purely imaginary, it was an excellent subject for voluminous writing. The writing was mystical and contradictory; why it was done at all is difficult to understand, because the alchemists did not want to disclose their secrets to anyone outside their group.

In line with their practice of secrecy, the alchemists used many signs, symbols, enigmas and other confusing devices. Some of their symbols, of course, were a kind of shorthand and some came from astrology. For example, the metals were associated with the heavenly bodies: gold with the sun, silver with the moon, copper with Venus, iron with Mars, lead with Saturn, tin with Jupiter and quicksilver with Mercury. In this last case the name of the planet became the name of the metal, and the term "quicksilver" has been obsolete in chemical language for more than two centuries.

Some of the symbols used by the alchemists for shorthand and for secrecy were

Gold	☉	Air	△ (with bar)	Mercury	☿
Fire	△	Earth	▽ (with bar)	Soap	◊
Water	▽	Salt	⊖	Glass	⌀⎯

As time went on, alchemy accumulated more complex symbols, some adopted from mythology or from religion—the serpent appears frequently and the Greek god Hermes was the first alchemist according to their own reckoning. The alchemists sometimes called themselves the sons of Hermes, and alchemy was called the divine art by its practitioners before it became the black art of its detractors.

Our knowledge of alchemy is fragmentary, and the historians have pieced it together from bits of writing by alchemists and from books written about alchemy by authors who had no direct connection with those who practiced the art. Diocletian's decree against alchemical books discouraged writers and eliminated most of the books already written. However, some alchemists continued to write despite the decree—a practice reminiscent of prohibitions the world over and in all ages. Only a few manuscripts have survived from the first thousand years of alchemy.

ZOSIMOS

One of the early alchemists whose manuscripts have survived was Zosimos. Who he was is somewhat doubtful, but he seems to have been a teacher and writer in Alexandria about the year A.D. 300. His writings are mainly laboratory directions for making or imitating gold, but they are not devoid of mysticism. At one point he describes a dream in which he saw a priest, an altar and various ceremonies. His dream was long and eventful, as the following quotation from his tale indicates:

> The priest stood there, and I heard a voice from above saying —"I have accomplished the art of descending the fifteen steps walking toward the darkness and the act of mounting the steps going toward the light. It is the sacrifice that renews me eliminating the dense nature of the body. Thus by necessity consecrated, I become a spirit." . . . In short, my friend built a monolith temple as of white lead, as of alabaster having neither commencement nor end in its construction. . . . A serpent is lying at the entrance guarding the temple. Seize him, immolate him, flay him and taking his flesh and his bones, separate his members. Then joining the members with the bones, make them a step to the entrance of the temple, mount upon it and enter. Thou wilt find what thou seekest.

If these isolated quotations seem jumbled they are no more so than the complete text. Chemists can only guess what this is all about, but those who have studied the matter think it to be a discussion of the transmutation of the metals. One sentence, however, is clear enough, "Never reveal clearly to anyone any such property, but be sufficient unto thyself for fear that in speaking thou bringest destruction upon thyself." This might be called the theme song of the alchemists.

JABIR

Scattered throughout the libraries of Europe there are short manuscripts by various alchemists, but the next writer of importance after Zosimos was the Arabian alchemist Jabir ibn-Hayyan, who is frequently called Djeber or Geber by later writers. He lived and wrote in Baghdad in the latter part of the eighth century or some five hundred years after Zosimos.

From the beginning, the theoretical side of alchemy stressed the unity of matter and the philosopher's stone. Later the sulfur-mercury theory appeared and its invention has been attributed to Jabir. Like most of the alchemical writing the theory is rather muddled, but the idea seems to have been that all metals are composed of sulfur and mercury, and that the different metals contain these two components in different proportions. The mercury and sulfur, however, were not the common substances we know by those names. The alchemists referred to them as *our* sulfur and *our* mercury to distinguish them from the common substances with those names. They were apparently somewhat short of words. The alchemist's sulfur appears to be the same as the Greek element *fire*, and the mercury the Greek *water*. Jabir's writings are in the usual mystic and obscure style common to the alchemists, but they deal with the theories of alchemy and do not describe laboratory methods like the manuscripts of Zosimos and the early Egyptian papyri.

Just what Jabir did write is uncertain. Over a thousand manuscripts have been attributed to him—many more than one man might be expected to write. Furthermore, some of them obviously were written long after Jabir's death. French, German and English scholars have done an enormous amount of work trying to solve the puzzle and have reached the conclusion that some of the early writing was done by Jabir, but that most of it was done by different members of the Ismailia, some of it a century or more after the early Jabir writings. Although they were a religious sect the Ismailia were interested in the science of their day and were practicing alchemists as well as theorists. Their habit of ascribing authorship of their papers to Jabir was fully in accord with alchemical practice. The idea was that everybody reads and believes a famous author and that the unknown writer is seldom read and never taken seriously.

AVICENNA

Another Mohammedan writer of great renown was born in Persia and lived in various places in the Middle East from 980 to 1037. He is known to Europeans as Avicenna, or sometimes as ibn-Sina, which is the last part of his long Arabic name. He was not a very orthodox alchemist. He did laboratory work with metals and minerals, but he did not believe transmutation possible and was fully convinced that no alchemist had ever carried it out, although he admitted that they could make good imitations of gold. He was primarily a physician and his writings on medicine were the basis of medical practice for over six hundred years. His fame as a physician, however, does not seem to have caused his ideas on transmutation to be accepted by his alchemical colleagues. They probably felt that as an alchemist he was a good doctor.

The Arabs invaded Spain in 711 and for the next four hundred years Europeans learned their alchemy from the Arabian-Spanish alchemists. Then came the crusades of the twelfth and thirteenth centuries. Alexander had spread Greek culture throughout the Middle East fourteen centuries earlier, and now the crusades brought back to Europe a Greek culture much contaminated with Persian, Arabian and Egyptian ideas. Scholars began to translate Greek and Arabic manuscripts into Latin, which was the scholarly language of Europe.

Robert of Chester was one of the first translators. In an introduction to a translation made in 1144 he explains the situation: "Since what Alchymia is, and what its composition is, your Latin world does not yet know, I will explain in the present work." Most of the translators of the twelfth century did not sign their work as Robert did, but, by the year 1200, hundreds of manuscripts had been translated into Latin, and these manuscripts became the chief source of material for the writers of books in the thirteenth century.

The year 1200 saw the beginnings of much new scholarly activity. In addition to the translation of manuscripts into Latin from Greek and Oriental languages, universities were established at Naples, Salamanca, Padua, Piacenza, Arezzo, Siena, Montpellier, Paris, Toulouse, Orléans, Seville, Valladolid, Oxford and Cambridge. Men wrote many books. Although they now had paper to write on, all copies had to be made by hand. The most important authors were the writers of the encyclopedias. Some of these encyclopedias were large and, like those in modern libraries, they aimed to cover the whole field of knowledge. Each author, of course, had to decide how much of the available knowledge was worth his attention. Several writers included the subject of alchemy and so helped to spread the knowledge of that art, for these books were widely used in the universities.

VINCENT DE BEAUVAIS

One of the first and most important of these writers was Vincent de Beauvais. Not much is known about his personal life, but he was born in Beauvais in Normandy about 1190 and died there, about 1264. He joined the Dominicans and lived the life of a monk of that order. He called his work *Speculum Majus*, which might be translated *The Great Mirror*. It was in three parts according to the general nature of the subject matter. One part, *Speculum Naturale*, treated the science of the day in thirty-two books, with a total of 3718 chapters. It contains long quotations from three hundred authors whose manuscripts were in Greek, Latin, Arabic and Hebrew; many of these manuscripts are no longer in existence.

Vincent was no alchemist, but he had read so much that he did not hesitate to offer his opinion. He quotes one author: "Let the artisans of alchemy know that it is not possible for species to be transmuted, but they can make things similar to these, as by tincturing white metal to a yellow color so that it may seem to be gold, also by removing the impurities of lead so that it may appear to be silver; but it will always be really lead." Vincent's encyclopedia was a success by any standard; more than three hundred years later it was in print in several editions.

VON BOLLSTÄDT

Another prolific writer of the period was Albert von Bollstädt, a Swabian born in Lannigan about 1200. His reputation as a scholar was so great that in later years he became known as Albertus Magnus. He too was a Dominican and held several important positions in the Church. Albertus was also a teacher; in his late years he taught in a convent in Cologne. His scholarship was mainly in theology and philosophy, but his writing was encyclopedic. He wrote nearly forty volumes and, in accord with the practice of the times, several books written by others were signed by his name. Albertus was not an alchemist, but he did travel through Europe, where he picked up considerable information besides what he read. Instead of presenting long quotations, such as those in the books of Vincent de Beauvais, Albertus digested the material he read and then wrote the information in his own words. He described many chemical substances and processes including the coloring of metals to resemble gold or silver, but he did not commit himself in the matter of transmutation.

ROGER BACON

A third writer of importance was Roger Bacon. Personal records are again scarce, but he was born in a wealthy family somewhere in England between 1210 and 1220. He died about 1292 and was buried in a Franciscan church in Oxford. He had a good education, and for a time lectured on Aristotle at the University of Paris. In 1247 he went to Oxford where he met some scientists and became interested in their subjects. He spent a lot of money on books and laboratory equipment and also trained assistants. For ten years Bacon worked in alchemy, astronomy, optics, mathematics and languages. Then, in 1257, he became a Franciscan friar, developed poor health and complained about being forgotten, all at about the same time.

Bacon had a very poor opinion of anyone who differed from his views and was very free in the expression of such opinions. Consequently, he was disciplined by his order. He complained to Pope Clement IV in 1266 and, in his letter, made some proposals for the welfare of the Church and the universities. The Pope wrote him to send along details, whereupon he proceeded to write three books. Bacon's main theme was apparently the teaching of science in the universities. The Pope urged him to keep his work secret, which seems to have been a good idea because, among other things, Bacon wrote that he could have covered quires of vellum with the puerilities and vain speculations which filled the commentaries of the leaders of the schools.

Clement IV died in 1268 and Bacon's project came to an end. Later the Franciscans sent him to prison for ten years because of his unorthodox teaching. In all, he wrote over thirty books and, as usual, there were several others signed with his name but written years after his death. His chief claim to fame rests on his urging the importance of experimentation in science and the earnest perseverance with which he tried to get his ideas accepted.

THE GEBER MANUSCRIPTS

There was one writer who is a totally unknown person. He wrote about the year 1300 and signed the name of Geber to his manuscripts. For many years these manuscripts were thought to have been written by the Arabic Geber (Jabir) of the eighth century, despite the fact that an Italian writer as early as 1330 referred to the author as the Spanish Geber. A close examination of these manuscripts by scholars of the nineteenth century revealed that they could not possibly have been written within four hundred years of the Arabic Geber's death. They were most likely written by a Spanish alchemist as the Italian writer six hundred years earlier had said they were. These Geber manuscripts were a great help to alchemists because they described many laboratory procedures without any mysticism or enigmas. The writer's theories are the same as those of all the other alchemists, and he must have been very active in the laboratory, for his descriptions of the processes indicate that they were written by someone who knew how to carry them out. Among them are processes for purifying common salt, alum and several other salts. He also told how to purify metals and how to dissolve them in acids. He also describes several pieces of laboratory apparatus. In fact, the four books that he wrote gave complete information for setting up a laboratory and carrying out the usual alchemical experiments. The difference between the books of this pseudo Geber and the three encyclopedias just mentioned is similar to the difference between a modern chemical student's book of laboratory directions and the chemical articles in a current encyclopedia.

THE DECLINE OF ALCHEMY

As more books on alchemy were written and the number of universities grew, alchemy developed enemies in both the Church and the government. In addition to the sixteen universities founded in the twelfth century, over twenty were established in the thirteenth century and more than forty in the fourteenth. By the year 1400 there were some seventy universities scattered over western Europe.

In 1317 Pope John XXII issued a decree that began, "Alchemies are here prohibited and those who practice their being done are punished. They must forfeit to the public treasury for the benefit of the poor as much genuine gold and silver as they have manufactured of the false or adulterated metal. . . . If they are clerics, they shall be deprived of any benefices that they hold and be deprived of holding others."

In Barcelona in 1323 an order of the Church pronounced a penalty of excommunication against clerics who practiced alchemy or who did not burn their books on the subject within eight days. Governments were not far behind the Church in their condemnation of alchemy. In 1380 Charles V of France forbade the practice of alchemy or even the possession of alchemical equipment. Henry IV in England prohibited the practice of alchemy in 1404, and the Council of Venice did the same in 1418.

In literature the alchemists fared no better. Dante, in the *Divine Comedy*, consigned them to the tortures of the lowest regions of his Inferno. Petrarch made fun of them in 1366 and Chaucer took a dim view of them in a Canterbury tale written about 1388.

The alchemists never accomplished the transmutation of any of the cheaper metals into gold or silver, nor did they find the elixir of life, but they did increase our knowledge of descriptive chemistry and they invented several pieces of chemical equipment such as bottles, furnaces, and apparatus for the distillation of liquids. The invention of an apparatus that enables a chemist to perform new experiments or to perform old ones better is a big contribution to the advancement of the science.

Spain may have contributed materials to the alchemists long before the Arabic invasion. Gold, silver, lead, tin, mercury and iron are all found in Spain, and these metals were probably carried to the eastern Mediterranean by traders before the Christian Era.

In the Middle Ages the nobility of Europe had personal alchemists and astrologers. The alchemist was housed, clothed, fed and given a place to work. In return, his sponsor expected to profit by his alchemist's discoveries. This system encouraged dishonesty—the alchemist was inclined to report valuable discoveries to keep his patron satisfied with his work. He surrounded the results of his experiments with secrecy and greatly exaggerated their importance. In the search for the elixir of life, many poisons were discovered and these did prove useful to some of the rulers in dealing with their rivals. However, none of the poisons was ever so potent as the novels of Dumas, Scott and other romanticists would have us believe. One novel has an episode based on a poison so powerful that a drop of it put on a rose proved fatal to anyone who smelled the flower. No such poison has ever been known. Novelists are famous for the creation of their own chemistry. A much more recent writer than Dumas has a murderer completely disposing of his victim's body with a small bottle of nitric acid—hardly enough to destroy a tropical cockroach.

The alchemists made alloys of copper and other metals,

which looked like gold. How well they matched the color of gold can be seen in a bright new penny, which is made of an alloy of copper, zinc and tin. One enterprising alchemist made bricks of lead and covered them with a thin layer of gold. He sold them in Switzerland and promptly left the country.

Some European alchemists were also druggists and some were physicians; these were the ones that did most of the work on the elixir of life. The court alchemist and the private operator were the hopeful metallurgists. Although alchemy was active for more than forty generations it accomplished very little. The Chinese invented gunpowder before the year 1150. The European alchemists made alcohol, nitric acid, sulfuric acid and several other chemicals, but many of the substances known to the alchemists, as well as their processes, were known to chemical artisans several centuries before the first alchemist stepped into his laboratory.

Alchemy was in full swing in Europe in the Middle Ages. During those years, by way of variety, the alchemist began looking for the universal solvent. Since this liquid was supposed to dissolve everything, it is not clear how the alchemist expected to keep it after he found it.

With the upsurge of learning about the year 1500, alchemy began to decline; it never really ended. The transmutation of metals, the elixir of life and the muddled theory of the alchemists made such an appeal to the imagination that many people, ignorant of science, believe in it to the present day. Just a few years ago I met a college senior who thought that the four elements, fire, air, earth and water were still considered to be the foundation of the composition of matter, and rather recently I received a serious inquiry as to the identity of the universal solvent. Alchemy cast a long shadow.

CHAPTER THREE

The Search for Drugs

By the year 1500 alchemy had certainly been in existence for fifteen hundred years and possibly for over three thousand. During all these centuries alchemists had experimented with the properties of matter, but they had made few attempts to solve the mysteries of its composition. The ideas of Aristotle had satisfied them: all matter is composed of fire, earth, air and water, or some such pronouncement. With good logic but very bad premises the alchemists saw no reason why gold could not be made from lead, tin or copper, nor why there should not be a drug to cure all diseases. We must admire their persistence, for fifteen centuries of failure did not restrain them from further efforts.

Alchemy did not disappear in a day; the decline was gradual, over more than a century; but its doom was sealed by the stirring events around the end of the fifteenth century.

Among the first of these events was the invention of printing from movable type. The process was in use as early as 1446 in both Germany and Holland. The Italians were printing by 1465 and the English in 1477. No more copying of books by hand: once the type was set any number of books could be printed, and then the type could be thrown down, sorted and used to print another book—the greatest improvement in recording and spreading information since the invention of the alphabet.

Explorers were on the move in those days. In 1486 Diaz sailed around the Cape of Good Hope and twelve years later Vasco da Gama also rounded the Cape and went on to India. In 1492 Columbus, having decided that a shorter route to India would lie west across the Atlantic and having finally gotten financial support, set out to prove it. The results are well known. These and other explorers were extending the knowledge of geography and of strange peoples, strange customs, strange minerals and new plants.

In politics Europe was seething. In 1499 Switzerland became a free country, and Europe was graced by such luminaries as Henry VIII who ascended the throne of England in 1509. Leo X was made Pope in 1513 and Francis I took over the rule of France in 1515. Five years later Suleiman the Magnificent ruled from Baghdad to Hungary and from 1519 Charles V ruled all of Europe that those just mentioned left him. Rivalries and intrigues made these years one of the most exciting periods in all political history.

Religious matters were also in an evolutionary stew. In 1517 Martin Luther criticized the Pope and the practices of the established Church and touched off the Reformation. In 1534 Henry VIII separated the Church of England from the authority of the Pope.

In addition to the rulers of Church and state there were other illustrious men of the times—in art, literature and adventure. These were the days of Shakespeare and Spenser, of Raleigh and Frobisher in England. Germany had Hans Sachs and the artists Dürer and Holbein. Rabelais was writing in France and Cartier was exploring North America. Spain had her Cervantes and Italy had a host of notables, such as the artists Botticelli, Michelangelo, Raphael, Titian and

Leonardo da Vinci—who was also a scientist and inventor. There were Ariosto and Castiglione and the famous Cesare Borgia and Lorenzo de' Medici. And let us not forget Amerigo Vespucci without whom the Americas would be called something else.

This was the period the historians call the Renaissance—a rebirth or upsurge of learning that was caused by many things. The invention of printing, the vast increase in geographical and other knowledge that followed the explorations, and the special quality of the minds and activities of the men of the period, all played important parts in the sudden popularity of knowledge.

Ferdinand and Isabella, rulers of Spain, had sponsored the voyages of Columbus and soon the Spaniards had conquered the Inca, Aztec and Mayan Indians and learned much about their civilizations. Spanish ships were able to supply Spain with gold, silver, strange botanical specimens and strange people. The explorers, and the adventurers who followed them, provided facts and materials for the advancement of science. The scholarly spirit of the Renaissance made alchemy seem futile and a bit silly. Aristotle's philosophy began to lose caste, but it needed someone like a Columbus or a Luther to change the course of alchemy and to give it new life. He soon appeared.

PARACELSUS

Theophrastus Bombastus von Hohenheim, who changed his name to Philippus Aureolus Paracelsus, was the man of the hour, and has been known to writers ever since simply as Paracelsus. He has often been looked upon as a quack or a fraud—an unprincipled, ignorant individual going about doing nothing of his own and criticizing the work of everyone else. On the contrary, he was one of the best educated and most successful physicians of his day. His evil reputation came from his sticking to a doctrine that was attributed to George Bernard Shaw some four hundred years later: "If you don't say a thing in an irritating manner you may as well not say it at all." This seems to have been the creed of Paracelsus, for he certainly excelled in the strength and persistence of his irritating speech.

Paracelsus was born in 1493 at Einsiedeln in the canton of Schwyz in northern Switzerland. When he was nine years old the family moved to Villach in Carinthia, a mining region in southwestern Austria. His father was city physician in Villach and also taught science in the local school of mines. Paracelsus was educated in a nearby monastery and also learned considerable chemistry, medicine, mining and metallurgy from his father and from his environment. His university career is difficult to trace for, at one time or another, he seems to have been a student in various universities in Austria, Germany, Italy, France, Sweden, Portugal, Poland, Russia, Spain and England. He apparently got his bachelor's degree in Vienna in 1511 and the doctorate at Ferrara in 1515.

Paracelsus was dissatisfied with the medical education of his day, which accounts for his visits to so many universities. In one of his books he says: "And in all these countries and places I was diligently investigating and inquiring into the certain and true art of medicine. This I tried not only with learned doctors, but also at the hand of barbers, bath keepers, shearers and with experienced surgeons; even with old women, with necromancers, alchemists and in monasteries; with the nobles and with common people, with the cleverest and with simpletons." In other words, he did his best to learn all he could of the healing art. With all this background he came to believe in the importance of experiment, observation and

experience; an idea that Roger Bacon had urged three centuries earlier also in an irritating manner, but apparently not
irritating enough or not to enough people, for Bacon had very
little effect on the science of his times.

After Paracelsus received the doctor's degree in 1515 his
medical practice became as diverse as his education. He was
an army doctor in Naples and in Holland; then he settled
down for a time and practiced medicine in Strasbourg. About
1526 he left there and went to Basel where he treated and
cured some prominent patients, who had him appointed city
physician and professor of chemistry and medicine at the
university. He didn't last long at either job.

During the Middle Ages, which were just coming to a
close, scholarship had consisted mainly in learning what was
in the books of the day, especially the older books. Medicine
was based chiefly on the writings of Galen (A.D. 130–200)
and Avicenna. Paracelsus thought it about time for apothecaries, alchemists and doctors to learn something new, and
so to emphasize his point he made a most impressive gesture.
On Saint John's Day in 1527 the university students were
having a bonfire in the public square by way of celebration of
the holiday, and Paracelsus, after the example of Luther
burning the papal bull seven years before, gathered up the
books of the ancient writers and added them to the fire. He
also made a speech for the occasion in which he paid his
respects to the habits and beliefs of alchemists, doctors and
anyone else who disagreed with him. This was not his only
offense; he lectured in German, whereas Latin was the language of the scholar, and he wore clothes that showed signs of
his laboratory efforts instead of the dignified robes of the
university professor. The bonfire was just the last straw; the
university promptly fired him, and his personal attacks on the

doctors made him so many enemies in the city that he had to leave Basel after living there less than a year.

He went to Colmar for a short time and then to Nuremberg, but he didn't stay long in either city. He spent the rest of his life wandering over Europe. Each place he went he practiced alchemy and medicine when he could; but his criticism of his colleagues made him so many enemies that he soon had to move on. He died in Salzburg in 1541 an old man, burned out at the age of forty-seven. Of the several books that he wrote not one was published during his lifetime. He was such a controversial figure that no publisher dared print them.

Paracelsus had many followers and his image grew. About twenty years after his death there was a sudden demand for his writings in alchemy, medicine and surgery. The demand, of course, brought forth publication of his books and they went through several editions, one of them as recently as the twentieth century.

IATROCHEMISTRY

As an alchemist Paracelsus believed in the four elements of Aristotle and the transmutation of the metals, but he did not consider either of these notions important. He was more interested in the sulfur-mercury theory and added salt as a third element; this was his *tria prima* theory of matter. For example, when wood burns, the mercury evaporates, the sulfur burns and the salt is left as ashes. He also believed the human body to be composed of three elements and disease to be caused by the shifting of their proportions. Curing the disease, then, consisted in bringing the elements back into balance. With this purpose in mind Paracelsus proceeded to make salts of iron, copper, mercury, antimony and other metals and to experiment with the effects of these salts as drugs. He argued violently that work of this kind was far more important than the traditional searchings of the alchemists, and that they should all get into the drug business and give up their search for the philosopher's stone. Some of them took his advice, but in addition to the salts made in the laboratory many new drugs were introduced into Europe from America, India and elsewhere by the adventurers of the sixteenth century. Thus began the science of *iatrochemistry*, the science of healing. Paracelsus did not contribute many drugs, but his example and continual argument persuaded many others to give up alchemy and try their hands at making remedies.

In addition to his contributions to iatrochemistry, Paracelsus made a few incidental contributions to the language of the science. He dropped the *al* from alchemy and was the first to use the word *chemy*. He also introduced the word *alcohol* for spirits of wine, and invented the word *gas*.

The chief opponents of Paracelsus were the physicians, which is no great surprise, for he constantly called them numerous uncomplimentary names, and continually called them stupid because they adhered to the old medical practices instead of trying new methods and using their observations and experience as guides. The alchemists and the apothecaries were less sensitive than the doctors, but they too came in for unrestrained criticism for their efforts to make gold and the elixir instead of making drugs.

As always happens in the case of a radical reformer, Paracelsus not only made bitter enemies, but also ardent disciples—some of them as bitter and outspoken as the master. Only a few of these Paracelsians can be mentioned here for we are more concerned with the development of chemistry than with its history.

One of the first iatrochemists of note was Basilius Valentinius, a German monk. In fact, he claimed to have written before Paracelsus and so the latter's enemies accused him of stealing the ideas of Valentinius. The controversy was long and bitter, and many scholars have made exhaustive studies of the matter. Result: Valentinius was not a monk and wrote several years after Paracelsus. As nearly as the scholars can make out, Valentinius was the pen name of an alchemist and printer by the name of Johann Tholde. Several books appeared under the pen name, but the most important one was *Triumphal Chariot of Antimony,* published in 1604. This was an inordinately fancy title, for the book was simply a treatise on the properties of antimony and its salts and their use in medicine. It was a good book on the chemistry of antimony, but its medical recommendations may have been disastrous to the patients of the doctors who followed them.

Another Paracelsian was Andreas Libau (1540–1616) who is generally called by his Latin name of Libavius because he wrote in Latin. He was born in Halle and educated in Jena. He began as a schoolteacher at Coburg and later went to Jena as professor of history and poetry. In 1591 Libavius went to the city of Rothenburg, where he became city physician, an inspector of schools and a teacher in the local gymnasium (a sort of cross between our high school and a junior college). In 1607 he went back to Coburg as head of the gymnasium in that city. Libavius was a chemist on the side and, being a teacher, he of course wrote a book, which has been called the first textbook in chemistry. It appeared in print in 1597. But his complete works on chemistry and medicine were not published until 1616.

Libavius was a follower of Paracelsus but not so extreme in his methods. He had a mind of his own and although he made several chemical salts and tested them as drugs, he used them rather cautiously. Because of his clear thinking and writing his book influenced chemists for more than a century.

The private lives of chemists and teachers are often unknown to both their associates and their successors. About the year 1600 there was an iatrochemist by the name of Jean Beguin. Very little is known of his personal history except that he lived in Paris and died around 1620. In 1604 he and some others opened a school for the teaching of chemistry and pharmacy. In 1610 he published *The Chemical Beginner*, which presented the iatrochemical point of view and contained directions for the preparation of chemical medicines. It appeared in nearly fifty editions and in several languages; its popularity lasted until the decline of iatrochemistry nearly a century later.

One of Beguin's associates in the founding of the school was Turquet de Mayerne (1573–1655), a physician who came to Paris from Geneva and became professor of chemistry and medicine at the University of Paris. Turquet was a Paracelsian in the matter of chemical medicines but also used the remedies of the ancient Avicenna and Galen. In 1603 the use of salts of antimony as drugs was banned in France and Turquet was ousted from his university post by the faculty of medicine and, furthermore, physicians were forbidden to have anything to do with him. A few years later he left France and became physician to James I of England. The introduction of new drugs was no bed of roses or, at least, the thorns were included with the flowers.

Paris seems to have had a great attraction for chemists in the early part of the seventeenth century, for there was another arrival in 1618. He was a Scot from Aberdeen by the name of Davidson, and he took over the work of Beguin, who died soon after Davidson arrived. By way of becoming a Frenchman Davidson changed his name to d'Avissone, which was probably what the French called him anyway. He was very successful, for in 1647 he was appointed professor of chemistry at the Jardin du Roi—the first of many famous chemists to hold that position. D'Avissone was a strong advocate of the use of the salts of antimony, mercury and other metals in medicine and, like Paracelsus, believed in the insulting approach. He advised doctors who were ignorant of chemistry to keep their mouths shut because they should know something about a subject before opposing it. However, he did better than Paracelsus for he held his job for four years before he was fired.

For a century and a half after Paracelsus there were numerous iatrochemists scattered throughout western Europe and Great Britain. Most of them were also physicians or apothecaries. Some were ardent supporters of Paracelsus, a few were lukewarm and some opposed his theories and recommendations but continued to search for drugs. The majority supported the chemical theory of disease. One of them became more specific and attributed disease to too much acid or alkali in the body. With this theory the cure was obvious: if the body contains too much acid give the patient alkali, or vice versa, because acids and alkalis neutralize each other. After a century of use this theory became doubtful because it failed to give satisfactory results in many cases. It was a noble effort but, alas, humanity had to wait two hundred years for Pasteur and his bacterial theory of disease.

The laboratory preparation of salts of metals and their introduction as drugs was an innovation of the iatrochemists. Among the many salts that were made a few proved to be useful remedies and some are still in use. However, the iatrochemists did not limit their search for drugs to the metallic salts, but continued to search for remedies among the natural substances, chiefly the leaves, seeds, barks and roots of plants. Consequently, the alchemist's furnace began to give way to equipment used to extract the drug, the odor or the flavor of a plant material, and so the extract was often called the essential oil.

Oil is more easily described than defined. It is usually thought of as a somewhat greasy liquid that is insoluble in water. However, there are three kinds of oils: fatty oils, such as olive and castor oil, which are greasy; petroleum, which comes from wells drilled into the earth and which is also greasy; and essential oils, which still retain the original meaning of extracts of plants and which are not greasy. The true essential oils are thin, colorless liquids that evaporate readily and are somewhat soluble in water. Some of the plant extracts are solids, especially the drugs, and, of course, are not oils at all. Among the common essential oils are oil of rose, oil of violet and oil of lilac, used in perfumery; then there are oil of peppermint, oil of wintergreen and oil of cloves, used as food and beverage flavors.

Plants with strong odors or flavors have always been thought to have medicinal value. Many an elderly person today can remember the catnip, horehound and boneset teas of his youth. The iatrochemist naturally attempted to separate the essences of such plants in order to test their effectiveness as medicine. He wanted also to get the essence into a bottle so he could keep it because many plants lose their essential oil by evaporation as the plant dries out—a phenomenon that is very familiar to anyone who has tried to keep cinnamon, nutmeg or other natural spices in a hot climate.

One of the processes used to get the essence from a plant is called *steam distillation*. The process is a very simple one and it has been widely used from the earliest times. The plant, let us say peppermint, is put into a large pot or still, designed somewhat like a big teakettle. The spout is connected to a pipe that is coiled into a helix. The coil is placed in a tub of cold water, or better yet, running water. Some water is added to the peppermint in the still and then boiled. The heat evaporates the water and the oil of peppermint, and the vapors pass into the coil where they are condensed back to a liquid. The oil floats as a clear layer on the surface of the water. The two liquids are easily separated by skimming off the oil, or by the use of a separatory funnel or a similar device invented for the purpose of separating two immiscible liquids. The separatory funnel is simply a funnel

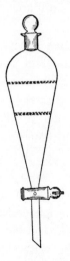

Figure A. A modern separatory funnel.

with a stopcock in the stem so that the bottom liquid can be drawn off and the stopcock closed, leaving the top liquid in the funnel. A similar vessel was found in ancient Sumer and so the process of steam distillation is very old, but the iatrochemists made several improvements in the stills, condensers and separating equipment used in the process.

Few of the essential oils were ever found to have any value as drugs, but many of them found their way into the perfume or flavor industries. Everyone is now familiar with the flavors of oils of orange, lemon, peppermint, wintergreen, cloves, spearmint and juniper (gin) and the odors of many others that are used in perfumes, cosmetics and soaps.

All odors are properties of either gases or the vapors of liquids or solids; otherwise the odorous substance could not reach the nose. The odor of sulfur water is the odor of the gas hydrogen sulfide; the odors of flowers and the flavors of seeds, leaves and roots are generally the odors of vapors of liquids; the odorous substances in camphor and vanilla, however, are the vapors of solids.

Some plant essences cannot be separated from the plant by steam distillation. Such are the sweet taste of sugar, the bitter flavor of quinine and the sour taste of grapefruit. These flavors do not evaporate and so the iatrochemist had to use a different process to get such substances out of the plant material. They used the ancient process of extraction; there are many ways to carry it out. If beets are sliced thin and soaked in water, the sugar passes through the cell walls of the beet into the water. The water solution can then be drawn off and filtered through cloth or some other porous material to remove particles of beet or other trash. Then the chemist evaporates the water at a low temperature to avoid scorching the sugar, which is left in the pan. The sap of the sugar maple tree and of sugar cane are solutions of sugar and some other substances in water. Today, cane and beet sugars appear on the market with all their impurities removed. Maple sugar retains most of its impurities to supply its characteristic flavor. When sugar was first extracted from plant sources it was used as a medicine. It was never effective as a drug, but it has become our favorite flavor.

Extractors that were used by the iatrochemists and those that have been invented since are of many types and designs in order to get the best type for each particular purpose. A drip coffeepot is a modern batch extractor, and a coffee percolator is a continuous extractor. The woody part of the coffee bean is insoluble in water, but the caffeine, flavoring substances and color are all soluble. The design of these extractors, together with the grinding of the coffee, are intended to extract most of the flavor and make a satisfactory beverage. If the idea were to get all the extractives out of the coffee then the chemist would arrange to have several portions of fresh water pass through the finely ground coffee. If the water is evaporated from the coffee extract a solid remains, and this is the process of making "soluble coffee." One difficulty that the manufacturer of soluble coffee encounters is the volatile flavor of the coffee, which makes it inclined to evaporate along with the water. This effect is sometimes noticed in the kitchen where the air smells more like coffee than the coffee does. Engineering methods have reduced the loss of flavor considerably in the manufacturing process, and the modern coffeepots have lessened the loss of flavor that was common in the older types in which coffee was boiled with water. Probably the simplest type of extractor is the tea bag in a cup of water—a principle that is sometimes used in industrial extractions.

With their stills and extractors the iatrochemists searched the plant kingdom for drugs and found several including quinine and morphine, which are still in use. They also found many odors and flavors, and hundreds of them are still in use from the rare attar of roses to the common vanillin.

Among the many salts that were made by the iatrochemists sodium sulfate was outstanding. It was discovered, or at least promoted, by the German chemist Glauber (p. 66), who thought so highly of its medicinal properties that he called it *sal mirabile* and touted it about Europe in language that could compete with any of the claims made by a present-day advertiser of nostrums. The salt is still used somewhat in medicine as a mild laxative, and both chemists and druggists are likely to call it Glauber's salt.

The iatrochemists investigated some of the physiological properties of their salts and their plant essences. The testing of the salts was more difficult than that of the plant essences, because, in most cases, the plants were known to be nonpoisonous, whereas the toxicity of the salts made in the laboratory was totally unknown. The usual procedure was to test the drug on one of the lower animals. Then, if no ill effects occurred, the chemist tried it on himself. The early alchemists, searching for the elixir of life, often omitted the animal test and swallowed the drug directly. It has been reported that some of the early Chinese emperors, working as alchemists, killed themselves in pursuit of such knowledge.

When a chemist made or discovered a new substance he named it anything he chose. Such were the names aqua vitae (alcohol), aqua fortis (nitric acid), oil of vitriol (sulfuric acid), corrosive sublimate (mercuric chloride) and calomel (mercurous chloride). These and many other such names were given to chemical substances by the alchemists and the iatrochemists, and some of them still persist, mainly on the labels on bottles in the drugstore or in books on the history of science. Chemists seldom use them. The habit of secrecy was not so great among the iatrochemists as it had been among the alchemists, and so the chemists made some feeble attempts to systematize the names. When copper dissolves in sulfuric acid it produces a blue salt, with iron the salt is green, and with zinc it is white. The iatrochemists named these salts blue vitriol, green vitriol and white vitriol, respectively, to connect them with the acid, which was oil of vitriol.

In the century following the death of Paracelsus the iatrochemists examined the more common salts and the available herbs and found a few drugs. They also eliminated many salts and extracts as useless, or worse still, as poisonous. Iatrochemistry then began to decline and by the year 1700 the search for drugs had become incidental to other practical work in chemistry. So ended the third period in the history of chemistry with still no solution of the mystery of the composition of matter. The four elements of Aristotle were almost forgotten. The *tria prima*—mercury, sulfur and salt— was losing caste. One iatrochemist substituted water for mercury in this trio, but nobody pretended to explain the composition of anything by stating how much of each of these three elements was present in any particular kind of matter.

The ancient chemists of the practical-arts period had made their contributions to civilization with their ink, paint, soap, tile, bricks, porcelain, glass and seven metals. The alchemists had contributed little of consequence to the development of chemical science in more than fifty generations. The iatrochemists had signed the death warrant of alchemy and, in their brief century and a half, had not only contributed some drugs to the relief of the ills of their fellow men but, through their books, had also given impetus to the study of chemistry. Industrial processes were improved and chemistry began to be studied for its own sake—simply for the increase in knowledge.

CHAPTER FOUR

The First Chemical Theory

THERE WERE CHEMISTS in the sixteenth and seventeenth centuries who were not iatrochemists. The healers stole the show because of the popular interest in drugs and the persistence with which the healing art was promoted, but others advanced the science by experiment and publication that did not concern medicine.

BIRINGUCCIO

Vanoccio Biringuccio (1480–1538) was strongly opposed to the views of the alchemists and had little interest in iatrochemistry. Born in Siena, the city with the famous horse race in the public square, Biringuccio lived there most of his life and worked for the ruler of the city as architect, gunsmith, metallurgist and chemist. He was not a university graduate but picked up his education as he traveled over Europe. Biringuccio wrote a book, but it was not published until two years after his death. Written in Italian, it was the result of his vast practical experience.

Biringuccio was a foundryman as well as a metallurgist and cast a bronze gun barrel twenty feet long—the longest on record. He also must have cast bells for he knew that when antimony is added to the bell metal it improves the bell's tone.

The alchemists had insisted that there were only seven metals: gold, silver, copper, iron, lead, tin and mercury; but the miners knew that there were more and Biringuccio includes both arsenic and antimony in his book. The book, *De la Pirotechnia*, was in ten volumes, or a work in ten books as it was called in those days. The first volume was about mining the ores of the principal metals. The later volumes treated the ores of less importance; the recovery of metals from their ores; alloys of the metals; casting cannon, bells and other objects; furnaces and their equipment; gunpowder and other materials of warfare.

Black powder was the only powder used until near the end of the nineteenth century, when smokeless powder began to replace it. The Spanish-American War was fought with black powder, and it is still in use for some purposes. It has always been made from charcoal, sulfur and saltpeter. Sulfur occurs naturally in Italy and elsewhere and charcoal is easy to make, but saltpeter is hard to come by. Biringuccio describes the method used in his day to produce and purify saltpeter—the method used for the next three hundred years. He says:

> The best saltpeter is obtained from animal manure converted to earth in stables, or from latrines which have not been used for a long time, and above all from pigpens. This manure must be converted into earth by time and entirely dried and powdered. Vats are then filled alternately by layers of this earth about four digits deep, and layers one digit deep of a mixture of two parts of quicklime and three parts of the ashes of bitter oak. The vats are filled to about four digits or half an arm's length from the top and then filled with water. The water seeps through this earth, dissolves the saltpeter and trickles through the holes in the bottom of the vats into conduits that carry it to other vats.

Then Biringuccio tasted the solution and if it was not strong and salty enough he passed it through the vats again, or through newly charged vats, until it was strong enough to suit him.

Saltpeter is potassium nitrate, and like other nitrates, it is very soluble in water and so the nitrates do not occur in nature in any great quantity except in caves and deserts. In Chile there are deposits in Atacama Desert. The origin of nitrates found in caves and in the Chilean desert is much the same as that of Biringuccio's saltpeter—these natural deposits are mostly from the excrement and the body remains of birds. The nitrate is formed by the oxidation of organic nitrogen compounds by the oxygen of the air.

For making gunpowder one must have a nitrate that does not take up moisture from the air. If powder is to explode it must be dry. Potassium nitrate meets this requirement, but the natural nitrates are seldom compounds of potassium. The wood ashes in Biringuccio's process contained potassium carbonate, which the quicklime changed to potassium hydroxide, and that reacted with the nitrate of the manure to form saltpeter.

Biringuccio's ten-volume *De la Pirotechnia* was a great success. It was first published in Italian in 1540 and then went through four Italian and three French editions; the last edition was published in 1678, nearly a century and a half after the first one.

AGRICOLA

Another chemist of the period, Georg Bauer (1494–1555), was famous for his book on mining, metallurgy and chemistry. Writing in Latin, he changed his name to Georgius Agricola —and Agricola he has been ever since. He was born in Glauchau in Saxony, and his higher education consisted of studies in theology, philosophy, and philology at Leipzig University. Agricola taught school for two years in Zwickau, wrote a Latin grammar and then decided that he needed more education and went to Italy to study medicine at Bologna, Padua and Venice. In those days the study of medicine was the study of most of the known sciences and students were not satisfied with what one university had to offer.

In 1527 Agricola returned to Germany and became city physician in the mining town of Joachimsthal. He lived there six years and in 1533 became city physician of Chemnitz where he spent the rest of his life. Mining was the main industry in this part of Germany and it seemed to interest Agricola more than the iatrochemistry of his colleagues. He published his first book in 1530 and in it classified all the minerals then known. This classification was one of the first steps in developing chemistry into an organized science.

Agricola's major work, the twelve-volume *De Re Metallica*, was published in Basel in 1556, a year after his death. The book was first published in Latin, but within a year there was a German edition. Although Agricola's book appeared sixteen years after Biringuccio's *Pirotechnia*, it did not replace the Italian work, partly because of the difference in languages and partly because the books were somewhat different although they treated the same general subjects. Agricola was neither a miner nor a metallurgist, but he lived all his life in a mining region and was a very close observer of the processes and equipment the miners and metallurgists used. Then too, a friend in Venice gave him a copy of Biringuccio's book, which he mentioned in his preface and then proceeded to draw upon for much of the material he needed for his book. Both books are well illustrated with woodcuts of machinery, tools and processes. The first volume of Agricola's book is a review of the history of minerals, mining and metallurgy. He then goes on to discuss ores and their geographical location, methods of mining, how the metals are obtained from their ores and the manufacture of acids and salts. He includes the new metals, bismuth, cobalt and zinc, but does not treat the casting of cannons, bells or other objects as Biringuccio had done. Despite the popularity of *De Re Metallica* it was not translated into English until the late President Hoover and Mrs. Hoover translated it in 1912.

PALISSY

A third chemist and writer of the sixteenth century was the Frenchman, Bernard Palissy (1510–1589), who was an artist and no student of classical languages, but a self-made chemist. Palissy started out with no training but great determination to improve the enamel on dishes and other porcelain ware. His method indicates more ambition than judgment. He admitted that he knew nothing about clay and never had heard how enamels are made; even so, he collected materials that he thought might be useful and ground them to a fine powder. Next, he got some unglazed pots and broke them up. These pieces of broken pottery he covered with his fine powder and baked in a furnace. This was trial-and-error experimentation of the first order. However, after repeating the process through fifteen or sixteen years, he finally got some pretty fair enamels, although they were probably not as good as those made in Italy at the time, and certainly inferior to those from China. One of his several books describes his method of making enamels and the difficulties he encountered.

Aside from his work in ceramics Palissy was interested in salts and wrote a book on the subject. One of the ideas in this book was ahead of its time. This was the belief that plants deplete the fertility of the soil by taking salts out of it, and that salts should be added to the soil to replace those taken out by the plants. He did not know which salts were involved, but his general idea was developed into the fertilizer industry more than three hundred years later. Palissy also wrote a book on alchemy and made it clear that attempts to make gold and silver always ended in failure. He thus drove another nail into the coffin of alchemy.

In spite of the writings and experiments of Paracelsus, Biringuccio, Agricola and Palissy, progress in chemistry was very slow and it was nearly a century before another chemist of their stature carried the science forward. Iatrochemistry had to wear itself out before chemists would turn their attention to the study of chemistry solely for the purpose of learning something about it.

VAN HELMONT

Among the first and greatest chemists to appear on the scene was Jan Baptista van Helmont (1577–1644), who was born into the nobility at Brussels. For his higher education he went to the University of Louvain where he studied philosophy, theology and classical languages for a time, and must have learned Latin very well for he later wrote his books in that language. However, Van Helmont became interested in the sciences at the university and turned his attention to mathematics, astronomy, chemistry, physics and medicine. He received the doctor's degree in 1599 and then took the usual tour of Europe and England. He did not return home until 1605 when he married and settled down for the rest of his life at Vilvorde, a suburb of Brussels.

Van Helmont was Count of Merode and, since he did not have to work for the necessities of life, he took his medical practice rather lightly and spent most of his time working in chemistry. He was a follower of Paracelsus, but he did not follow very closely. In his medical views he was not only independent of Galen and Avicenna but also of Paracelsus. His claim to fame rests mainly on some of his chemical experiments. He discovered carbon dioxide, which he called *gas silvestre*, and learned that it is formed by burning charcoal and alcohol, by wine fermentation and by the action of acids on sea shells. He also learned that the gas is found in caves and in some natural waters. This is a lot of information, but Van Helmont did not have a satisfactory method for collecting a gas and so the only properties he discovered were that the carbon dioxide is heavier than air and that it will put out a fire.

Among the observations of Van Helmont was the fact that animal and vegetable matter, and also many minerals, give off water when they are heated. He also noted that fish and other marine life grow in water and concluded that they are made of water. These observations gave him the notion that everything, at least in part, is composed of water, and he planned an experiment to prove it. Van Helmont dried a large quantity of soil as thoroughly as he could and then placed exactly 200 pounds of it in a large ceramic pot. In this soil he planted a 5-pound willow tree and covered the pot as well as he could with sheets of iron to keep out the dust and to prevent mechanical loss of soil by accident. He watered his tree for five years with distilled water, or rain water, which is naturally-distilled water. Each fall the tree shed its leaves, but Van Helmont collected and weighed them. After five years he removed the tree and cleaned the soil from the roots. The tree weighed 169 pounds, a gain of 164 pounds. To complete the experiment he dried the soil and weighed it. It still weighed 200 pounds.

To Van Helmont, the results of this experiment proved his point. The soil had lost nothing and the water was all that had been added; therefore, the 164 pounds that the tree gained must have come from the water. Besides, he had used distilled water and so there could not have been any earthy matter in that. His reasoning was better than his experiment. If he had burned the tree he would have found some ashes, which came from the soil. Of course, he did find that the soil had not lost any weight, which was the result of one of two possible errors: either his scales were not good enough to weigh such a heavy object accurately or, more likely, he did not get the soil as dry the second time as he did the first. Drying 200 pounds of soil is a major operation. Even drying a few ounces is a problem—it either is not quite dry or some of the components have been decomposed by the heat. Therefore, we can forgive Van Helmont for missing the loss from the soil. However, there was a much greater error in the experiment. He assumed that a tree feeds only through its roots and so neglected the possibility that the tree might take something from the air through its leaves.

The composition of the air was unknown in Van Helmont's time and, moreover, it would be almost impossible to discover the effect of air in an experiment of that kind. The facts are, as chemists learned long afterward, that a tree takes carbon dioxide from the air and combines it with water taken through the roots to make the wood and other materials of its composition. Ironically, Van Helmont had discovered carbon dioxide, but the air contains only 0.04 per cent of it, and he had no tests that would detect such a small amount.

Although the celebrated willow tree led to a wrong conclusion it was an important advance in the progress of chemistry, for it was the first recorded quantitative experiment. Van Helmont measured how much the tree gained and how much the soil lost, or at least he tried to. Furthermore, it was a controlled experiment; that is, he took into account everything he could think of that might affect the results. He dried the soil to remove the water because he knew that to weigh a sample of the soil as it came from the ground would not mean anything—it might be dry, damp or wet. He guarded against mechanical gain or loss through dust or spillage. He weighed the leaves. With the state of chemical and botanical knowledge of the day these were all the conditions there were to take into account.

Van Helmont wrote a lot but published very little. His complete works were published by his son in 1648, four years after his father's death. His works had a great influence on chemistry in the latter half of his century, for his quantitative experiment and his experiments with carbon dioxide and several other gases, purely for gaining information, were new ideas in a science that had been devoted to making gold or drugs for more than fifteen centuries.

JOHANN GLAUBER

The first half of the seventeenth century was a troublesome time in Europe. There were civil wars in England (1642–1649), France (1648–1653) and Germany (1618–1648). Of these the most devastating was the Thirty Years' War in Germany. It is not surprising that progress in chemistry and the other sciences was slow. However, there was one German chemist who managed to do a lot of work in industrial chemistry although he had to retire to Holland a time or two to do it. This was Johann Rudolf Glauber (1604–1668), who was born in Karlstadt, the son of a barber, and became an orphan while he was still very young. Consequently, he had very little formal schooling and picked up his education as he wandered about Europe and worked at various jobs to support himself—a very different life from that of Van Helmont.

Glauber was attracted to chemistry by a personal experience; he had a fever and was cured by a mineral water. Being of a curious turn of mind, he examined the water to find what there was about it that made it such a good medicine. The investigation disclosed the salt, sodium sulfate, which Glauber called *sal mirabile*—his main contribution to iatrochemistry, which we have mentioned in Chapter Three.

Glauber settled in Amsterdam about 1646, worked there for two years, and returned to Germany after the peace of Westphalia had ended the Thirty Years' War. After trying out a few places he settled in Kitzingen where he sold wine, manufactured vinegar and continued his experimental work in chemistry. By 1654 he had trouble of some sort and moved back to Amsterdam where he worked all his remaining years. Here he set up a laboratory that employed several assistants. It was an experimental laboratory and also a small factory that made sulfuric, nitric, hydrochloric and acetic acids and several salts including the famous *sal mirabile*. In his research activity Glauber heated some coal in a closed brick furnace, condensed the vapors given off in a crude apparatus and discovered phenol (carbolic acid) and benzene in the tarry liquid that came from the coal. Glauber's large-scale production of so many chemicals gives him a fair claim to the title of founder of industrial chemistry.

Like Van Helmont and many other chemists of the day, Glauber was a prolific writer—he wrote forty books. In 1666 he became partly paralyzed, but he kept on working and writing until his death in 1668.

ROBERT BOYLE

Several chemists on the continent of Europe had made their contributions to the decline of alchemy and the crude beginnings of a chemical science, but England had lagged behind. For four hundred years after the valiant efforts of Roger Bacon, we hear very little about the progress of chemistry in England; then came the first of a long line of famous English chemists, Robert Boyle (1627–1691).

Boyle's father, Richard Boyle, was an Englishman who went over to Ireland on a government job. As soon as he was established there he went into real estate and politics and, with some royal favors, he did very well. He came into possession of large tracts of land, became Earl of Cork, and was said to be the richest man in England and the most influential in Ireland. However, the Earl anticipated trouble in Ireland and bought some land in Dorset where he built a house to which he could move his family in case of necessity. This estate he named Stalbridge.

Robert, who was the youngest of fourteen children, was born at Lismore in the province of Munster. His early education was from tutors; when he was eight, he and his brother Francis, who was thirteen, were sent to Eton accompanied by a servant. After four years the two boys went to Paris, Lyons and Geneva, where they studied for twenty-one months with another tutor. Robert studied Latin, Aramaic, Hebrew, Syriac, the Bible, rhetoric, mathematics and Roman history. One of his early tutors at home was a Frenchman, and Robert spoke French well enough to pass for a French boy.

In 1641 the two boys and their Swiss tutor moved on to Italy and studied in Venice, Florence and Rome. Robert was always a great reader, and while they were in Florence, Galileo died there and Robert began to read his books, chiefly from curiosity. It was his first introduction to science.

The boys did not stay long in Italy. They started home and got as far as Marseilles when they received a letter from their father, which not only did not contain a remittance, but did contain the sad news that trouble had come and the Boyle estates in Ireland had been confiscated. Consequently, there would be no more money forthcoming. The boys were very short of funds, but Francis managed to get back home and Robert went back to Geneva. Their tutor was still with them in Marseilles and apparently loaned Robert money for the trip to Geneva and to live on for the next two years. In 1644 Boyle sold some of his jewelry and returned to England. He moved in with his favorite sister, Katherine, Lady Ranslagh, who was a widow living in London. At his father's death in 1643 Robert had inherited Stalbridge and after a year or so in London he moved down to his estate.

Boyle was a quiet, retiring person wrapped up in his books. He was tall and thin, stuttered and always imagined himself sick. Consequently, he was always taking nostrums to cure his imaginary ills. He never married but lived alone with his servants at Stalbridge and spent his time in writing—he even wrote a novel. Then, in 1649, Cromwell suppressed the Irish uprisings and restored the estates to their former owners. This gave Boyle considerable land in Ireland and in 1652 he went over there and spent two years getting his estates in order; then he returned to London.

During Boyle's years at Stalbridge he had gone up to London frequently to meet with a group of men for informal discussion—just a talkfest. Boyle called this group the Invisible College, but when he returned to London in 1653, the city was suffering from the effects of the Civil War and the Invisible College had disbanded. Boyle returned to Stalbridge, but found it rather lonely and in 1654 he left his country estate and moved to Oxford. Up to this time Boyle's main interest had been in religion and ethics, but when he got to Oxford he met several scientists, became interested in their subjects and proceeded to establish laboratories, hire assistants and get down to serious work in physics and chemistry. He remained in Oxford for fourteen years and in November 1668 moved back to London with his sister Katherine.

Besides his scientific work Boyle was interested in public affairs. In 1660 he and eleven other men founded the Royal Society of Great Britain, which was chartered by Charles II two years later; Boyle was its president from 1680 until his death. He was a very religious person and became one of the governors of a trust fund to bring religion to the American Indians.

In June 1670 he had a stroke, which did not incapacitate him entirely, for he remained active until his death. Oddly enough, his sister died December 23, 1691, and a week later Boyle died. Such, in brief, was the life of the Honorable Robert Boyle.

Wrong ideas die hard. Boyle tried the transmutation of metals but soon abandoned the project. He had become skeptical of the doctrines of both the Greeks and Paracelsus. His doubts were not purely philosophical, for he heated some gold for several months and found that it had lost no weight nor could he extract anything from it. He reasoned that if gold were composed of sulfur, salt and mercury, or any two of them, the gold should lose weight when heated because both sulfur and mercury are evaporated by heat. He even offered to finance the cost of any experiment that would show gold to be composed of mercury, sulfur and salt. Furthermore, he heated a lot of other substances and found that they decomposed but gave different products in each case. The mercury, sulfur and salt theory just did not seem possible.

Boyle also pointed out one of the most fundamental principles in chemistry, namely, that after a chemical reaction has occurred the properties of the new substance may be, and usually are, very different from those of the parent substance. He dissolved copper in sulfuric acid and studied the properties of the resulting substance. The red, metallic copper dissolved in the acid and made a blue, crystalline salt that was soluble in water and had other properties that were very different from those of the metallic copper or the colorless liquid sulfuric acid. This fundamental principle is familiar to everyone today. Bright and shiny steel exposed to moist air turns to a brown powder. Solid yellow sulfur burns to a pungent, choking, colorless gas. Common salt bears no resemblance to the poisonous, yellow chlorine gas or the bright, metallic sodium that combine to form it.

Boyle did a large number of experiments in chemistry. He worked out a method for obtaining phosphorus from its compounds. He discovered some colored substances that are one color in an acid and another color in an alkali. These substances are called *indicators* and are still very useful for determining whether an unknown liquid is acidic or alkaline. He studied combustion and learned that it stopped when the air is exhausted or withdrawn. Boyle also worked with metals. He heated lead, tin and copper separately in both open and closed vessels and found that each of them changed to a powder, or *calx*, and that the calx weighed more than the original metal. He said that the increase in weight was caused by particles of fire that passed through the glass and were absorbed by the metal.

TORRICELLI'S BAROMETER

An Italian scientist and mathematician, Evangelista Torricelli (1608–1647), who had been educated in Rome, went to Florence in 1641 to become secretary to Galileo. Three months after his arrival Galileo died, but Torricelli stayed on in Florence to become a professor of mathematics in the

Florentine Academy. He was also a physicist and in 1643 he made his famous contribution to physics, chemistry and meteorology—the barometer. Torricelli took a straight glass tube about 3 feet long and sealed one end of it. He filled the tube with mercury, inverted it and placed the open end in a dish of mercury and then secured the tube in a vertical position. The mercury in the tube fell somewhat but remained at a height of about 30 inches above the level of the mercury in the dish. This device of Torricelli's was and is the barometer; although the modern ones use a smaller tube and a small cup at the bottom instead of the dish of mercury, the principle is exactly the same. Torricelli explained the result by saying that the weight of the air on the surface of the mercury in the dish is the same as that of a column of mercury 30 inches high, and the 6-inch space between the mercury and the closed end of the tube is a vacuum. He was right and the space is still called a Torricellian vacuum.

The strange results of Torricelli's experiment intrigued others. Blaise Pascal (1623–1662), the French philosopher, mathematician and amateur scientist, thought that if Torricelli were right about the air holding up the mercury, then the column should be less than 30 inches on the top of a mountain because the air would be lighter up there. Pascal was something of an invalid, but in 1648 he persuaded his brother-in-law, M. Périer, to climb the 4800-foot Puy de Dôme near Clermont-Ferrand in south central France and set up a barometer. Pascal was right; the height of the mercury was less on the top of the mountain.

Boyle had a library of three thousand volumes and kept up with what was going on in science. He learned about these experiments by Torricelli, Périer and others and also that the German physicist Otto von Guericke had invented an air pump. One of Boyle's assistants in the laboratory was Robert Hooke (1635–1703), who later became a famous scientist, curator of the Royal Society and a professor at Gresham College in London. Hooke was a good mechanic and made several improvements on the Von Guericke air pump. Then he and Boyle began to experiment with it. They proved that air has weight and also, following Pascal's reasoning, they placed a tall bell jar over a barometer and pumped the air out—a procedure that was much easier than climbing a mountain. As the air pressure diminished the barometer fell. This established once and for all that the height of the barometer depends on the pressure of the air and explains why your radio announcer tells you that the barometer is 29.90 inches, which means that the mercury column stands at 29.90 inches above the level of the mercury in the cup at the bottom of the tube. Since 30 inches is the average reading of the barometer at sea level, 29.90 inches means that the reading is below normal and perhaps it will rain; the more water vapor there is in the air the lighter it is since water vapor is lighter than dry air. Boyle discovered that the barometer reading changes from hour to hour, but he did not know why.

BOYLE'S LAW

Boyle also put a lamb's bladder, with a little air sealed in it, under a bell jar and pumped the air out of the jar. The air in the bladder expanded and distended the bladder and thus proved that air has a pressure of its own that does not depend on its weight. Now Boyle was all set for his most famous experiment; the results constituted his first scientific paper, which was published in 1660. The title of the paper was *New Experiments Physico-Mechanical touching the Spring of the Air and its Effects.*

For these experiments Boyle and his assistants bent a glass tube somewhat in the shape of the letter J, making the two arms of the tube as nearly parallel as possible. Then the shorter section was sealed at the end. They broke the first tube and then got another that was so long that the ceiling was not high enough to accommodate it and so they set it up in a stair well. They poured enough mercury into the tube to seal off the short end and carefully tilted the tube to equalize the pressure so the mercury would be at the same height in each arm of the tube. Then they pasted a paper scale on each arm of the tube so they could measure the height of the mercury. The scales were in inches divided to eighths.

One of the men went up the stairs and poured a little mercury into the tube, which forced the mercury up into the short arm a little way. The other member of the team was at the bottom to read the height of the mercury in the tubes. Once a reading was made and recorded, they added more mercury and took another reading. The pressure on the air in the closed arm, of course, would be the pressure of the air at the open end of the tube plus the height of the mercury in the open tube above the level in the closed tube. They took twenty-five readings. They could have taken more because they only used seven feet of their long tube, but they ran out of mercury and were also afraid that the weight of the mercury might break the tube. Boyle had determined the specific gravity of mercury to be 13.76 and so knew that the pressure on the tube at the bottom was nearly 60 pounds to the square inch.

The following table gives some of their results. A is the length of the air column in the short end of the tube; B is the excess height of mercury in the long arm of the tube; C is the air pressure at the time of the experiment; D is the sum of B and C; and E is what the pressure should have been

if the volume of the air were inversely proportional to the
pressure upon it. That is, as the table shows when the volume
is reduced from 12 to 6, the pressure is twice the original.

Some of Boyle's Results

A	B	C	D	E
12	0	$29\frac{2}{16}$	$29\frac{2}{16}$	$29\frac{2}{16}$
10	$6\frac{3}{16}$	$29\frac{2}{16}$	$35\frac{5}{16}$	35
8	$15\frac{14}{16}$	$29\frac{2}{16}$	$44\frac{3}{16}$	$43\frac{11}{16}$
6	$29\frac{11}{16}$	$29\frac{2}{16}$	$58\frac{13}{16}$	$58\frac{2}{16}$
4	$58\frac{2}{16}$	$29\frac{2}{16}$	$87\frac{1}{16}$	$87\frac{7}{16}$
3	$88\frac{7}{16}$	$29\frac{2}{16}$	$117\frac{9}{16}$	$116\frac{6}{16}$

After they had finished this experiment they started over
again with the mercury levels the same in the two arms of the
tube. This time they reduced the pressure on the imprisoned
air by pumping some air out of the open end of the long tube.
In this experiment they took eighteen readings, and so in all
they had the volume of a fixed amount of air under forty-
three different pressures. If the volume of air is strictly proportional to the pressure on it, the corresponding values in
columns D and E should be the same. They are not quite
the same, but Boyle did not see to it that the temperature
was exactly the same during all the readings. Also he assumed that the volume of air in a 6-inch column was exactly
half that in a 12-inch column and this would not be true unless the tube was absolutely uniform in diameter. It probably
was not, for it is very difficult to make a tube of uniform
bore. When we consider the simplicity of the apparatus, with
its hand-drawn tube, paper scale and lack of temperature
control, Boyle's results are remarkably accurate.

This first scientific paper by Boyle was an enormous contribution to science. It was the first elaborate quantitative
experiment since Van Helmont grew his willow tree fifty

years earlier. It also gave to science the invaluable *Boyle's law*, which is now stated as follows: If the temperature does not change, the volume of a sample of gas is inversely proportional to the pressure upon it. Boyle worked with air only, but his followers have found that the law applies to all other gases.

Chemists often find it necessary to work with a gas, and over the past three centuries they have found Boyle's law indispensable. If a chemist measures the volume of a gas he still does not know how much he has, for any sample fills the vessel that contains it whether it be a pill bottle or a barrel. Therefore, the chemist must know what the pressure on the gas is, and then he can calculate what the volume would be if the pressure were 1 atmosphere (30 inches of mercury), which is the pressure all physicists and chemists use for reporting gas volumes. For example, when you read that the weight of air is 1.293 grams per liter, it means that that is the weight of pure, dry air at a pressure of 1 atmosphere and at zero degrees Celsius (frequently called centigrade). Boyle's law provides the chemist with a method for the pressure calculation, and another law, which was discovered several years later, tells him how to make the calculation of the volume at 0° C, the standard temperature. Imagine having to wait to measure a gas until the temperature is zero (the freezing point of water) and the barometer reads 30 inches. If you lived in Denver you would have a long wait for a barometer reading of 30 inches because in that elevated city the average barometer reading is about 25 inches. And if you lived in Miami, which is about as close to sea level as you can get without getting wet, there would be a long wait for the zero degrees. Besides, who wants to work at a freezing temperature? Boyle's law and its temperature companion relieve chemists of this arduous necessity.

After the publication of his paper in 1660, Boyle turned his attention to chemistry. The next year, in August, he published a small book, *The Sceptical Chemist*. The book was written in English and later translated into Latin for the benefit of the Europeans. It was very popular and ran through several printings. In 1680 Boyle published a second edition with some new material added.

Boyle not only doubted the theories of Aristotle and Paracelsus, but in his book he proposed a somewhat elaborated version of the ancient atomic theory of the early Greek philosophers. He said that all matter is composed of corpuscles—particles too small to be seen. His statement of his theory is not very clear, but he seems to have thought that the corpuscles of different materials are of different shapes and sizes and in constant motion. Different clusters of them produced the characteristic properties of the various substances.

Whether or not Boyle began to change his idea of the composition of matter is doubtful, but in the 1680 edition of his book he suggests the modern idea of chemical elements in these words: "And to prevent mistakes, I must advertize you that I now mean by elements . . . certain Primitive or Simple, or perfectly mingled bodies, or of one another, are the ingredients of which all those call'd perfectly mixt Bodies are immediately compounded, and into which they are ultimately resolved." Translated into twentieth-century English this is the modern definition of an element, but with Boyle this idea was philosophical in nature, because he did not make any experiments to distinguish simple from compound substances and did not propose any list of elements. Even so, Boyle was a century ahead of his time with this idea.

One of Boyle's contemporaries was also ahead of his time. This was John Mayow (1640–1679), a London physician who was also a chemist and a member of the Royal Society.

Mayow inverted empty jars over water, supported several substances above the water in them and burned the substances by heating them with sunlight through a lens. He found that the volume contracted as the substances burned and the water rose in the jar. When the material would no longer burn, the air left in the jar would not support life. These and other experiments led Mayow to the conclusion, published in 1674, that both air and saltpeter contain "nitro-aerial spirit" which supports combustion and also life. In other words, Mayow was the first to discover certain effects of oxygen, but he did not explore its properties except its effect on fire and life.

THE PHLOGISTON THEORY

A new development occurred in the middle of the seventeenth century that tended to distract the attention of chemists from the work of Boyle and Mayow. This was the invention of the phlogiston theory of Becher and Stahl.

Johann Joachim Becher (1635–1682) was the son of a Lutheran preacher. His father died while Johann was a boy and so he had to make his own way in the world. At one time he was one of Boyle's assistants. He had neither the wealth nor the education of Boyle, but he did manage to get a doctor's degree from the University of Mainz. Like many a self-made man Becher became very versatile. He was personal physician to the Elector of Bavaria and others of the nobility and he also served as a diplomat for some of them. In his spare time he planned a Rhine-Danube canal, devised a world language, proposed colonies for Germany, engaged in several industrial enterprises and wrote sixteen books. But he seems to have had a little trouble holding a job. He moved to Munich, Vienna and Holland among other places and in 1680 went to England, where he died two years later.

Becher resembled Paracelsus in his wanderings, his theories and his death at forty-seven. He gave different names to the three elements of Paracelsus and expanded the idea of one of them. The sulfur of Paracelsus became the *terra pinguis* of Becher and the cause of fire. This was no new idea, but Becher bore down upon it and explained fire very simply: any substance that will burn contains terra pinguis and as it burns the terra pinguis escapes. When metals are heated the terra pinguis escapes and the calx is left. One weakness of this theory is obvious: when metals are heated they gain weight, as Boyle and other chemists had shown, whereas if something escapes they should lose weight. That metals do gain in weight when they are heated in air was well known and probably Becher knew it too. But he set forth his theory in a book published in the year of his death and so he never explained the theory in any detail. This was done very ably, however, by Stahl.

Georg Ernst Stahl (1660–1734) had a career vaguely similar to that of Becher, but he was much more fortunate. He was born in Ansbach in 1660—after the end of the Thirty Years' War. He studied medicine at Jena and at the age of twenty-three began to teach there. In 1693 he became professor of chemistry and medicine at the University of Halle and taught there for twenty-two years; he then went to Berlin as personal physician to King Frederick William I, and held that position until his death in 1734.

Stahl was a great student of Becher's books and in 1702 he republished Becher's *Subterranean Physics*, which had first been published in 1669. Stahl published about two hundred writings of his own including a book in 1687 and another in 1713. In these books he elaborated Becher's explanation of fire.

Stahl changed the name of Becher's terra pinguis to

phlogiston and so the explanation of fire became the phlogiston theory, and the period in the history of chemistry from about 1670 to 1770 is the Phlogiston Period to the historian of the science. The theory dominated the thinking of chemists for that entire century.

The chemist of today is quite familiar with all the phenomena of burning and sometimes wonders why anybody ever believed the phlogiston theory. It had very little experimental support, but it is called a theory because it was the only explanation of burning and related phenomena for more than a hundred years.

The phlogiston theory came from casual observation. Consider the main premise: anything that will burn contains phlogiston and when it burns the phlogiston escapes. Also, the more phlogiston a substance contains the more violently it burns. Anyone who has seen a bonfire or a burning building must agree that it certainly looks as though something is escaping. Metals, on the other hand, burn very slowly, at least those known at the turn of the eighteenth century do. Stahl recognized that the conversion of metals to a powder by heating them was the same as the burning of wood or anything else. Wood was mostly phlogiston and so very little ash was left, but metals contained very little phlogiston and so did not burn very well and left abundant ash, that is, calx. Stahl knew that the calx from a piece of metal weighs more than the metal from which it was formed. But he did not let that worry him; if he considered it at all, he probably thought that phlogiston was weightless or had negative weight —a buoyancy effect like the gas in a balloon. The negative weight explanation was a favorite one with some of the later supporters of the theory.

Phlogiston also entered into biology. Plants took it from the air and stored it. Animals got it from eating plants, and then returned it to the air as they breathed, for the heat of the animal body was caused by slow burning. Fermentation that produced wine also gave off phlogiston. When air would no longer support burning or life it was because it was phlogisticated, that is, the air was full of phlogiston. Stahl knew that air was necessary for both breathing and burning, but thought that its effect was purely mechanical—it just swept away the phlogiston.

If the calx of copper, tin or lead is heated with coal, charcoal or fats, the metal is set free again. Stahl explained this very simply: coal, charcoal and fats are all rich in phlogiston and so they transfer some of it to the calx during the heating.

Not all chemists at the dawn of the eighteenth century were phlogistonists, but the vast majority of them were. The theory had originated in Germany, but it had its advocates in England, France, Holland and Sweden, in fact, all over Europe and among the few chemists in America. The wide acceptance of the theory is surprising because nobody ever claimed to have isolated phlogiston and studied its properties. It was as elusive as the philosopher's stone. However, many substances burned completely, leaving no ash at all; two such substances were alcohol and ether, both well known to Stahl. Complete combustion would indicate that these substances are pure phlogiston and yet they differ in odor, taste, density and many other properties; but nobody seems to have suggested that there are different kinds of phlogiston. And then there was still the troublesome fact that metals gain weight when they burn and so apparently gain rather than lose something.

Two hundred years before Stahl, Leonardo da Vinci (1452–1519), the Italian artist, inventor and scientist, said: "The fire destroys without intermission the air that supports it and would produce a vacuum if other air could not come to supply it. As soon as the air is in no condition to sustain a flame, no earthly creature can live in it. . . ." A century later the French doctor and chemist Jean Rey, in 1630, found that lead and tin increased in weight when he heated them in open vessels. His explanation was that "this increase in weight comes from the air, which has been condensed, made heavy and rendered somewhat adhesive by the . . . heat of the furnace." But neither Leonardo nor Rey had a Stahl to advertise his theory.

Here and there another voice was raised, but the phlogiston theory survived until chemists began to investigate gases and devised better methods for handling them. This they began to do in the middle of the eighteenth century. By the time the American colonists had declared their independence the phlogiston theory had received several blows.

The books of Biringuccio, Agricola and Palissy and the experimental work of Van Helmont, Glauber and Boyle constituted the advances in chemistry that accompanied and followed the wave of iatrochemistry. They were the first vague efforts to produce an organized science of chemistry. But a theory always stirs the imagination; the phlogiston theory was the glorious event of those years and so, out of all proportion to its importance, it furnished its name to the Phlogiston Period of chemistry.

CHAPTER FIVE

The Beginning of Chemical Science

Before the year 1700 Becher had advanced a hypothesis to explain fire and respiration. Van Helmont had investigated some sources of carbon dioxide with its more obvious properties and had performed the famous willow tree experiment. Several chemists had discovered that some of the metals form a calx when they are heated in air and that the calx is heavier than the metal from which it was formed. Boyle had expressed his skepticism of the notions of Aristotle and Paracelsus, and had suggested that some substances are elements, which combine to form all other substances, but he did not elaborate this idea although he lived more than a decade after he suggested it. Most of the chemists were too busy trying to support the phlogiston theory to pay any attention to Boyle's suggestion of elements and compounds. This was the state of chemistry in the early eighteenth century, but by the end of that century chemistry had become a science.

Why should chemists accomplish more in less than one century than they had accomplished in the previous fifty? There were many reasons, but two of the major ones were the formation of scientific societies and the fact that some chemists began to study gases seriously just to learn what they could about them.

SOCIETIES AND JOURNALS

Groups of scientists who join together to discuss their subjects call themselves by a variety of names; the most common are club, society, association, academy, institute and college. The name "academy" was the most common in the eighteenth century although one of the earliest groups was the Royal Society in England, which was chartered by Charles II, July 15, 1662. In 1666 the Royal Society began publication of a journal, *Philosophical Transactions*. A member of the society sometimes performed experiments before the others or read a paper to report the results of experiments that he made in his laboratory. Such presentations would be discussed by the members and later the paper would be published in their journal as a permanent record. This journal was widely distributed in England and on the Continent and soon the work of the English chemists became widely known. The Royal Society also elected a few foreign members, and through its meetings and its journal it became a powerful factor in the advancement of the science of the time.

The French Academy of Sciences was established in 1666. It was similar to the Royal Society and its scientific papers were published in its *Memoirs* (reports). Other academies of science were established in Italy (1560), Spain (1657), Germany (1672), Russia (1725), Sweden (1739), Denmark (1742), and Portugal (1779).

There were also journals that were not connected with any society or academy. In 1778 Lorenz von Crell began publication in Germany of the *Chemisches Journal*, the first journal devoted only to chemistry. Crell's journal ran for three years and then, in 1784, he resumed publication but changed the name to *Chemische Annalen*, which continued until 1803. In April 1789 several French chemists published the first number of *Annales de Chimie*, which has survived to this day. In some cases a chemist would publish the results of his research in pamphlet form and distribute copies to his friends, to libraries or to anyone who asked for a copy. Publication had reached a fairly satisfactory state by 1775, but it had one defect that still persists—delay. Such delay, as we shall soon see, often led to controversy over who was the first to make a discovery.

Today, there are hundreds of scientific groups and over ten thousand periodicals that publish papers on chemical subjects, in addition to thousands of books, pamphlets, patents and bulletins. Modern precautions reduce controversies over priority of discovery to a minimum. If a paper is read before a scientific meeting, the date on which it was read is given in a footnote to the article when it appears in a journal, perhaps a year after it was read. For example, an article in the *Journal of the American Chemical Society* may have a footnote that reads: "Read before the meeting of the American Chemical Society, September 10, 1957." This date then becomes the date of the discovery announced in the paper. In case a paper was never read before a meeting, the journal will have some statement such as: "Manuscript received for publication August 12, 1957." Chemists and other scientists and inventors are anxious to get credit for their discoveries and inventions whether the reward is money or a bit of glory but, despite all the precautions, doubts sometimes remain. Some cases of priority have been decided by the courts, others have been the study of historians and some have never been settled.

Although there are still many academies and other scientific groups of a general nature, many specialized societies have sprung up. There is not only an American Chemical Society, but also an Oil Chemists Society, an Association of Cereal Chemists, a Society of Cosmetic Chemists and several other specialized groups in the United States alone. The academies admit members from all fields of science.

THE STUDY OF GASES

Aside from Boyle's work on the pressure of gases, which was purely physical, and Van Helmont's primitive study of carbon dioxide, almost nothing had been done to investigate the gases before the beginning of the eighteenth century. Even the nature of air was unknown; it had been called an element and few had questioned that conclusion. One reason for the neglect of the gases was that there were so few of them. Even today, there are only ten gaseous elements and some twenty-five or thirty gaseous compounds out of a total of over two million known substances. Chemists had not discovered more than half a dozen of these forty gases before the middle of the eighteenth century. The fact that nearly all gases are colorless was also a factor in their neglect because it was not obvious that they were different substances.

The gases were all still called *airs* until near the end of the eighteenth century despite the efforts of Paracelsus and Van Helmont to introduce the word *gas*. This ancient nomenclature tended to obscure the fact that the gases are as different from each other as the liquids and the solids are. In fact, the first investigation of the eighteenth century that involved gases led to this conclusion. The Reverend Stephen Hales (1677–1761), an English clergyman and amateur botanist, had read the work of Boyle and Mayow that had been done fifty years earlier and was impressed by the fact that both plants and metals absorb air and fix it, that is, make it into a solid. This information started Hales heating various materials and collecting and measuring any air they gave off. Among the many things he heated were blood, tallow, horn, wood, peas, mustard seed, tobacco, brandy, water, saltpeter and oyster shell—apparently anything that came to hand. He also collected airs from fermentation and putrefaction and from the action of acids on metal.

Hales used a musket barrel for a retort in which to heat his materials and connected the end of it by means of a tube to a jar of water inverted in a pan of water so he could collect the gas. Judging from the materials he heated we can assume that he must have got oxygen, hydrogen, carbon dioxide, nitric oxide and methane, but he did not examine any of them for he was only interested in how much air each substance had fixed. He just assumed that they were all ordinary air and so his chief contribution to chemistry was his method of collecting gases. He published only two papers, one in 1727 and the other in 1733.

In the early years of the century the University of Leyden was probably the leading university in Europe, at least, in the field of medicine. Hermann Boerhaave (1668–1738) was the rector and professor of medicine, botany and chemistry. His students became the most famous chemists of the day and were Boerhaave's main contribution to chemistry. However, he did publish a textbook in 1724, *Elementa Chemiae*, which was translated into English, French, German, Russian and Turkish. It was the leading textbook of chemistry for the next fifty years. Although the book was written in the Phlogiston Period he did not mention the phlogiston theory.

The alchemists had claimed that heating mercury would convert it into a solid and Boerhaave's best-known research was done on that problem. He heated mercury for fifteen years and distilled it four hundred times, but it was still a liquid. By then almost everybody was convinced that the alchemists were wrong, but the time and effort that Boerhaave spent on the problem indicates the difficulty of proving a negative statement, that is, proving that something does not happen. In Boerhaave's research a skeptic could say that perhaps if he had heated the mercury twenty years or distilled it five hundred times he would have converted it into a solid. Beware of negative statements.

Boerhaave also thought that the atmosphere contains a food for life and that chemists should investigate it. Some fifty years later they did, and the first chemist to do so was Joseph Black, who learned his chemistry from one of Boerhaave's students. Joseph Black (1728–1799) was a Scot born in Bordeaux where his father was a wine merchant. He studied chemistry and medicine at the University of Glasgow and later at Edinburgh where he was graduated as a doctor of medicine in 1754. After teaching anatomy and chemistry at Glasgow for ten years, he became professor of chemistry at Edinburgh in 1766 and held that position until his death thirty-three years later.

Black was a great teacher. Latin was going out of style as a spoken language and so he lectured in English and illustrated his lectures with demonstrations. He was the instructor of many famous chemists; one of them, Benjamin Rush, became professor of chemistry at the University of Pennsylvania—the first professor of that subject in North America.

CARBON DIOXIDE

The chemical research for which Black was most noted was on carbon dioxide, or fixed air as he called it. Mild and caustic alkalis were both used as drugs at the time and Black undertook to find the difference between them as his thesis for the doctor's degree. He began with the mild alkali magnesia alba, which we now know as a basic carbonate of magnesium. His first experiment consisted of heating the drug and collecting the gas. He found that the alkali lost seven-twelfths of its weight and that the gas was mostly fixed air. This was the first time a gas had been weighed indirectly, for the loss in weight of the solid was the weight of the volume of the gas he collected.

He carried out the same experiments with marble and chalk and got the same results that he obtained with the magnesia alba. This time, of course, the calx was quicklime. The calxes that Black got from his heating experiments were both caustic alkalis, but he found that they would take up fixed air and become mild alkalis again. In modern chemical language Black found that magnesium and calcium carbonates give up carbon dioxide when they are heated and become the oxides and when these oxides are exposed to carbon dioxide they combine with it to form the carbonates again. He also found that the oxides and carbonates of each of these metals give the same salt when they are treated with acid.

Lime is slightly soluble in water, and Black discovered that a clear solution of limewater can be used as a test for carbon dioxide. Bubble a gas through the limewater and if it is carbon dioxide a white cloud of calcium carbonate forms. With this test he showed that the atmosphere contains a small amount of carbon dioxide and that the breath contains more. I suppose that every chemistry student since the days of Black has tested his breath by Black's method. Nobody has improved the test yet. Black's thesis on the carbonates was published in 1756 and he never investigated gases any further. Although he did much research in other fields his big contribution to chemistry was the thorough manner in which he planned and carried through his experiments, the use of the balance for quantitative work and the matter-of-fact manner in which he interpreted his results. This was the Phlogiston Period, but Black paid no attention to that theory. In fact, he set a pattern of work that others followed and that finally gave the deathblow to phlogiston.

HENRY CAVENDISH

Black was a professional chemist. He made his living teaching the science and also did research in the field. His English contemporary, Sir Henry Cavendish (1731–1810), like Boyle a century earlier, was a wealthy English gentleman with a consuming passion for experimentation. Cavendish, the grandson of the second Duke of Devonshire, was born in Nice in the south of France where the family had gone in search of a milder climate because of the mother's health. He entered Cambridge University in 1745 and spent four years there, but for some reason did not take a degree. He was what most of us would call an eccentric. He wore old clothes of the style of his youth or before and was very shy in the presence of others. He did not care for religion, money or women. He never married and instructed his female servants to stay out of his sight. He kept his money in the Bank of England and when the bankers tried to consult him about some investments he told them that if they didn't quit bothering him he would withdraw his account. They quit, but they apparently did quite well with the investments for at the time of his death his wealth was about seven million dollars.

Cavendish had a house in London in which he lived and had his laboratory. His library was so large that he had to have a separate house for it. He also had a country house in which he had another laboratory—his sole interest was experimentation. If his clothes wore out, he got some more just like them and so avoided any time lost in selecting the style and kind of cloth. All he asked was to be left alone. Nobody seems to know what Cavendish did during his first ten years out of Cambridge, but in 1766 he read his first paper before the Royal Society.

HYDROGEN

Cavendish worked in mathematics, physics and chemistry. His first experiments in chemistry were with inflammable air (hydrogen). He used Hales's method of collecting gases by an inverted bottle of water in a pan of water, except that Cavendish, who had more money than the Reverend Hales, used mercury instead of water for most of his gas collecting. He showed that zinc, iron and tin all produce the inflammable air when dropped into either hydrochloric or dilute sulfuric acid. The other metals available to Cavendish did not produce the gas and neither did nitric acid or concentrated sulfuric acid when they were used with the zinc, iron or tin. He weighed the metal he used and measured the volume of gas it produced, which led to the discovery that each metal gave a different volume of the gas for the same weight of the metal. Then he weighed the gas itself by weighing a dried bladder, filling it with the gas and weighing it again. He calculated his results as specific gravity using air as a standard, that is, he took the weight of the air as 1. For his inflammable air he got the value 0.09. This is a good value when we consider the difficulty in getting the same temperature and pressure on the gas every time, and also the fact that the dilute acid is mostly water and so the gas would be mixed with water vapor. The correct specific gravity of hydrogen is 0.069.

Cavendish performed many experiments with this gas that we now call hydrogen. One of the most important of them showed that 423 volumes of hydrogen combine with 1000 volumes of air to form water. This alone was a brilliant achievement. Air is about 21 per cent oxygen and so 1000 volumes of air would contain 210 volumes of oxygen. He thus established very accurately the important fact that hydrogen combines with half its volume of oxygen to form water. Water had always been considered an element and the fact that it is not was revolutionary. Cavendish is usually considered to be the discoverer of hydrogen although Boyle and several others had prepared it previously and had shown that it will burn. However, the inflammable airs reported by these earlier chemists were not always hydrogen: some were carbon monoxide and some were methane. Cavendish measured the specific properties of hydrogen and thus showed it to be a definite substance. No other gas, for example, has a specific gravity as low as the 0.09 Cavendish got for that property.

NITROGEN

After the discovery of oxygen in 1775 Cavendish proceeded to show that the air contains 20.84 per cent oxygen, and after four hundred experiments he decided that air has the same composition regardless of its geographical source. He published this conclusion in 1784. Hales had discovered a colorless gas that reacts with air to form a brown gas that is soluble in water. Cavendish used this reaction to analyze the air. He added the gas, which is now called nitric oxide, to air confined in a jar over water and found that as the brown gas (nitrogen dioxide) formed and dissolved in the water, the volume of the air in the jar diminished. He kept on adding the gas until the air no longer lost volume, and concluded that when the air didn't shrink any more there was no more oxygen in it. The amount of shrinkage was 20.84 per cent. The present value is 20.94 per cent.

Cavendish passed air over burning charcoal in a closed apparatus and then bubbled the emerging gas through a solution of potassium hydroxide, which he knew would absorb the carbon dioxide formed. The gas that he collected he called *mephitic air* because it would not support life and neither would it support combustion. However, this gas was somewhat lighter than air. This was the discovery of nitrogen, but Cavendish was no more interested in fame than he was in money, and so he delayed publication of this discovery for ten years; meanwhile, another chemist got credit for the discovery. Cavendish studied nitrogen rather thoroughly. He arranged to produce an electric spark in a jar of air confined over water. He added extra oxygen to the air and noticed that the spark produced the brown, soluble gas, the volume of the air decreased and the water contained nitric acid. Over 99 per cent of the air disappeared, but however long he continued the spark, the other 1 per cent remained. This was the first that anybody knew that nitric acid is composed of oxygen, nitrogen and hydrogen. The last 1 per cent of the air was apparently so small that Cavendish did not investigate it. A century later another chemist found it to be argon.

Cavendish, like Black and several others, investigated carbon dioxide. He prepared the gas by several methods and studied its properties. He found that at 55° F water dissolves about its own volume of the gas and that the gas is completely removed from the water by boiling for fifteen minutes. His determination of the specific gravity of the gas gave a value of 1.57—the best modern value is 1.53. Cavendish worked quantitatively whenever he could. Marble gave up carbon dioxide when heated and thus lost 40.8 per cent of its weight. In this work on carbon dioxide Cavendish also studied fermentation and putrefaction to see if these processes gave off any other gas. He found that they did give off other gases, but he did not identify any of them.

In addition to his work on gases, Cavendish hit upon the

principle of equivalence. For example, if it requires twice as much nitric acid as sulfuric to dissolve one ounce of marble then it will take twice as much to dissolve one ounce of any other carbonate. In other words, sulfuric acid has twice the dissolving powder of nitric acid. Several years after Cavendish made this discovery, another chemist stated the matter of equivalence in the form of a law.

In brief, the eccentric Cavendish, in his half-century of work, showed how to establish the identity of a gas, proved the composition of air, water and nitric acid, and furnished the idea that later became the important law of equivalents. These outstanding accomplishments, together with several lesser ones, make Sir Henry Cavendish one of the immortals of science. When he discovered hydrogen he thought it was pure phlogiston, but he gave up that idea after he had read some of the papers of his French contemporary, Lavoisier.

JOSEPH PRIESTLEY

A very different person from Sir Henry Cavendish was his fellow countryman, Joseph Priestley (1733–1804), whom Cavendish knew very well, for both were members of the Royal Society and read their papers at the meetings. Priestley was poor. He was the son of a weaver in a village near Leeds. From 1752 to 1755 he attended Daventry Academy where he studied theology, philosophy and foreign languages including Arabic, Chaldean, Hebrew and Syriac. After Daventry he became a country preacher. He was a Calvinist and a very vocal dissenter from the doctrines of the Church of England. His salary as a clergyman was low and he taught to get enough money to live on. Then in 1761 he became a full-time teacher of various subjects, mostly history and languages, at Warrington Academy. After six years on that job he returned to preaching, this time at a church in Leeds where he lived near a brewery.

Priestley was now thirty-seven years old and had no training in chemistry, but the gas from the fermentation vats in the brewery aroused his curiosity and he began to experiment with it. The gas, of course, was carbon dioxide, which had already been worked over pretty thoroughly by several chemists. The only new thing that Priestley discovered about it was that a water solution of it tastes good; he thus discovered soda water. For this discovery the Royal Society gave Priestley its Copley Medal in 1773. The members seemed to think that the soda water had some medicinal value, especially for scurvy, which was a troublesome disease of sailors on long voyages. However, the soda water turned out to be useless as a drug and scurvy remained a problem.

While Priestley was at Warrington he published several papers on education, history and biography. In recognition of one of his papers on biography, the University of Edinburgh gave him the honorary degree of Doctor of Laws. Also during the Warrington period he went to London where he met Benjamin Franklin. Franklin told him about electricity, which inspired him to collect more information on the subject and write a book, *The History and Present State of Electricity*. This publication earned him election to the Royal Society in 1773.

In 1772 Priestley became librarian to the liberal politician, Lord Shelburne. His pay was £250 a year, a summer home in Calne, a winter home in London and an annuity of £150 for life to start at the end of his work for the generous Shelburne. After eight years of service Priestley's religious and political views became too strong for his patron and he went back to preaching. He was a supporter of the American Revolution and later of the French Revolution. Neither attitude was popular with either the British aristocracy or the government. Nearly all of Priestley's scientific work was done while he was with Lord Shelburne who, incidentally, continued Priestley's annuity until the latter died in 1804.

Priestley's most important chemical work was with gases and was purely qualitative. He was attracted to the gas that Hales had gotten from the action of nitric acid on pyrites. He discussed this with Cavendish who suggested that he could probably get the same gas from the action of nitric acid on other substances, including the metals, since the gas likely came from the nitric acid. Priestley explored this idea and found that Cavendish was right. He prepared the gas by several methods and used it to devise the method that Cavendish used to find that the air contains 20.84 per cent oxygen. Priestley was not as good an analyst as Cavendish—he reported that the air is about one-fifth oxygen.

Priestley used Hales's method of collecting gases but, like Cavendish, he often substituted mercury for water. He also improved the method by inventing the pneumatic trough to replace the pan of water. He prepared sulfur dioxide, carbon monoxide, hydrogen chloride, ammonia and nitrous oxide, all of which were new to chemists. Most of these gases were prepared by heating something, but his heating equipment was not very good until 1774 when he got a lens a foot in diameter—the best heating device of the day, that is, when the sun shone.

DEPHLOGISTICATED AIR

On August 1, 1774, Priestley heated *mercurius calcinatus per se* with his new lens and collected the gas over mercury. He found that a candle, wood, and even iron burned brilliantly in this gas and that mice would live longer in it than in an equal volume of air. He also found that when the air is exhausted so that it will no longer support animal life, a plant placed in the exhausted gas will restore its respirable property.

The *mercurius calcinatus per se* was a red powder prepared by heating mercury exposed to air for a long time at a low temperature; we now call the powder mercuric oxide. Priestley also prepared this gas from a mercuric oxide made by dissolving mercury in nitric acid and then heating the salt that was formed. These two oxides of mercury were the same, but chemists did not know that at the time. In fact, Priestley's experiments helped to establish the identity of the two substances made by the two different methods. He also got the same gas by heating red lead.

In October 1774 Lord Shelburne went to Paris and took Priestley with him. Here Priestley met several French chemists including Lavoisier and told them of his discovery, although he had not named the gas or completed a study of its properties. He bought more oxide of mercury in Paris and went back to London in November, but he did not do any more work on his gas until the spring of 1775, possibly because of a scarcity of sunlight for his lens. After he resumed his work he inhaled the gas himself and from the effects he concluded that the gas might be of value in lung disorders. He also found that when a stream of the gas was passed over burning wood the wood burned more violently. Priestley predicted that the gas would be used to make fires hotter. Present-day use of the gas bears out both these predictions.

Priestley also showed that the gas from mercuric oxide is the same as one of the gases of the air and so he called it *dephlogisticated air*—he was an ardent phlogistonist. Later, Lavoisier gave the gas its present name of oxygen.

The discovery of oxygen was Priestley's greatest contribution to chemistry and his last of any importance. In 1780 he left Lord Shelburne for a church in Birmingham. Here he spent most of his time writing religious and political tracts and becoming increasingly unpopular. On July 14, 1791, when Priestley and other supporters of the French Revolution were preparing to celebrate Bastille Day, a riot broke out and a mob burned Priestley's church, his house and all his personal property. The riot went on for three days and then the army stopped it. His friends helped Priestley to escape and he went to London. Here, however, he found the members of the Royal Society unfriendly and he resigned from that organization. Later he sued the city of Birmingham for damages and recovered £2500.

Living in London became uncomfortable for Priestley and in April 1794 he sailed for New York. America was more hospitable; he was offered a church in New York and a professorship at the University of Pennsylvania. He refused both offers and went on to Northumberland, Pennsylvania, where three sons had settled several years before. There he built a house and a laboratory, but he kept up his interest in religion also. He had no need to worry about politics for his ideas agreed with those of the early Americans. He did meet several American politicians, however, including President Jefferson. At Northumberland he published a *History of the Church* and a *Defense of Phlogiston*. He was a phlogistonist to the end and believed in defending his views.

In his later years at Northumberland, Priestley prepared water gas, a mixture of carbon monoxide and hydrogen, by passing steam over hot charcoal, and he also did some work with compounds of mercury. It has been rumored that he was poisoned by his enemies. Nothing is more unlikely, for neither his politics nor his religion caused any flurry in Pennsylvania. The symptoms of his last illness did indicate poisoning, but he had just been working with carbon monoxide and volatile compounds of mercury and both are extremely toxic. He died in 1804.

KARL WILHELM SCHEELE

In Sweden a contemporary of Cavendish and Priestley was making his contribution to the chemistry of the gases. Karl Wilhelm Scheele (1742–1786) was the youngest son in a merchant's family of eleven children. His father became bankrupt in 1745 and Scheele's education was rather scant. He went to a private school for a time but at fourteen was apprenticed to an apothecary in Gothenburg. Here he had access to books, chemicals and apparatus. He was a born student and the druggist encouraged him in his studies, but the druggist died in 1764 and Scheele, who had already completed his apprenticeship, went to another druggist as an assistant and remained there four years. In 1768 he moved on to another drugstore in Stockholm and in 1770 to still another in Uppsala. Finally in 1776 he went to Köping and bought a drugstore of his own. In all these places he carried on his studies and his experiments in chemistry.

Scheele was not entirely self-taught. In Stockholm he worked with a Professor Retzius and they together isolated tartaric acid from cream of tartar, which is a by-product of the manufacture of grape wine. Retzius read the paper before the Swedish Academy and it was published in 1770—the first publication of Scheele's work, although his name was not on the paper. Then, in Uppsala, Scheele met Professor Bergman of Uppsala University, who encouraged him in his researches. In 1775 Scheele was elected to the Academy of Sciences, which was an unusual honor for an apothecary's assistant.

Scheele made an enormous number of contributions to descriptive chemistry, especially when we consider that he was also a pharmacist with the usual duties and that he died at the age of forty-four. He discovered citric, tartaric, malic and gallic acids—all of them from plant juices. He also made oxalic acid from sugar and obtained glycerin from olive oil. He showed that graphite is carbon by burning it to carbon dioxide. A study of the mineral pyrolusite, which is an oxide of manganese, led him to the discovery of chlorine and several manganese salts. Among Scheele's other discoveries were deadly poisonous gases: arsine, hydrogen sulfide and hydrogen cyanide.

Although Scheele contributed a host of new compounds to the list of known chemicals, he is best known for his discovery of oxygen and his bad luck with publication. As early as 1771 he prepared and collected oxygen. He prepared it by heating some ten different substances including mercuric oxide and saltpeter, which he decided were the best sources of the gas. In addition to the omission of his name from his first paper, he was constantly having papers delayed or refused altogether, so that he became discouraged with publication and sometimes did not even bother to write reports of his research in form for publication. All his work on oxygen was done in the years 1771 and 1772, but he did not submit the results for publication until 1775 and then the publisher did not get around to printing the paper until 1777. Meanwhile, Priestley had discovered the gas and published the results of his work. Scheele called the gas *fire air* and found that it reacted with many substances. He also weighed it and found that it is a little heavier than air, constitutes about one-fifth of the common air and is the part of the atmosphere that supports combustion. Like Priestley, Scheele had some practical ideas, for he wrote: "If the atmosphere consisted of fire air only, water would furnish poor service in extinguishing conflagrations."

Scheele had little tendency to theorize; like Priestley he

died a phlogistonist. It has always been thought that Scheele's early death was caused by his work with poisonous gases, but a recent biographer attributes his death to rheumatism and respiratory ailments that developed from his working in an unheated shed in cold weather.

The experiments that were made with gases in the eighteenth century were sufficient to destroy the phlogiston theory, but, alas, those who performed the experiments did not realize that they could explain fire without phlogiston. It remained for the French chemist Lavoisier to combine the results of other chemists' work with some of his own to destroy the phlogiston theory and establish a new system of chemistry—a system that has survived all the experiments of the past two centuries. After more than five thousand years, chemistry became a science, largely through the thinking of one man.

ANTOINE LAVOISIER

Antoine Laurent Lavoisier, born in Paris on August 25, 1743, was the son of a lawyer. His mother died when he was four years old and his father moved in with his mother-in-law. Antoine and his sister Marguerite were raised by their aunt who was twenty at the time of the mother's death. Marguerite died at the age of fifteen and left Antoine as the sole heir to the family fortune.

Lavoisier received his first education at the Collège Mazarin. This was not like an American college, but corresponded more nearly to our elementary and high schools. After he finished at the college, Lavoisier studied law and earned the bachelor's degree at the age of twenty. Law was traditional in the family, but Lavoisier was more interested in science and studied anatomy, astronomy, botany, chemistry, geology, meteorology and mineralogy. Meteorology seems to have been his first love and he began taking barometric readings several times a day. He kept this up all his life and took his barometer with him wherever he went. In 1790, four years before his death, he drew up a scheme for predicting the weather and suggested the daily publication of forecasts.

One of Lavoisier's closest friends was the botanist and geologist Jean Guettard (1715–1786), with whom he had studied. Guettard undertook to make a geological and mineralogical map of France and invited Lavoisier to join him. Lavoisier liked the idea and worked at the project from 1763 to 1766 and again for a short time a few years later.

Lavoisier not only collected minerals on these trips with Guettard, he studied them. For example, he collected several samples of gypsum, now commonly called plaster of Paris, and determined its solubility in water; he also showed that water is part of its composition. Then he discovered that when gypsum is heated this water is expelled and when the dehydrated gypsum is mixed with water the two combine again and set to a hard plaster. He even discovered that if the gypsum is heated too hot it will not combine with the water to form the plaster. These results constituted the first of many papers that Lavoisier presented to the Academy of Sciences; it was read February 25, 1765. This was remarkable research for a chemist who was not yet twenty-two years old, for his explanation of the chemistry of plaster of Paris is still included in textbooks that discuss the subject.

In the year that Lavoisier published his first paper the Academy offered a prize of two thousand livres for the best essay on lighting the streets of a big city. Lavoisier was willing to tackle any problem and so he studied this one thoroughly and submitted an essay. He did not win first prize, but he did get a gold medal for his effort and on

June 1, 1768, he was admitted to membership in the Academy.

The Academy of Sciences was the official scientific body in France. For example, Lavoisier's gold medal was awarded by the king and the members of the Academy were appointed by him. The Academy itself selected the candidates for admission and presented them for appointment, but the king could refuse to appoint a member and sometimes did. In its official capacity the Academy appointed committees to investigate all kinds of scientific matters that concerned the public welfare. The committees on which Lavoisier served were those investigating water supply, prisons, animal magnetism (Mesmerism), adulteration of cider, the location of slaughterhouses, Montgolfier's balloon, bleaching, tables of specific gravity, paper, a powder magazine for the arsenal and nearly a hundred others. He had more committee work than a United States senator or an American college professor.

In 1771 Lavoisier married Marie Anne Pierette Paulze, who was then fourteen years old, and in 1775 he was appointed *Régisseur des Poudres*, that is, one of the supervisors of the manufacture of gunpowder. This appointment gave the Lavoisiers a house at the arsenal where they lived for seventeen years and where he did the greater part of his chemical work. Madame Lavoisier was an alert and talented person and a great help to her husband in his scientific work. She learned English and translated the papers of Cavendish, Priestley and others and also drew the illustrations for her husband's textbook, *Traité élémentaire de chimie*, which appeared in 1789.

Although Lavoisier had a position with the government he spent much of his own money on his laboratory and as a result it was the best laboratory in Europe. It was visited by all the chemists and celebrities who came to Paris, among them Priestley, Benjamin Franklin, James Watt of steam-engine fame, and Arthur Young, the celebrated traveler. Some came to work with him as assistants.

One of the most important pieces of apparatus in Lavoisier's laboratory was the chemical balance, which differs from the old-fashioned grocer's scale chiefly because it is so constructed that it is sensitive to very small differences in weight. The first balance that Lavoisier used could weigh objects up to 6 pounds with a precision of about a grain—the French grain was equal to about 53 milligrams. Modern chemical balances are limited to the weight of objects of about a half-pound or less and will show differences in weight of about 0.1 milligram. The so-called microbalance is more sensitive than that. Although this seems like an enormous improvement in chemical balances since Lavoisier's day, the difference is chiefly between the sensitivity of a balance that will weigh 6 pounds and one that will weigh less than half a pound, although in the case of the microbalance the maximum load is much less.

Black, Rey and others had used balances long before Lavoisier did, but they used them mostly for analytical work, whereas Lavoisier used the balance mainly for research. With it he established the first law of chemistry and thus became the first physical chemist.

Lavoisier's first quantitative experiment was made to test the truth of the ancient idea that heat converts water into earth. The word *earth* as chemists then used it meant any solid substance. This belief was still common in the middle of the eighteenth century and there was considerable evidence to support it. Van Helmont had grown 164 pounds of tree on water alone, others had raised vegetables in a similar manner, and when water was distilled repeatedly from a glass vessel there was always a solid left after the water had all evaporated. One chemist claimed that he had distilled the same water two hundred times and that a solid residue remained after each distillation. All kinds of natural water had been tried. Some experimenters even melted snow or hail, but the results were always the same—a solid was always left after the water was evaporated.

Lavoisier had been interested for several years in the examination of water in connection with his survey of mineral resources. He began his laboratory studies by having a glass blower make him a pelican, which was an apparatus that had been widely used by the alchemists. It consisted of a large glass globe with a short tube connecting it with a smaller globe above it so that water could be boiled in the larger globe and the steam would condense in the upper globe and the water then run back into the larger one. The smaller globe had a bottle neck opening at the top, which was closed with a glass stopper ground to fit gastight. Lavoisier distilled some water eight times, poured it into the pelican and warmed the apparatus to drive out some of the air. He then stoppered and sealed the pelican to prevent any loss of vapor. He had weighed the empty pelican and than weighed it again with the water in it. He next set the apparatus on a pan of sand and heated it with an olive oil lamp from October 24, 1768, to February 1, 1769, more than three months, which would seem to be long enough for the heat to convert a considerable portion of the water into earth.

Lavoisier cooled the pelican and weighed it; the pelican and the water weighed just the same as they had before they were heated. The reason for taking this weight was the prevailing idea that heat passed through the glass and combined with the water to form the earth. Lavoisier reasoned that if this were true the apparatus should increase in weight, and since the weight did not increase he concluded that neither heat nor anything else had passed into the vessel.

There were some particles of solid floating in the water that settled to the bottom when the vessel was left at rest for a time. Lavoisier emptied the pelican, dried and weighed it, and found that it had lost 17.4 grains. Next he dried and weighed the solid that had settled out and found that it weighed only 4.9 grains. Then he evaporated the water from the pelican in another glass vessel and got a solid residue of 15.5 grains. This made a total of 20.4 grains or 3.0 more than the pelican had lost. Then it occurred to him that he had evaporated the water in another glass vessel and that the 3.0 grains had dissolved from it. This long and tedious experiment had shown that water is not converted into earth, but that any solid left after the evaporation of water is either dissolved in the water to begin with or dissolved from the glass during the evaporation. This conclusion has been amply verified by the evaporation of water from metal vessels. The results of Lavoisier's experiment were accepted by the other chemists of the day and so he settled a controversy of long standing. The notion that heat converts water into earth was soon forgotten.

COMBUSTION

After Lavoisier finished with the water problem he began to investigate combustion. It is hard to imagine what started chemists working on diamonds, but Boyle, who was very wealthy, had shown that a diamond loses weight and its polish when heated strongly for three hours. Others had repeated the experiment. Some thought the diamond evaporated, others thought it burned and still others thought it lost small solid particles. The diamond was supposed to be a mineral like other precious stones and so would hardly be expected to burn.

Lavoisier undertook work on the diamond problem in collaboration with three others, Macquer, Cadet and Brisson. A jeweler by name of Maillard agreed to furnish the diamonds if they would let him protect them from air during the heating. The chemists agreed and he put the diamonds in a clay pipe filled with charcoal and placed the pipe inside two crucibles, one inverted over the other. Then he sealed the crucibles with clay—he was determined to keep the air out. This apparatus was heated for two hours when the chemists decided the furnace was not hot enough and got another one in which the heating went on for two hours more. The crucibles and pipe were fused into a solid mass, which had to be broken to get at the diamonds. When they were recovered it was found that there was no change in either the weight or the polish of the diamonds, which proved that they did not evaporate or give off solid particles; therefore, when heated in air they must burn. This conclusion the experimenters proposed to verify.

In the eighteenth century the best method of heating anything was by means of the burning lens, sometimes called a solar furnace, which focused the rays of the sun on a small spot and thus produced a high temperature. The experimenters borrowed two large lenses, each nearly a yard in diameter. They placed a diamond in a glass bell jar set in a pan of mercury. The diamond was supported above the surface of the mercury and the rays of the sun focused on it with the lenses. They repeated the experiment several times and found that the diamond burned very slowly to carbon dioxide, and thus these four experimenters settled the chemistry of the diamond after four years' work.

It is now well known that the diamond is a crystalline form

of carbon, for other chemists have repeated the experiments of Lavoisier and his colleagues. Further research by various chemists also confirmed Scheele's conclusion that graphite is also a crystalline form of carbon and established the fact that anthracite coal, charcoal, lampblack and soot are non-crystalline or amorphous forms of the same element.

While the experiments with diamonds were in progress Lavoisier was also studying the combustion of phosphorus and sulfur. In both cases he found that the product of combustion weighed more than the phosphorus or sulfur used in the experiment and decided that the burning consisted of the union of the substance with the air.

In 1773 Lavoisier turned his attention to the effect of heat on metals. He used several types of apparatus and made a number of experiments with lead. It was well known that if lead is heated in an open vessel it changes to a red powder, or calx. Because of this name the process is sometimes called calcination. Lavoisier found that the lead calx weighed more than the lead that formed it and that the volume of air diminished when he used an enclosing vessel. He also found that if the calx were heated with charcoal a gas was produced and the original amount of lead recovered. One thing that puzzled him was the fact that the gas produced by heating the calx with charcoal was carbon dioxide and not ordinary air.

In 1774 Lavoisier arrived at his theory of combustion, namely that burning substances are combining with the air. He then reasoned that if this were true there would be no increase in weight if metals were calcined in a vessel that was sealed airtight. Accordingly, he planned a series of experiments to test this theory. He had several glass retorts made of different sizes. His retort was a rounded glass vessel with a neck drawn out to a small tube. Pieces of metal were placed in the retort and the end of the tube sealed by melting the glass until the tube closed completely. The retort was then heated on a charcoal furnace, which was somewhat like the charcoal grills now used for outdoor cooking. Under these conditions lead changed to a red powder and tin to a gray powder. Before and after each experiment he weighed the retort and found that it had not changed in weight. If the fire had passed through the glass and combined with the metal as Boyle had thought, the weight of the retort should have been greater, and if phlogiston had escaped, the weight should have been less. Therefore, the unchanged weight eliminated both these possibilities. But according to his new theory the weight should be unchanged because if the air in the retort had combined with the metal it was still in the retort as part of the calx.

Furthermore, if the air in the retort had combined with the metal there would be less free air in the retort, and so Lavoisier now took the next obvious step. He broke the seal and noticed the sound of air rushing into the retort, a sound that lasted longer in the larger retorts than in the small ones. He now weighed the retort again after it was opened and found that it had gained in weight. The larger retorts had increased more than the smaller ones, and in every case the increase caused by this influx of air was the same as the difference in weight between the weight of the metal and the weight of the calx. These experiments supported his theory very well—the metals did combine with the air.

We have referred to Lavoisier's explanation of the nature of calcination and combustion as the *theory of combustion*, which it later became, but Lavoisier repeatedly referred to it as his *hypothesis* of combustion. Perhaps the difference between these two terms should be explained. Both theories and hypotheses are explanations of something. A hypothesis is the first explanation offered and is usually just a good guess. The phlogiston theory was really just a hypothesis. Everybody advances hypotheses continually. Who has not offered an explanation of a long drought, a week of heavy rain, why a tree is dying, what caused an accident, why a cake did not rise or why taxes are so high? In such cases little or no attempt is made to test the truth of the explanation and so your hypothesis remains a hypothesis and is soon forgotten by you and everyone else, especially the latter.

The research scientist usually has an explanation of the results of his experiments as soon as they are completed, although he may not publish his hypothesis or even mention it. He knows that if he does someone else may promptly show that the explanation is wrong; consequently, he plans more experiments designed to furnish greater support for his hypothesis before he risks publishing it. If all the experiments that have been tried support the hypothesis it is called a theory. The two terms are used rather loosely by scientists because there is no agreement as to how much supporting evidence there should be before the change is made. The word "theory" is the more common, probably because it is easier to spell and pronounce; at least, that is my hypothesis.

By 1774 Lavoisier had studied the combustion of only four substances quantitatively: phosphorus, sulfur, lead and tin. Some similar experiments had been made by other chemists, but most of them were made with one or more of these same substances. Lavoisier noticed that none of these substances combined with all the air in the vessel even though there was some of the unburned substance left. He was personally convinced of the truth of his hypothesis, but saw very clearly that it needed more experimental support. His work and that of his contemporaries furnished that support within the next few years.

Lavoisier, like research chemists today, always began his projects by reading the records of all the work that had been done on the subject. His wife's translation of papers published in English helped, for in these years most of the work on gases was done in England. However, he attended the sessions of the Academy where papers were read and the subjects discussed. Also there were his visitors—I have already mentioned the visit of Priestley in October 1774. When two chemists get together they always talk shop and so Priestley told Lavoisier about the new air he had just discovered, although at that time Priestley had not made many experiments with the new gas.

After the 1774 meeting with Priestley, Lavoisier repeated Priestley's experiments with the new gas and made some further experiments of his own. From all this information he concluded that Priestley's dephlogisticated air was the part of the atmosphere that combines with the burning substances, and proceeded to study the atmosphere. He was not a phlogistonist and so he called the gas *eminently respirable air*. By 1777 he had found that nonmetallic substances such as carbon, sulfur and phosphorus combined with this air to form acids. This conclusion led him to call the gas *oxygen* from two Greek words that mean *acid* and *to form*, and he also decided that oxygen is an element—the element *oxygen* it has been ever since.

By the year 1778 Lavoisier's theory of combustion had been well established and air had been shown to be a mixture that contained over 20 per cent oxygen and another gas that does not support combustion. Cavendish had found the oxygen content of the air to be 20.84 per cent and had made several experiments with the other gas present, which is now called *nitrogen*. Cavendish had also discovered hydrogen and proved that it combines with oxygen to form water. The combined work of Cavendish, Priestley and Lavoisier had shown that neither air nor water is an element—the notions of Aristotle were at last defunct. After the year 1778 it was known that carbon, sulfur, phosphorus, lead and tin all increase in weight when they burn and that diamond, graphite and charcoal are all carbon. All this chemical knowledge indicated that the phlogiston theory was wrong, but some chemists, including Priestley, continued to support it well into the nineteenth century.

LAW OF THE CONSERVATION OF MASS

Another result of Lavoisier's quantitative experiments was the announcement of the first and most fundamental law in chemistry: the law of the conservation of mass. A scientific law is not like an act of Congress or of a state legislature; in fact, it is very different. It is simply a generalized way of stating experimental results. Boyle's law from the science of physics is an illustration. Lavoisier's law of the conservation of mass is a similar statement. He heated six substances and found that they reacted to form new substances, but that there was no change in weight of the closed vessel and its contents. Then he made a very different quantitative experiment. It was common knowledge that yeast converts the sugar of grape juice to alcohol and carbon dioxide in the production of wine. Lavoisier thought the must of wine too complicated to analyze and so undertook a similar reaction with a simpler mixture. He weighed some water, sugar and yeast, dissolved the sugar in the water and added the yeast. As the fermentation proceeded he collected the carbon dioxide and then weighed it and all the other products of the fermentation. The weight of the carbon dioxide, alcohol, acetic acid and water together with the unfermented sugar and remaining yeast was the same as that of the water, sugar and yeast before the fermentation. He even calculated the weights of the carbon, hydrogen and oxygen in each substance and found their weights to be the same before and after the fermentation.

Just when Lavoisier became aware of his law is unknown, but he announced it in his textbook of 1789 along with the report of the fermentation experiment. His statement as it appears in the English translation of his book is: "We may also lay it down as an incontestable axiom, that, in all the operations of art and nature, nothing is created; an equal quantity of matter exists both before and after the experiment; the quality and quantity of the elements remain precisely the same; and nothing takes place beyond changes and modifications in the combination of the elements."

In the same report Lavoisier says: "We may consider the substances submitted to fermentation, and the products resulting from the operation, as forming an algebraic equation. . . ." In these words he suggested the first chemical equation although he did not write it in his book. It would probably be

yeast+sugar$\longrightarrow$carbon dioxide+alcohol+yeast+acetic acid

One of the simplest statements of the law of the conservation of mass is: *The weight of the products of a chemical reaction is exactly the same as the weight of the reacting substances.* A popular version of the law is that matter can neither be created nor destroyed—a difficult statement to prove because of the size of the universe and the negative nature of the statement. Many chemists since the days of Lavoisier have tested his law by a great variety of chemical experiments and the law has survived all of them.

THE CHEMICAL ELEMENTS

Lavoisier, together with some of his colleagues, made two other contributions to the science of chemistry; they established the present idea of chemical elements and invented a system of nomenclature. Boyle had suggested the idea of chemical elements a century earlier, but he had not suggested any method for telling which substances were elements nor had he published a list; consequently his suggestion had been almost forgotten.

Textbooks of chemistry sometimes define an element as a substance that *cannot* be decomposed to simpler substances, and this is a good way to establish the concept in the mind of a beginner; but Lavoisier was not so positive. He always emphasized the idea that elements are substances that *have not been* decomposed to simpler substances. It is interesting to note that Comstock, in a book published in New York in 1848, maintains Lavoisier's caution in his definition of an element. Perhaps it should be pointed out that a substance can be shown to be a compound by decomposing it. If red oxide of mercury is heated it decomposes to oxygen and mercury and so the oxide of mercury is a compound. Also, an electric current decomposes water into hydrogen and oxygen and so water is a compound. Compounds can also be established as such by making them from simpler substances. Cavendish first proved water to be a compound by making it from the elements. Iron oxide is not easily decomposed, but it is easily made by burning iron in oxygen. On the other hand, there was no way to prove that a substance was an element for nearly a century after Lavoisier wrote his book. Chemists just assumed that a substance was an element until somebody proved it to be a compound. Lavoisier included a list of thirty-three elements in his book.

Lavoisier's List of Elements

GASES	NONMETALS	METALS		EARTHS
Light	Sulfur	Antimony	Mercury	Lime
Caloric	Phosphorus	Silver	Molybdena	Barytes
Oxygen	Carbone	Arsenic	Nickel	Magnesia
Azote	Muriatic	Bismuth	Gold	Argill
Hydrogen	radical	Cobalt	Platina	Silex
	Fluoric	Copper	Lead	
	radical	Tin	Tungsten	
	Boracic	Iron	Zinc	
	radical	Manganese		

Of the thirty-three elements in this list ten are now absent. Azote, carbone, molybdena and platina are the elements nitrogen, carbon, molybdenum and platinum. The physicists have proved that light and caloric are energy and both the acid radicals and the earths turned out to be compounds. Lavoisier had doubts about the earths as elements, but they had not been decomposed and, as he said, ". . . at the most this is mere conjecture [that the earths are compounds]. I hope that the reader will take care not to confound what I relate as truths of fact and experience with what is yet only hypothetical." Within thirty years the earths were shown to be compounds, as Lavoisier had guessed. They are oxides.

Today's list of elements contains 103 substances, including twenty from Lavoisier's list, and there are reasons to think that the list is now about complete. Some of these elements of special interest will be discussed in a later chapter. Only eighty-eight of them occur naturally and a chemist usually deals with less than seventy; all the materials seen by the reader in an ordinary day will likely be composed of less then forty.

The idea that a few elementary substances combine to form the thousands of substances then known caught on at

once, although there was much controversy as to which substances were elements. The concept of elements and compounds was the first statement that had ever been made
that related different substances to each other in any definite manner. In other words, it established a system of
chemistry.

NOMENCLATURE

Now that there was some system to chemistry, a systematic way of naming substances was both possible and de-
sirable. Accordingly, four French chemists undertook to
devise one. They were Lavoisier, Claude Louis Berthollet,
Antoine François de Fourcroy and Louis Bernard Guyton
de Morveau. Although Guyton de Morveau, who was a professor of chemistry at Dijon, was the first to suggest a system
of nomenclature, Lavoisier was the leader in devising such a
system. The system that they invented has not been changed
fundamentally since, although some changes have been
necessary to adapt the system to languages other than
French and to include the ever increasing number of substances that have been made or found in nature.

Instead of the old names such as aqua fortis, aqua regia,
sand, Glauber's salt and other arbitrary designations, the
new names were planned to indicate the composition of
substances in terms of the elements they contain. Translated
literally from French into English, there were the names
oxide of mercury, oxide of tin, chloride of zinc, sulfide of iron
and so on. Such names were used in English for more than
two generations before anyone seems to have thought of
the difference in the nature of the two languages. Every beginning student of French in this country is familiar with
la plume de ma tante, which means "the pen of my aunt."
In English, of course, it is "my aunt's pen," but the

French do not have a possessive and are not so free with the use of nouns as adjectives, such as in the common English expressions "barn door," "window screen," and "lamp shade." A textbook published in New York as late as 1848 uses the old names oxide of bismuth, sulfate of lead, borate of soda and all the rest. Eventually, English-speaking chemists got around to the names now used in English—zinc chloride, sodium borate, lead sulfate and so on. The old names are still used somewhat in industry, pharmacy, agriculture and elsewhere outside of the science of chemistry itself. Incidentally, the word "gas" did not come into general use until these Frenchmen included it in their system of nomenclature.

THE END OF AN ERA

In a sense a science is independent of its history. To a heart patient in an oxygen tent it does not matter who discovered oxygen or when he did it, and even a chemist who makes use of a substance seldom knows who discovered it. However, in order to get a clear idea of a science it helps to know something of its age and the procedures by which it was brought to its present state. If the name of the originator of a great discovery is known it should be mentioned along with the discovery, because it is often the only reward he ever receives. Just how much a discoverer owes to his predecessors and his contemporaries is often very difficult to learn.

There were many chemists in England, France, Italy, Germany, Sweden and Holland and a few elsewhere in the eighteenth century and before, and to many of these Lavoisier was indebted for the results of their experiments and he freely admitted it; but he was the best thinker of them all and had a confidence and energy that brought about the acceptance of his ideas. Consequently, history calls him "the father of chemistry," a title that is sometimes applied, less appropriately, to Boyle.

In 1790 Jean Antoine Claude Chaptal (1756–1832), professor of chemistry at Montpellier, published his *Éléments de Chymie* based on the new system and Lavoisier wrote him:

> To see you adopt the principles which I first announced is a great joy. The conquest of yourself, M. de Morveau, and of a small number of chemists scattered through Europe is all that I had the ambition of accomplishing, and the success surpasses my hopes, for I receive from all sides letters that announce new proselytes, and I see now that only aged persons who have no longer the courage to begin again their studies, or who can no longer turn their imagination to a new order of things, still hold to the doctrine of phlogiston. All young people adopt the new doctrine, and from this I conclude that the revolution in chemistry is accomplished.

The closing years of Lavoisier's life are a long, sad story. He had been a tax collector, and the system of tax collection in France was one of the causes of the French Revolution. In the purges of those troubled times, Lavoisier was tried, convicted and beheaded all on the same day, May 8, 1794. He was fifty-one years old. Later a statue of him was erected in a public square near the Church of the Madeleine in Paris. It is interesting to note that on the day of Lavoisier's execution, Priestley was at sea, bound for New York.

By the date of Lavoisier's death the foundations of the science of chemistry as we now know it had been laid. The material substances that compose the crust of the earth are either elements or compounds of them. The metals are elements and when they corrode they combine with the oxygen of the atmosphere—all except silver, which prefers sulfur. Likewise, combustion is the combination of elements with oxygen, free elements in the case of carbon and sulfur, combined elements in the case of wood and gasoline. When a chemical change occurs the elements merely change places, so that the weight of all the products of the change is the same as that of all the substances that entered into the change. After Lavoisier was no longer on the scene, other chemists came to the fore and before the end of the century another law had been added to the science.

LAW OF CONSTANT COMPOSITION

Joseph Louis Proust (1754–1826) was born in Angers, the son of a pharmacist. He worked for a time as a pharmacist at home and in Paris before he began the study of chemistry with the younger Rouelle at the Jardin du Roi. After some research there and elsewhere in France, he was invited to Spain by Charles IV who gave him a laboratory in Madrid that was said to be better equipped than any other laboratory in Europe. Proust taught chemistry and did both industrial and pure research. In 1799 he announced the law of constant composition in French equivalents of these words: "The proportions of true compounds are invariable as is the ratio of their constituents." Originally, there was considerable doubt as to whether all samples of the same substance had the same properties. The doubts were mostly the results of impure samples and poor analyses. For example, limestone is calcium carbonate, but some samples contain magnesium carbonate. By 1799, however, the situation was pretty well cleared up and chemists generally agreed that the qualitative properties of the same substance were always the same. Their quantitative properties had not been systematically examined. Proust made many analyses, and he was the first to announce that the copper carbonate that occurs in nature has the same composition as that made in the laboratory.

Claude Louis Berthollet (1748–1822), who was one of the

leading chemists in France, had ideas opposite to those of Proust. He thought the composition of a substance depended on how it was made. His arguments were based partly on solutions and alloys, which do vary in composition, and partly on poor analyses, for he seems to have reported any analysis he found in the literature to support his views. Also, some work that he was doing at the time did seem to support his arguments. The controversy between these two French chemists was quite friendly, but it lasted for eight years during which time each of them published several papers to support his views. Proust not only analyzed several substances, but also supported his claims very vigorously. In fact, his rhetoric may have won more converts than his analyses. Among other things, he said that in all the known parts of the world you will never find more than one variety of sodium chloride, potassium nitrate, calcium sulfate and several other substances that he named. Just how many samples from all parts of the world he had analyzed is not clear. He also said that cinnabar (mercuric sulfide) from Japan is the same as that from Almadén, Spain. He also proved that there are two oxides of iron, tin, lead, copper, antimony, nickel and cobalt and that each of them has a definite composition. We now state this law of constant composition: *All samples of the same substance contain the same elements in the same ratio by weight.* As a specific example, all pure samples of common salt contain 39.32 per cent sodium and 60.68 per cent chlorine.

By 1808 Proust had prevailed over Berthollet and the law was firmly established, which was fortunate, for in that year the French army invaded Spain, Proust's laboratory was destroyed and his generous patron Charles IV was forced to abdicate. Proust lost all his possessions and returned to France in poverty. Napoleon offered him a job as supervisor of the manufacture of grape sugar and, although Proust had discovered the presence of sugar in grapes, for some unknown reason he refused the offer. He continued his research in France on a much smaller scale and in 1814, when Louis XVIII came to power, Proust was given a pension and made a member of the French Academy.

Such was chemistry in the year 1800. It consisted of two laws, one theory and the accumulated descriptive chemistry of fifty centuries.

CHAPTER SIX

The Glamorous Atomic Theory

THE THREE IDEAS—chemical elements, conservation of mass and constant composition—that were introduced into chemistry before 1800 had been firmly established over the previous twenty-five years by several chemists and with many difficulties. One of the difficulties the analytical chemist had to contend with was the awkward system of weights and measures in use at the time. Moreover, each country had a different system, which made it difficult for the chemists to read each other's papers. The system of weights used by Lavoisier consisted of

72 grains	equal	1 gros
8 gros	equal	1 once
16 onces	equal	1 livre

The livre was equal to 0.93 English pound. With 9216 grains in a livre and the livre less than a pound, the French grain was much lighter than the English grain.

In England the situation was worse than it was in France. There were three systems of weights. In the apothecaries' system,

20 grains	equal	1 scruple
3 scruples	equal	1 dram
8 drams	equal	1 ounce
12 ounces	equal	1 pound

Some chemists had been trained as apothecaries and used this system.

The troy system was used to weigh gold and silver and it has a different system of weights, but chemists seldom used it.

The avoirdupois system was, and still is, used in trade in English-speaking countries, although some of the units have different values in different countries. Great Britain uses the system with the following units:

GREAT BRITAIN

437.5	grains	equal	1 ounce
16	ounces	equal	1 pound
14	pounds	equal	1 stone
2	stones	equal	1 quarter
4	quarters	equal	1 hundredweight
20	hundredweight	equal	1 ton
1	ton	equals	2240 pounds
1	pound	equals	7000 grains

Since the apothecaries' pound has only 5760 grains, it was vital to know which pound was used when the literature reported a pound of anything. The weight of the grain, however, is the same in all the English systems.

The English system for the measurement of length and volume is no better than the system of weights. Furthermore, measures of volume are different for the measurement of different things.

Some of the variations in the measures of volume are indicated in the following tables:

LIQUIDS				SOLIDS		
4 gills	equal	1 pint		8 quarts	equal	1 peck
2 pints	equal	1 quart		4 pecks	equal	1 bushel
4 quarts	equal	1 gallon		1 bushel	equals	2150.42 cu. in.
1 gallon, U.S.	equals	231 cu. in.		1 quart	equals	67.19 cu. in.
1 gallon, Eng.	equals	277.42 cu. in.				
1 quart, U.S.	equals	57.77 cu. in.				

One hardly needs to say that calculations in these systems are very difficult. Try calculating the volume of a cube that is 2 ft. 7½ inches on an edge. Aside from the difficulties in calculation, the smallest unit in these several systems is too big for use in the laboratory: the ounce, the gill and the cubic inch are all much larger than the amount the chemist usually works with.

Another problem was the accuracy and uniformity of the units of weight, length and volume. Originally, the grain was the weight of a grain of barley, but grains of barley do not all weigh the same. Obviously, one could not make a set of weights from them, and there were similar difficulties with the units of length and volume.

Before discussing the standards that were adopted for weights and measures it is necessary to consider in some detail another system of measurement. Calculations are much simpler in a decimal system, which is evident from a comparison of English and American money.

ENGLISH MONEY			AMERICAN MONEY		
4 farthings	equal	1 penny	10 mills	equal	1 cent
12 pence	equal	1 shilling	10 cents	equal	1 dime
20 shillings	equal	1 pound	10 dimes	equal	1 dollar
21 shillings	equal	1 guinea	10 dollars	equal	1 eagle

Suppose that the price of an item is 1 pound, 6 shillings and 3 pence, what will five such items cost? Obviously, 5 pounds 30 shillings and 15 pence, but when the bill is presented it becomes 6 pounds 11 shillings and 3 pence. If an item costs 1 dollar, 6 dimes and 3 cents, the decimal system combines these into 1.63 dollars and five will cost 8.15 dollars. If this illustration is not convincing, try to calculate a 3 per cent sales tax on each of these bills.

A decimal system of weights and measures was proposed in France as early as 1670, but it was over a century before the officials got around to devising one. A committee of the Academy of Sciences was appointed for the purpose and made its report in 1791. They named their system the *metric system*. The units in the older systems had developed from ancient standards such as the weight of a grain of barley or the length of the foot of a king, but the metric system was made by a group of scientists who at once began to look about for something that could be used as a standard; something that would be exact and invariable. Think for a moment. What would you use for a standard of length? Well, these Frenchmen decided upon a quadrant of a great circle of the earth, that is, the distance from the Equator to the North Pole, and they proceeded to measure this distance on the meridian that passes through Dunkirk. The method used to make the measurement is beyond the scope of this book, but once they made it they decided that one ten-millionth of the distance would be a good length for their basic unit and they named it the *metre*, which is the French word for "measure." In English we spell the word "meter." Once the length of the standard was decided upon, a bar was made of an alloy that contains 90 per cent platinum and 10 per cent iridium. The bar is a little longer than a meter and two lines were etched across it exactly a meter apart. The bar was deposited in the archives of the French government and is still there. It is the official standard of the metric system. Platinum was cheaper then than it is now and the alloy has several advantages over other metals. It does not corrode, it is harder than gold and takes a high polish so that very fine lines could be used and thus lessen the error caused by the width of the lines. The meter is a little longer than the yard—39.37 inches to be exact.

Having settled the length of the meter, the next problem was to decide the names of the multiple and fractional units; it was to be a decimal system and so the units must vary by tens. The names were made by adding the Greek prefixes for the multiples and the Latin prefixes for the fractions as given in the following table:

1 kilometer	(km)	equals	1000	meters
1 hectometer	(hm)	equals	100	meters
1 decameter	(dkm)	equals	10	meters
1 meter	(m)	equals	1	meter
1 decimeter	(dm)	equals	0.1	meter
1 centimeter	(cm)	equals	0.01	meter
1 millimeter	(mm)	equals 0.001 meter, or 10^{-3} meter		

The size of these units is readily grasped by comparison with the more familiar English units. The kilometer is about ⅝ of a mile, the meter is a little longer than a yard, a decimeter is about 4 inches and an inch is 2.54 centimeters.

The metric system is used for general purposes in most countries except those in which English is the prevailing language. In France, Italy and Mexico, for example, the highway signs and speed limits are in kilometers, cloth is measured by the meter, waistlines in centimeters and small dimensions, such as the diameter of a wire, in millimeters.

In recent years scientists have had occasion to measure both larger and smaller dimensions than their predecessors were confronted with and have introduced several additional units for the purpose. These are:

1 terameter	(tm)	equals 10^{12}	meters
1 gigameter	(gm)	equals 10^{9}	meters
1 megameter	(mgm)	equals 10^{6}	meters
1 micrometer	(μ)	equals 10^{-6}	meter
1 nanometer	(nm)	equals 10^{-9}	meter
1 picometer	(pm)	equals 10^{-12}	meter

These units and their names were adopted by the International Committee on Weights and Measures in 1958. The micrometer has long been called the micron, abbreviated by the Greek letter *mu* (μ), and the nanometer is the millimicron, abbreviated by mμ. In addition to the above units the physicists use the old Angstrom unit (A), which is one-tenth of a nanometer, or 10^{-10} meter. These older units appear in the chemical literature before 1960 and sometimes more recently.

Units of area are simply the square of the units of length: square millimeters, square centimeters, etc. Units of volume are cubes of the units of length as in the English system. The metric system also introduced the *liter* as a unit of volume. Its volume is the same as the cubic decimeter, or 1000 cubic centimeters (cc). It is used for general purposes where we would use the quart, such as the measurement of milk, wine, oil and other liquids sold at retail. Its volume is just over a quart (1.057). The names of the other units of volume are similar to those of the units of length: milliliter (ml), centiliter (cl), etc.

The chemist uses the liter to measure large volumes of

gases and liquids and the milliliter for small volumes. Since the liter is a cubic decimeter and the milliliter a cubic centimeter, calculations that involve volumes are easily made.

Units of weight are very simply tied to the units of volume. The gram was taken as the weight of a cubic centimeter of water, but water, like everything else, changes in volume with changes in temperature. The volume of a given weight of water is smallest at $4°$ C ($39.2°$ F). For this reason the gram was defined as the weight of 1 cubic centimeter of water at $4°$ C. The names of the multiples and fractions of a gram use the same prefixes as the units of length: kilogram, hectogram, etc. The microgram is 10^{-6} gram and is abbreviated by the Greek letter gamma, γ. It is often used to record extremely small weights. For estimating the English equivalent of these weights all we need to know is that a kilogram is 2.2 pounds and that an ounce is 28.3 grams.

One great advantage of the metric system is evident from a single comparison. Suppose an object weighs 2 pounds 5 ounces 7 grains. Try to multiply or divide this number by 5, or perhaps by 17 would be better. If an object weighs 2 grams 5 decigrams 7 milligrams, the 5 dg is 0.5 g and the 7 mg is 0.007 g and the total is 2.507 grams. In fact, a chemist would set the number down as 2.507 grams from the weights on the balance and would not mention the other units at all.

The metric system soon spread from France to other countries. It is official in the United States for those who care to use it, but it is seldom used outside of scientific laboratories. There are, however, some manufacturers of drugs and other chemicals who sell their products by the gram or the kilogram, and a few give the customer his choice of pounds or kilograms. Both England and the United States are considering a complete change to the metric system.

It is obvious that any system of weights and measures is purely arbitrary, and that there must be some official standard for the units so that their values will be the same throughout the countries in which they are used. In addition to the International Committee, each country has an office that deals with the standards within the country; we have the United States Bureau of Standards. Most of the national bureaus adopt the international standards, but the national bureau may devise other standards and it controls all the standards within the country. For example, a manufacturer or user of weights, thermometers or other measuring devices can have our Bureau of Standards check and certify one of his instruments and then he can check the rest of his stock against the certified one. Almost any chemist has access to a set of certified weights; if not, then he had better get one, for some of the weights bought in the market are far from correct. The states, too, get in on the act by checking the weights and measures used by grocers and other vendors to the public.

THE THERMOMETER

Besides length, area, volume and weight there are many other things to be measured; one of the most important is temperature. Without a thermometer nobody could report how cold it was on his back porch this morning and the weather bureau would be out of business. The doctor uses temperature in his diagnoses, the chemist regulates the temperature in order to control his experiments, and even the cookbooks indicate temperatures to be used in the kitchen.

How do we go about measuring temperature? Here again the system is purely arbitrary. The familiar thermometer consists of a glass tube with a bulb at the end, filled with mercury. It dates from 1654. The earlier thermometers used alcohol colored with a dye as the liquid in the tube, and many use this same liquid today. Water cannot be used because it freezes at very common temperatures and expands and breaks the tube. The principle of the thermometer is very simple. As the liquid in the bulb is warmed it expands and the excess runs up the tube; the warmer it is the farther the liquid rises. Of course, a liquid must be selected that boils and freezes beyond the limits of the temperatures to be measured. Deciding what temperature to call each position of the liquid was the real problem.

Gabriel Daniel Fahrenheit (1686–1736), a German instrument maker who lived and worked in Holland, hit upon the idea of using mercury as the liquid and devised the familiar Fahrenheit scale in 1714. The mercury thermometer is used in scientific work because the boiling point of mercury (674° F) is much higher than that of alcohol (172° F). The alcohol thermometer is still commonly used to measure weather temperatures. Fahrenheit made his scale by placing the bulb of the thermometer in a mixture of snow and salt and marking the position of the mercury in the tube 0°. Then with the bulb in ice and water, but no salt, he marked the position of the mercury at the freezing point. Finally with the bulb in boiling water he marked the boiling point. These three temperatures are called the "fixed points" of the thermometer. The boiling point of a liquid changes with the pressure, but Holland is a low country and so the boiling point was about that at the normal pressure of 30 inches of mercury. After he established his fixed points, for some unknown reason Fahrenheit divided the space between the boiling and freezing points into 180 equal spaces and called them *degrees*. Then he found that it took 32 more spaces of the same size to go on down to the zero point, which was the lowest temperature he knew how to get. By calling this lowest temperature zero degrees the freezing point of water became 32° and the boiling point 212°. This was a very convenient scale because all common atmospheric temperatures fell somewhere on it. For use in colder climates than that of Holland the scale has been carried below zero and indicated by the minus sign. When you hear that it was ten below this morning, it of course means that the temperature was —10° Fahrenheit. This thermometer is still used by the weather bureaus in England and the United States, by many industries and by the population at large although I hear that England is about to abandon it. Most thermometers in common use have the tube mounted on wood, plastic or metal background with the scale printed on the background. Clinical and other scientific thermometers have the scale etched on the tube itself where it can be read more accurately.

It is an interesting coincidence that three men devised thermometers at about the same time. René Antoine Ferchault de Réaumur (1683–1757), a Frenchman, used two of the fixed points Fahrenheit had used, the boiling and freezing points of water, in 1730. He made his scale with the freezing point as 0° and the boiling point at 80°. Why he used eighty degrees between these two points is no more apparent than why Fahrenheit used one hundred and eighty. Réaumur's thermometer was used by Lavoisier and is still used in parts of Europe, and I encountered one in use by a Swiss cheese maker in Wisconsin just a few years ago. So few people in this country are familiar with the Réaumur scale that it is a very convenient thermometer when a chemist or a manufacturer does not care to have everybody know what temperatures he is using in his operations.

The third thermometer scale was devised by a Swedish

astronomer, Anders Celsius (1701–1744) of Uppsala. He
also used the freezing and boiling points of water as his
reference points but divided the space between them into
100 degrees. This seems to be the most logical scale of the
three. The fact that there are one hundred degrees between
the fixed points has led to the name *centigrade* scale. If you
ask a scientist what 30° C means he will probably say
"thirty degrees centigrade," but a few with better memories
or a better historical background will say "thirty degrees
Celsius."

The centigrade scale is used by the general public in the
countries that use the metric system and by physicists and
chemists everywhere in their professional work. A few days
ago I noticed that the temperature of a Florida hospital
patient had been recorded in degrees Celsius. Some journals
print the temperatures in two forms, such as 60° C (140° F),
although it is not difficult to change a reading from one
scale to the other. If the two scales are placed side by side
it will be noticed that the boiling point is 212° F or 100° C
and the freezing points are 32° F and 0° C. Between these
two points there are 180 Fahrenheit degrees and 100 centigrade degrees. Since these cover the same range of temperature, 100 degrees C equal 180 degrees F, or 1 degree C
equals 1.8 degrees F. A temperature of 60 degrees C then
represents the same expanse of liquid as 108 degrees F, but
since these are measured above 32 degrees the temperature
is 140° F. For the mathematically inclined, here are the
formulas:

$$F = 1.8C + 32$$
$$C = \frac{F - 32}{1.8}$$

In case the reader wonders what all this has to do with
chemistry it must be realized that the invention of the

metric system simplified the task of measurement and calculation, and thus contributed nearly as much to the advancement of chemistry as the invention of printing or the chemical balance. Chemists depend on many things outside their own field for the study of the composition of matter. A library is essential in order to follow the work of other chemists because the subject is too vast for each chemist to begin at the beginning. Measurement of weight, volume, temperature and many other quantities is necessary and the chemist generally adopts the system of measurement devised by others, although there are times when he must devise his own for he may wish to measure something that does not interest anyone else.

Around the year 1800, chemists were busy learning the metric system, trying to verify the laws of the conservation of mass and constant composition, and continuing the study of gases that the English and French chemists had begun several years before. There is always much routine work that goes on between the eruptions of great discoveries. These are quiet periods in which chemists are discarding old ideas and learning new ones. After Lavoisier and Proust made their contributions, phlogiston was being forgotten and chemists were beginning to take these laws and the explanation of fire for granted. Suddenly there appeared a new theory which was destined to become the fundamental basis of all chemistry—*the atomic theory*.

JOHN DALTON

John Dalton (1766–1844) was the son of a weaver. The Daltons were Quakers who lived in the village of Eaglesfield, Cumberland, in the north of England. There were six children in the family and not much money, although young John managed to get a good elementary education. He was an excellent student and was teaching in a private school in his village when he was twelve years old. From then until his death he was a teacher. His main hobby was meteorology and he worked at making barometers and other meteorological instruments. All his life he took barometer and thermometer readings and recorded them in notebooks along with other weather data. In all he made over 200,000 readings, which resulted in a book on meteorology published in 1793.

Young Dalton was a busy boy with his school, his work on his father's farm and his study of Latin, Greek and science. After two years he gave up his teaching in his home town and went down to Kendal in the next county to teach in a school run by his brother Jonathan. He taught there twelve years and in 1793 he moved on south to Manchester where he had received an appointment as a tutor in Warrington Academy, where Priestley had taught before him. He became a member of the Literary and Philosophical Society of Manchester in 1794 and in 1817 was elected president of the Society; he held that office the rest of his life. In the course of his fifty years' membership he read 116 papers before the meetings of the Society. The Society had a building in which Dalton set up a laboratory where he did most of his meteorological and chemical work. In 1799 the Academy moved away from Manchester, but Dalton remained in the city and made his living as a tutor at two shillings a lesson.

Dalton was always the Quaker. He wore the usual somber gray clothes, coat and vest, white neckcloth, knee breeches, gray stockings and buckled shoes. He retained the *thee* and *thou* of his Quaker speech and was always stiff and awkward in company. His manner of speaking was so dry and uninteresting that he was not much of a success as a lecturer. He never married—he said he could not afford the luxury of marriage.

Dalton's meteorological activities led him to a study of the composition of the atmosphere and he began to collect samples from different places and analyze them. His results, and those of others that he read about, convinced him that air has the same composition wherever it comes from. The fact that all samples of air are alike indicates that air is a compound, but Dalton proved that it is simply a mixture of gases, and that each gas in the mixture has the same pressure that it would have if it occupied the same space alone, which is Dalton's *law of partial pressures*.

One thing about the air bothered him. Carbon dioxide is heavy, oxygen is lighter, nitrogen is lighter still and water vapor is the lightest of all—the water vapor is not half as heavy as the carbon dioxide. Why, then, did the gases not stratify with a layer of carbon dioxide at the bottom and the water vapor at the top? Gay-Lussac had certainly shown that they did not. Dalton had read Lavoisier's textbook in which he found the suggestion that the particles of a gas are separated from each other by a layer of heat that keeps them apart. This idea started a train of thought that ended in the most useful and most famous theory in the history of chemistry. Dalton concluded that everything is made up of particles.

Unlike the ancient Greeks, Dalton was not just trying to explain the nature of matter, but rather trying to explain some troublesome facts that had come to his attention—a mixture of gases does not settle out like so much sand and water. Also, all samples of the same compound substance contain the same elements in the same ratio by weight, and chemical action neither creates nor destroys anything. Also, unlike the Greek philosophers, Dalton was not above making experiments. He continued with his experiments while he was thinking about the hypothesis and, among other things, he analyzed the two gases now known as methane and ethylene. Each gas contains carbon and hydrogen only, but the strange thing was that for a given weight of carbon the methane contained exactly twice as much hydrogen as the ethylene. In the methane the ratio of the weights of carbon to hydrogen was 6 to 2 and in the ethylene 6 to 1.

LAW OF MULTIPLE PROPORTIONS

Dalton next analyzed the two oxides of carbon and here he found the same thing—one contains exactly twice as much oxygen as the other for the same weight of carbon. It began to look as though this curious result was a habit and so Dalton next analyzed the oxides of nitrogen. This time he had three gases to work with and he found that one contained nitrogen and oxygen in the ratio of 7 to 8, another was 7 to 16 and the third was 7 to 4. At this point Dalton announced the *law of multiple proportions*, which is easier to understand than it is to state. One of the most common ways of putting it is: *When two elements combine to form more than one compound the same weight of one element combines with weights of the other that are in a simple whole-number ratio.* For example, in the case of the oxides of nitrogen, for 7 grams of nitrogen the ratio of the oxygen is 1 to 2 to 4.

Analysts soon began to turn up other examples of the law of multiple proportions to add to the three that Dalton had found. One example was the two oxides of copper. One of these oxides is red and the other is black. The black one contains 1 part of oxygen to 4 of copper and the red one 1 part of oxygen to 8 parts of copper. The ratio is not always 2 to 1; there are examples where it is 1 to 3, 2 to 3 and other ratios, but the weights of the elements are always in the ratio of small, whole numbers.

Speculation on the nature of gases, the conservation of matter and multiple proportions led Dalton to an explanation of the cause of it all. His explanation is his famous atomic hypothesis, for such it was called for the next fifty years. As more and more experiments supported it, the name gradually changed to the atomic theory. Today, most chemists consider it a simple statement of fact. But we are getting ahead of our story.

Dalton's atomic theory contained so many ideas that four statements are required to express them:

1. All substances are composed of atoms.

2. Atoms of one substance are all alike and have the same weight; atoms of other substances are different and have different weights.

3. Chemical action consists of union, separation and interchange of atoms. In other words, the atom is the unit that takes part in chemical action and it does not split into fractions in the process.

4. If there are two or more compounds composed of the same elements, the most common compound contains one atom of each element.

Dalton used the word *atom* for the unit particle of both elements and compounds; he called the former *simple atoms* and the latter *compound atoms*. The atom is still the basic unit of an element that enters into a chemical reaction. When hydrogen burns in oxygen to form water, atoms of hydrogen combine with atoms of oxygen to form compound atoms of water. Likewise atoms of copper combine with atoms of oxygen and in each smallest particle of the black copper oxide there is one atom of each element. In the red oxide of copper there are two atoms of copper to one of oxygen. All the atoms of copper weigh the same and so two weigh twice as much as one, which is the explanation of the 2 to 1 ratio in weight mentioned above as an illustration of the law of multiple proportions.

Dalton first mentioned his hypothesis in a speech before the Manchester Literary and Philosophical Society on October 21, 1803, and included it in a book that he published in 1808. A friend of Dalton's, the Scottish chemist Thomas Thompson, had included the hypothesis in a book that he published in 1807. The circulation of these books at once opened a new field for investigation and brought forth many new names of chemists as others began to seek evidence for or against the hypothesis.

One of the obvious problems was the determination of the weights of the atoms. They were so small that to get one alone and weigh it was out of the question. What the chemists did was to determine the relative proportions in which the elements combine. They found that 1 gram of hydrogen combines with 8 grams of oxygen, therefore, the relative weights of the atoms is 1 to 8 if 1 atom of hydrogen combines with 1 of oxygen. There was no way to tell how many atoms of each element were present in a compound atom of water or of any other compound. It was for this reason that Dalton assumed that the most common compound of two elements contained 1 atom of each, the simplest possible ratio. This assumption was wrong, but it took fifty years to prove it so. Meanwhile, chemists went on with the business of determining relative weights and calling them *equivalent*, *combining* or *atomic* weights, each according to his own notion. The first two names were correct because they depended on experiment and did not make any assumption.

JÖNS BERZELIUS

One of the most outstanding chemists who worked on the determination of combining weights was, like Dalton, of humble origin. He was Jöns Jakob Berzelius (1779–1848), born of poor parents at Wäfversunda, Sweden. His father died when he was very young and Jöns was raised on the farm of his stepfather. His schooling was at Linköping where he, like Dalton, financed himself by work on the farm and by tutoring. He then went to the University of Uppsala where he received a medical degree in 1796. By 1808 Berzelius was professor of chemistry, biology and medicine at the University of Stockholm and the next year he was elected to the Swedish Academy of Sciences; also in the year 1809 Berzelius went to England and visited several English chemists. When he returned the king appointed him director of the Academy of Agriculture, which had just been established. Here, Berzelius had a small laboratory in which he did his chemical work and taught a few students in chemistry—only two at a time.

Berzelius' chemical work was mostly analytical. Excellent analytical work was characteristic of Swedish chemists at that time, and with no lack of ambition Berzelius set out to establish the truth of the law of constant composition. Then after he heard about Dalton's hypothesis he added the law of multiple proportions to his project. In the course of several years he analyzed more than two thousand substances. Many other analytical chemists were working at the same time, but even if they hadn't been, Berzelius' results would have put both laws on a firm foundation.

Dalton had taken the weight of the hydrogen atom as 1 because it was—and it still is—the lightest element known. But most of the elements are metals and do not combine with hydrogen; therefore, Berzelius suggested using oxygen as a standard and calling its weight 100 so that none of the elements would have a combining weight less than 1. To illustrate the advantage of oxygen as a standard: copper does not unite with hydrogen, but does combine with oxygen in the ratio of 4 to 1. If oxygen has the combining weight of 8 then copper is 32, but the accuracy of this value for copper depends on two analyses: the ratio of oxygen to hydrogen and the ratio of copper to oxygen. If the H to O ratio happens to be wrong then the combining weight of copper and all the others metals are wrong also; if oxygen were the standard then each metal would have its combining weight determined by the analysis of its oxide only. As it turned out, Dalton's ratio of hydrogen to oxygen was wrong, for he got a ratio of 1 to 7. But others did a better job of analysis and 1 to 8 is still almost the exact ratio. Despite the disadvantages of the hydrogen standard, it was used for a hundred years. In 1905 chemists changed over to the oxygen standard, but they set the weight of oxygen at 16 and not 100 as Berzelius had suggested.

Establishment of the laws of constant composition and multiple proportions and the determination of combining weights were by no means the only contributions Berzelius made to chemistry. He discovered the elements silicon, selenium and tellurium, invented several pieces of apparatus that are standard equipment in the chemical laboratory today and devised a host of names that are still in the language of chemistry.

ELECTROCHEMISTRY

Berzelius also did some of the first work in electrochemistry. About the year 1800, Alessandro Volta (1745–1827), professor of natural philosophy at the University of Pavia, made the first electric battery. The battery was called a *voltaic pile* —named after its inventor and its nature. It consisted of alternating disks of either copper or silver and zinc separated by pieces of paper soaked in a salt solution. A wire was attached to a copper disk at one end and another wire to a zinc disk at the other end of the pile. When the free ends of these wires were brought together a current of electricity flowed through the wires. The invention seized the imagination and soon physicists and chemists all over Europe were building voltaic piles from various metal combinations. Copper and zinc proved to be the best as silver was expensive and other combinations gave less electricity. Two English chemists found that the electric current would separate water into hydrogen and oxygen. In 1803 Berzelius repeated this experiment and went on to study the effect of electricity on salt solutions. Some salts gave acid at one terminal and alkali at the other. Thus began the science of electrochemistry.

One of Berzelius' greatest contributions to chemistry was designating the symbols of the elements. To write the names of the elements and their compounds is a tedious business. For example, one atom of copper combines with one atom of oxygen to form one molecule of black copper oxide. In order to express such information more briefly, Dalton indicated the atoms with symbols such as the alchemists had used centuries earlier except that each one of Dalton's symbols represented a definite amount of the element, namely, one atom. Some of Dalton's symbols were:

Hydrogen	⊙	Nitrogen	⓪
Oxygen	◯	Sulfur	⊕
Carbon	●	Phosphorus	⊗

With these symbols he could write

$$\odot + \bigcirc = \odot\bigcirc$$

instead of "One atom of hydrogen combines with one atom of oxygen to form one compound atom of water." This is a chemical equation such as Lavoisier had suggested, but now it was based on the atomic theory and used symbols instead of words.

These symbols were a great convenience, but new elements were being discovered and it was difficult both to devise new symbols and to remember them. In 1814 Berzelius had a better idea. He proposed the use of the initial letter of the name of the element as the symbol. Chemistry is international and the question was what language to use for the names. Iron is *fer* in French, *eisen* in German, *ferro* in Italian and *hierro* in Spanish, and I suppose that every other country has its own idea of what the metal should be called. Berzelius' solution of the problem was to take the initial letters from the Latin names of the older elements, because Latin had been the language of European scholars for ages and every chemist knew the Latin names of these older elements. This proposal was adopted although some of the English chemists complained about the harsh sound of the Latin names. However, it soon became the practice for the discoverer of an element to name it, and then all nationalities used the name he proposed. To this statement there are two important exceptions. Sodium and potassium were discovered by the English chemist Sir Humphry Davy and named by him, but a German chemist later changed the names to *natrium* and *kalium*. For some strange reason Berzelius used the German names and so we have the symbols Na and K for these elements. The symbols are now the initial letters of the Latin names of the older elements and the modern names of the newer ones. The names of several elements begin with the same letter, but this difficulty was met by using a second letter in some of the symbols. Thus, we have argon, Ar; arsenic, As; boron, B;

barium, Ba; bismuth, Bi; carbon, C; calcium, Ca; Cadmium, Cd; chlorine, Cl; and so on. The elements with the Latin names are the seven metals of the ancients, and antimony:

Antimony	Stibnium	Sb
Copper	Cuprum	Cu
Gold	Aurum	Au
Iron	Ferrum	Fe
Mercury	Hydrargyrum	Hg
Silver	Argentum	Ag
Tin	Stannum	Sn
Lead	Plumbum	Pb

The symbols represent one atom and therefore a definite weight of the element; they are not abbreviations and are not followed by a period. The acceptance of these symbols simplified the matter of notes and also the publication of papers. The modern chemist would be lost without them. He remembers them more easily than the names of his acquaintances or his distant relatives.

Dalton by his keen thinking and Berzelius by his exact analytical work soon placed the atomic hypothesis on a firm foundation. Each of them received numerous honors. Dalton was elected to membership in the French Academy of Sciences and the Royal Society of England. Oxford University contributed the degree of doctor of laws. The Royal Society gave him a gold medal and the government gave him a pension of three hundred pounds a year.

Berzelius was the more prolific writer; he wrote some 250 papers and a three-volume book. Like Dalton he received many honors and a pension. In addition to his professional honors, he was made a baron by King Charles XIV of Norway and Sweden. Unlike Dalton, he married; at the age of fifty he married the twenty-four-year-old daughter of one of Napoleon's marshals.

ATOMIC WEIGHTS

The chemists of the early nineteenth century had a bothersome problem with the atomic weights of the elements. Careful analytical work had determined the ratios in which the elements combine with each other, but these were not necessarily the relative weights of the atoms. They were the atomic weights only if Dalton's assumption were true, that is, if the most common compound of two elements contained just one atom of each element. For example, analysis showed that the relative weights of hydrogen and oxygen in water is 1 to 8. The atomic weight of 1 had been arbitrarily selected for hydrogen and so there was no question about that and the atomic weight of oxygen would be 8 if water contained just one atom of each element. But if water contained two atoms of hydrogen to one of oxygen then the atomic weight of oxygen would be 16 because it would be eight times as heavy as two atoms of hydrogen. This was a serious difficulty because the combining weights of carbon, sulfur, phosphorus, nitrogen and all the metals were determined by the analysis of their oxides, and if oxygen were wrong all the others were wrong. Furthermore, after 1814, when Berzelius introduced the symbols to represent the atomic weights of the elements, chemists began to combine these symbols into formulas to represent compounds. These formulas were calculated from an analysis of the compound and the atomic weights of the elements. If the atomic weight of oxygen were 8 then the formula of water was HO, but if it were 16 then the formula was H_2O.

The first break in the dilemma came in 1819 with the publication of a paper by two French physicists, Pierre Louis Dulong (1785–1838) and Alexis Thérèse Petit (1791–1820). These two physics professors were studying the *spe-*

cific heats of metals in their laboratory at the École Poly-technique in Paris. Specific heat is *the amount of heat re-quired to raise the temperature of a specific weight of a substance 1 degree.* The units now used to measure specific heat are the *calorie* and the gram. The calorie is the amount of heat required to raise the temperature of 1 gram of water 1 degree centigrade. As it happens, water has a greater specific heat than does anything else, which makes the spe-cific heats of all other substances fractions of a calorie. Du-long and Petit had the idea that the heat required to raise the temperature of the solid elements should depend only on the number of atoms in the sample that was heated and not at all on the kind of atoms. If this were true it would take more heat to raise the temperature of 1 gram of copper 1 degree than to raise the temperature of 1 gram of lead the same amount, because the copper atom is lighter than the lead atom and so there are more of them in a gram. If the lead atom is three times as heavy as the copper atom then there would be three times as many atoms in a gram of copper as there are in a gram of lead. Dulong and Petit measured the specific heats of about a dozen metals and found their reasoning to be correct. The combining weight of copper was 32, but its specific heat showed that its atomic weight should be about 64. The present value is 63.54. The combining weight of lead is 103.5, but its specific heat in-dicated that this is only half the atomic weight. The present value is 207.19.

The combining weights of the metals have always been determined from the proportions with which they combine with oxygen or chlorine, and the weights of these two ele-ments were found from their combining ratio with hydrogen, the standard. The atomic weight of 8 for oxygen and 32 for copper depended on the assumption that water contains one atom of hydrogen and one of oxygen, and that copper oxide also contains one atom of each element in it. If the atomic weight of copper is 64, either water is not HO or copper oxide is not CuO. The law of Dulong and Petit established the atomic weights of the metals, but it was no help with the nonmetallic elements. This was unfortunate because the solids carbon, sulfur and phosphorus and the gases oxygen, hydrogen, nitrogen and chlorine are among the most common of all elements.

The settlement of the atomic weights of the gaseous elements began with the work of the French chemist Joseph Louis Gay-Lussac (1778–1850); that is, it began there unless we include the work of Boyle and his law a century and a half before.

Gay-Lussac was a country boy like many of his contemporaries. He was the son of a lawyer of Saint-Léonard in the region of Limousin. He received his early education locally, but went to Paris for his higher education. He became a most daring chemist; he was injured at least twice by explosions in his laboratory. He also went up to a height of four miles in a balloon several times to get samples of air for analysis. He held professorships in three of the most important scientific institutions in Paris: the Jardin des Plantes, which had been the Jardin du Roi before the revolution, the École Polytechnique and the University. In addition to his teaching and research he edited the famous journal *Annales de chimie* for fifty years.

About the year 1787 the physicist Jacques Alexandre Charles (1746–1823) announced the law of the constant expansion of gases with temperature; that is, a gas expands the same amount for an increase of 1° whether it is from 10° to 11° or 90° to 91°. In 1802 Gay-Lussac determined that the amount of this expansion is $\frac{1}{266}$ of the volume at 0°. It was several years before this value was corrected; then a compatriot of Gay-Lussac, Henri Victor Regnault (1810–1878), who was also a chemistry professor, found the expansion to be $\frac{1}{273}$ of the volume at 0°. To illustrate and keep the arithmetic easy: if we have 273 liters of a gas at 0° C and heat it 1° we will have 274 liters; at 100° the volume will be 373 liters.

If we wish to compare the weights of two or more gases we must have them at the same temperature and pressure. The usual practice is to measure the volume at whatever temperature and pressure prevails in the laboratory and then by means of Boyle's and Charles's laws calculate the volume the gas would have at 0° C and a pressure of 760 mm of mercury. These are the standard conditions that chemists use for gases.

Even though Gay-Lussac had the wrong value for the expansion of a gas, the use of it could still bring two volumes to the same condition and so he was able to discover his law of gas volumes. He first showed that the volumes of hydrogen and oxygen that combine to form water are in the simple ratio of 2 to 1. He then studied the reactions of several other gases, which enabled him to announce the law: *The ratios of the volumes of gases involved in a chemical reaction are expressed by small, whole numbers.* A few illustrations show the simplicity of the law:

One liter of hydrogen combines with 1 liter of chlorine to form 2 liters of hydrogen chloride.

Two liters of hydrogen combines with 1 liter of oxygen to form 2 liters of water vapor.

If 2 liters of ammonia are decomposed, they yield 1 liter of nitrogen and 3 liters of hydrogen.

One liter of ammonia combines with 1 liter of hydrogen chloride and the product is a solid.

In all these illustrations except the last, all the substances involved in the reaction are gases, but the law also applies to the two gases in the last illustration. If 1 liter of hydrogen combines with 1 liter of chlorine one would expect to get 2 liters of hydrogen chloride; but why should 2 liters of hydrogen and 1 liter of oxygen give 2 liters of the product? Or why should 2 volumes of ammonia decompose to 1 volume of nitrogen and 3 of hydrogen? Gay-Lussac did not attempt to answer these questions. He simply found the results by experiment and announced the law—no exception to it has ever been found. An explanation of why gases always react in these simple ratios was soon forthcoming, but it was not generally accepted for half a century.

In 1811 an Italian professor of physics at Vercelli (later at Turin), Amadeo Avogadro (1776–1856), announced a hypothesis that later became a fact. He first made a distinction between simple and compound atoms and named the latter *molecules.* His hypothesis stated that *equal volumes of gases at the same temperature and pressure contain the same number of molecules.* In other words, there are just as many molecules in a liter of hydrogen as there are in a liter of oxygen or ammonia. He also said that atoms of the same element can combine with each other. The molecule thus became the unit particle in a gas whether it was composed of one element as in the case of oxygen or two as in the case of carbon dioxide. These two ideas led to interesting conclusions. If the hydrogen and oxygen molecules each contained two atoms, then there would be twice as many atoms of hydrogen as of oxygen in a molecule of water because of the ratio of 2 to 1 in which the gases combine.

Suppose there are X molecules in a liter of a gas and

experiment shows that 2 volumes of hydrogen combine with 1 volume of oxygen, then,

2l of hydrogen+1l of oxygen———→2l of water vapor

2X molecules of H+X molecules of O———→2X molecules of water vapor

4X atoms of H+2X atoms of O———→2X molecules of water vapor

If we divide each term in the last equation by 2X it shows that a molecule of water vapor is composed of two atoms of H and one atom of O; consequently, the formula of water should be H_2O and the atomic weight of oxygen 16.

Avogadro also pointed out that if equal volumes of gases contain the same number of molecules then the relative weights of equal volumes of gases would be the relative weights of the molecules. If the hydrogen molecule is H_2, then its molecular weight is 2 because the hydrogen atom was the weight standard of 1. Gases are difficult to weigh and the weights in those days were not very accurate; the weight of a liter of hydrogen was 0.0721 gram and that of a liter of oxygen was 1.0359 grams—a ratio of 1 to 15.074. If the hydrogen molecule weighs 2 then the oxygen molecule weighs 30.148 and if the oxygen molecule is diatomic then the atomic weight is 15.074. But the ratio of the weights of hydrogen and oxygen in the molecule of water is 1 to 8 and so the atomic weight of oxygen is 16 and not 8.

Three years later the French physicist André Marie Ampère (1775–1836) independently came up with the same ideas that Avogadro had advanced, but the big authority of the day, Berzelius, did not think that atoms of the same element could combine with each other. Chemists, therefore, paid very little attention to the ideas of Avogadro and Ampère and so atomic weights were in a muddle for nearly half a century. Neither man lived to see his ideas accepted.

The reader may wonder why chemists made such a to-do about the atomic weights of the elements. There are at least two reasons. First, as a matter of pure science and curiosity, it was a problem to be solved and they were determined to meet the challenge. What may seem to be a better reason is the fact that the chemist uses these weights for several purposes, mainly three: to calculate formulas of compounds, to calculate the results of chemical analyses and to calculate the proportions of substances to be used in experimental or manufacturing operations.

A chemist likes to represent a substance by a formula because the formula is shorter than the name and tells him more about the compound than the name does. All formulas are groups of symbols that show what elements are in a compound and how much of each there is present. To find the formula of a new substance the chemist analyzes it and then calculates the formula from the analysis and the atomic weights of the elements present. For example, an analysis of water shows it to contain 88.88 per cent oxygen and 11.11 per cent hydrogen. In 100 grams of water there are 88.88 grams of oxygen and 11.11 grams of hydrogen. This does not mean that there are eight atoms of oxygen to one atom of hydrogen because the oxygen atom is much heavier than the hydrogen atom and so the ratio must be much less than 8 to 1. If the oxygen atom weighs 8 and the hydrogen atom 1, then the relative number of atoms is,

$$O = \frac{88.88}{8} = 11.11 = 1$$

$$H = \frac{11.11}{1} = 11.11 = 1$$

This ratio of 1 to 1 shows that the formula of water is HO. Some chemists of the early nineteenth century thought that the atomic weight of oxygen is 16. If this were the case, then,

$$O = \frac{88.88}{16} = 5.55 = 1$$

$$H = \frac{11.11}{1} = 11.11 = 2$$

and the simple ratio of hydrogen to oxygen atoms is 2 to 1 and the formula of water is H_2O.

The work of Dulong and Petit in 1819 had settled the atomic weights of the elements that were metals but had not helped with the nonmetals. The chemical literature after 1819 was filled with chemical formulas, but the uncertainty of the atomic weights resulted in different formulas for the same compound. Water, one of the most common of chemical substances, sometimes appeared as HO and sometimes as H_2O according to which of the above calculations the chemist had used to derive it.

By 1850 there was so much confusion because of the uncertainty of the formulas that chemists decided something should be done about it. There were sixteen different formulas for acetic acid, the common acid of vinegar, and all the other compounds of carbon had at least two different formulas. Three university professors decided to take action. Friedrich August Kekulé of Ghent and Carl Weltzien of Karlsruhe met Charles Adolphe Wurtz in Paris in the fall of 1859 to talk things over. They decided to send out a joint letter to prominent chemists to ask their opinion as to the advisability of a conference. The response to these letters was greatly in favor of the idea and so Weltzien sent out an invitation, which was signed by over forty chemists, to a three-day conference to be held in Karlsruhe, September 3,

1860. About 140 chemists from all over Europe came to the meeting, which has always been known as the Karlsruhe Congress. Differences in language were something of a handicap, but discussions went on for three days. The sessions were well organized and presided over by some of the ablest chemists of the day, but the meeting adjourned without reaching any conclusions. There were some ruffled feelings because of the forcefulness with which some of the members expressed or defended their opinions. They did not even plan another meeting.

The unsuspected hero of the Congress was Stanislao Cannizzaro (1826–1910). This Italian chemist was born in Palermo, the son of a magistrate. He graduated in medicine at the University of Palermo, but in 1845 he became interested in chemistry and went to Pisa to study with Professor Piria, who was the leading chemist in Italy. Cannizzaro remained in Pisa two years and in the summer of 1847 went home for a vacation. Those were revolutionary days in Sicily and the young chemist joined the army. He was on the losing side and in 1849 he fled to Paris where he spent two years working in the laboratory of Chevreul, the chemist famous for discovering the nature of fats and for living to the age of 103. By 1851 politics had settled down and Cannizzaro returned to Italy where he was appointed a professor of physics and chemistry at the National College of Alexandria in Lombardy. He now decided to give up politics and get down to work in chemistry. He did so well that he was appointed to a better professorship at Genoa in 1855.

By 1858 Cannizzaro had decided how to determine atomic and molecular weights, taught the method to his students and published it in *Il Nuovo Cimento*, a chemical journal founded by his old teacher Piria and another chemist and published in Pisa. Cannizzaro arrived in Karlsruhe with several reprints of his paper. During the Congress he spoke at great length on the subject of atomic and molecular weights but got more opposition than encouragement. I guess he got disgusted with the reception of his speeches, for he did not distribute his reprints. However, his friend, Professor Angelo Pavesi of the University of Pavia, did hand them out. Many of them were thrown away, of course—free handouts always are—but some of the chemists read them. With more leisure to study the subject these chemists began to see the truth of Cannizzaro's arguments.

Cannizzaro began with the law of Gay-Lussac, which was derived from experimental facts. With this law he combined the almost forgotten hypothesis of Avogadro in much the same way as Avogadro himself had done fifty years earlier. According to Gay-Lussac's results, 1 liter of hydrogen combines with 1 liter of chlorine to form 2 liters of hydrogen chloride. Both the elements and the compound are gases, and according to Avogadro equal volumes of gases contain the same number of molecules. In Cannizzaro's argument it does not matter what the number is, but if we assume the number to be 1000 molecules in a liter of gas, then

1 liter of hydrogen+1 liter of chlorine⟶2 liters of hydrogen chloride

1000 molecules of H+1000 molecules of Cl⟶2000 molecules of hydrogen chloride

Each molecule of hydrogen chloride must contain one atom of hydrogen and one of chlorine because, according to the atomic theory, there are no fractions of atoms. Therefore, in 2000 molecules of hydrogen chloride there must be 2000 atoms of hydrogen and 2000 atoms of chlorine. These 2000 atoms of hydrogen were originally in 1000 molecules of hydrogen and so a molecule of hydrogen gas must contain 2 atoms,

H_2. By the same reasoning the formula for the gaseous chlorine is Cl_2. From other examples of Gay-Lussac's law Cannizzaro showed that oxygen is O_2, nitrogen N_2, but the vapor of mercury is monatomic, simply Hg.

Cannizzaro's paper contained another idea. Following the reasoning of Avogadro fifty years before (p. 148), he showed that the atomic weight of oxygen is 16. But Cannizzaro went further than Avogadro had gone and showed how to get the atomic weight of a solid nonmetallic element such as carbon from the molecular weights and percentage composition of its gaseous compounds. The chemistry of the carbon compounds was the exciting subject of the day and the uncertainty about the atomic weight of carbon had been largely responsible for calling the Karlsruhe Congress. Carbon forms several gaseous compounds, and the following table shows how to find the atomic weight of this troublesome element.

GAS	MOLECULAR WEIGHT	PERCENTAGE CARBON	WEIGHT OF C IN 1 MOLECULAR WEIGHT OF THE COMPOUND
Carbon dioxide	44	27.27	12
Carbon monoxide	28	42.86	12
Methane	16	75.00	12
Ethylene	28	85.71	24

There are no fractions of atoms and therefore the smallest weight of carbon ever found in the molecular weight of one of its compounds must be its atomic weight. Besides the compounds in the above table, other gaseous compounds of carbon have been analyzed and the smallest value for carbon is 12. Similar methods applied to other elements give chlorine, 35.5; nitrogen, 14; sulfur, 32; phosphorus, 31; and mercury, 200.

It is so difficult to weigh a gas with great precision that the Cannizzaro method for atomic weights gave only approximate values. Oxygen was approximately 16 and not 8, nitrogen was about 14 and not 7 and so on. The precise values were obtained by the analysis of compounds to get the exact combining weight, which usually ends in a decimal fraction as shown in the table on p. 157.

One of the strongest arguments in favor of Cannizzaro's method was that it gave mercury the weight 200, and since mercury is a metal its atomic weight was already known to be 200 from the application of the law of Dulong and Petit. The method gradually gained acceptance and today chemists consider the matter of atomic weights to have been settled by the Italian professor. Since 1860, scores of chemists have worked to determine the combining weights with greater precision. Even today the final decimal of the weight of one of the elements is changed now and then by someone who thinks he has a better value than the old one.

In all the work on atomic weights of the nineteenth century calculations were made on the basis of 1 for hydrogen. This gave the value of 15.872 for oxygen. About 80 per cent of the elements are metals and do not combine with hydrogen, but despite this difficulty the hydrogen standard was used during the entire century. Chemists then revived the arguments and suggestions of Berzelius and in 1905 they adopted the oxygen standard; but they did not accept Berzelius' suggestion that oxygen be used at 100, for to do so would change the existing weights too much. Instead they made oxygen exactly 16, which changed the other weights very little, for the old value was nearly 15.9. The change to oxygen with which most of the elements combine directly made it possible to determine the atomic weights with greater precision and the oxygen standard was used for the next fifty years. After the Second World War, chemists and physicists began to use slightly different standards for the atomic weights and the literature again began to be a bit confusing. The International Union of Pure and Applied Physics adopted carbon 12 as a standard in 1960 and so in 1961 the International Union of Pure and Applied Chemistry adopted the same standard. This new standard will be explained in Chapter Eleven. In 1961 the first official table of atomic weights on the new standard was published (see p. 157). The weights are not changed very much, as the following comparison shows:

OXYGEN STANDARD		CARBON 12 STANDARD	
Al	26.97	Al	26.9815
Cl	35.46	Cl	35.453
Cu	63.57	Cu	63.54
H	1.008	H	1.00797
O	16	O	15.9994

The differences are so slight that the change makes no important difference in the great majority of chemical work.

And so we come to the end of an era as far as research chemists are concerned. Dalton's theory of 1803 said that the atoms of the elements have different weights, and it took scores of chemists sixty years to determine what these weights are. The theory also said that the atom is the indivisible unit in all chemical reactions, which also proved to be true, but the assumption that the most common compound of two elements contains one atom of each element was wrong. Water, the most common substance of all, is H_2O.

The discovery of the elements and the determination of their atomic weights was a greater advance in the science of chemistry than all the efforts of the ancients, the alche-

ATOMIC WEIGHTS OF THE MORE COMMON ELEMENTS
BASED ON CARBON 12

ELEMENT	SYM.	AT. NO.	AT. WEIGHT	ELEMENT	SYM.	AT. NO.	AT. WEIGHT
Aluminum	Al	13	26.9815	Molybdenum	Mo	42	95.94
Antimony	Sb	51	121.75	Neon	Ne	10	20.183
Argon	Ar	18	39.948	Nickel	Ni	28	58.71
Arsenic	As	33	74.9216	Nitrogen	N	7	14.0067
Barium	Ba	56	137.34	Osmium	Os	76	190.2
Beryllium	Be	4	9.0122	Oxygen	O	8	15.9994
Bismuth	Bi	83	208.980	Palladium	Pd	46	106.4
Boron	B	5	10.811	Phosphorus	P	15	30.9738
Bromine	Br	35	79.909	Platinum	Pt	78	195.09
Cadmium	Cd	48	112.40	Polonium	Po	84	——
Calcium	Ca	20	40.08	Potassium	K	19	39.102
Carbon	C	6	12.0115	Radium	Ra	88	——
Cerium	Ce	58	140.12	Radon	Rn	86	——
Cesium	Cs	55	132.905	Rhodium	Rh	45	102.905
Chlorine	Cl	17	35.453	Rubidium	Rb	37	85.47
Chromium	Cr	24	51.996	Scandium	Sc	21	44.956
Cobalt	Co	27	58.9332	Selenium	Se	34	78.96
Copper	Cu	29	63.54	Silicon	Si	14	28.086
Fluorine	F	9	18.9984	Silver	Ag	47	107.870
Gallium	Ga	31	69.72	Sodium	Na	11	22.9898
Germanium	Ge	32	72.59	Strontium	Sr	38	87.62
Gold	Au	79	196.967	Sulfur	S	16	32.064
Helium	He	2	4.0026	Tantalum	Ta	73	180.948
Hydrogen	H	1	1.00797	Thallium	Tl	81	204.37
Iodine	I	53	126.9044	Thorium	Th	90	232.038
Iridium	Ir	77	192.2	Tin	Sn	50	118.69
Iron	Fe	26	55.847	Titanium	Ti	22	47.90
Krypton	Kr	36	83.80	Tungsten	W	74	183.85
Lead	Pb	82	207.19	Uranium	U	92	238.03
Lithium	Li	3	6.939	Vanadium	V	23	50.942
Magnesium	Mg	12	24.312	Xenon	Xe	54	131.30
Manganese	Mn	25	54.9380	Zinc	Zn	30	65.37
Mercury	Hg	80	200.59	Zirconium	Zr	40	91.22

mists, the iatrochemists and the phlogistonists had been able to produce.

Writers of textbooks lag several years behind the state of the science as the research chemist knows it. J. L. Comstock, M.D., published the twenty-second edition of his *Elements of Chemistry* at Hartford, Connecticut, in 1848. He says in his preface that he has rewritten the book and brought it up to date and believes teachers will find it "as modern as any book written at the present day." The book was in use more than fifty years later. He does not mention Lavoisier on the conservation of matter, but he does emphasize the laws of definite and multiple proportions and includes Gay-Lussac's law of combining gas volumes as part of the law of definite proportions. He does not mention either Ampère or Avogadro or their ideas. He includes the atomic theory and uses it to explain the "doctrine of definite proportions," but being cautious, as textbook writers generally are, he says, "And whether the theory of atoms, which accounts for the facts on which the doctrine is founded, be true, or false, the doctrine itself will ever maintain its integrity, its elements being nothing more than the expression of facts which experiment and analysis have developed." He also says: "The atomic theory, however, must always be considered an elegant and probable hypothesis; and while it displays uncommon ingenuity, and great chemical research, has the advantage of agreeing, in general, perfectly with the facts obtained by analysis."

The book includes a table of "equivalent or atomic weights" and a few values taken from it show the unsettled state of these weights in 1848 and emphasize the need for the Karlsruhe Congress.

Atomic Weights Then and Now

	1848	1961
Aluminum	13.7	26.98
Calcium	20.5	40.08
Carbon	6.12	12.01
Copper	31.6	63.54
Hydrogen	1	1.008
Nitrogen	14.15	14.007
Oxygen	8	16.00
Phosphorus	15.7	30.97
Sulfur	16.1	32.06

Of the fifty-four elements in his table only fourteen had approximately correct values. The work of Dulong and Petit on the atomic weights of the metals was not mentioned.

Introducing symbols, Comstock says: "Chemists . . . believing symbols to be useful, adopted those which Berzelius had proposed. The consequence is that symbolic expressions called *chemical formulas* are now so much resorted to, and so identified with the language of chemistry that essays of great value are in a measure, sealed books to those who cannot read symbols." The formulas were then written in algebraic fashion and he dismisses them with these two sentences: "Thus bisulfate of potash as seen above, is thus expressed $(K+O)+(2S+3O)$. Now who does not see that the words themselves can be more quickly written than these signs made? and, when printed, close attention and much practice is required in order to avoid errors in reading them." He has a point there, but the modern formula, $KHSO_4$, answers it. Symbols were no help to Comstock and neither was the metric system, for his weights are expressed in ounces and grains.

And so the science progressed with lagging feet.

CHAPTER SEVEN

The Chemical Elements

B Y THE TIME the Karlsruhe Congress met in 1860, ten of Lavoisier's thirty-three elements had disappeared from the list, but the remaining twenty-three had grown to sixty while an undiscovered twenty-eight were lurking about in air, land and sea. The composition of matter was no longer a mystery. A great many things, of course, remained to be analyzed, and today, a century later, there is still plenty of matter of unknown composition. There probably always will be, for chemists have become quite blasé in such matters and only undertake to determine the composition of a substance when there seems to be a good reason for doing so.

The industrial chemists have always been interested in what the elements and their compounds can be used for, but the basic research chemists have concerned themselves with the fundamental nature of the elements and their behavior. The idea that all matter is composed of a few fundamental units still lingered in the minds of chemists. The four elements of the Greeks had been replaced with sixty and that seemed to be too many; some of these sixty elements must be related to each other.

In 1815 William Prout (1785–1850), an English physician and chemist, announced his famous hypothesis: the atoms of all the other elements are composed of hydrogen atoms. Hydrogen was the standard for the atomic weights and so its weight was exactly 1. If Prout were right, all the other weights should be whole numbers because there were no fractions of atoms. The hypothesis was a happy suggestion and inspired chemists to determine atomic weights with a high degree of precision. But alas! within the next twenty-five years it became obvious that the atomic weights were not all whole numbers although several of them were close to it. The weight of chlorine was 35.5 and this fraction was too big to be an error in determination, and so were several other fractional atomic weights. Consequently, Prout's hypothesis was soon abandoned but not forgotten. There were doubts in the minds of many chemists about atoms being indivisible, and Lavoisier's definition of an element as a substance that has not been decomposed was not very satisfactory.

While Prout's hypothesis was fresh in the minds of chemists, some of them began to try to classify the elements according to their weights. The first to publish was Professor Johann Wolfgang Döbereiner (1780–1849) of the University of Jena. In 1829 he discovered several groups of elements of three each with similar properties and with weights that had a strange relationship. These groups soon became known as Döbereiner's triads. The atomic weights in the following four triads are the modern ones given to the nearest whole number.

Li	7	Ca	40	S	32	Cl	35.5
Na	23	Sr	88	Se	79	Br	80
K	39	Ba	137	Te	128	I	127

The second weight in each triad is very close to the average of the other two, for these averages are 23, 88.5, 80 and 81.2 respectively for the four triads. In addition to this weight peculiarity, the chemical properties of the three elements in each triad are similar. For example, chlorine, bromine and iodine combine with hydrogen to form the acids HCl, HBr and HI, and the three acids are all colorless gases and all very soluble in water. They all react with a solution of silver nitrate to give the insoluble salts AgCl, AgBr, and AgI and they have many other properties in common. Likewise, the elements of the other triads are similar and form compounds that have similar properties.

Unfortunately, the triads did not include all the elements, in fact, not many of them; consequently, they were not a good classification and were not based on any general principle. They were simply picked out of the list of elements for the properties they were known to have, and so Döbereiner's triads became just a memory. Several other chemists tried to relate the properties of the elements to their atomic weights, or the atomic weights to each other, but the efforts made before 1860 were doomed to failure because the atomic weights of several of the elements were uncertain, unknown or wrong.

JOHN NEWLANDS

In 1863 John Alexander Reina Newlands (1837–1898), a chemist for a London sugar refinery, arranged the elements in the order of increasing atomic weights and found that the eighth element had properties similar to those of the first and that the fifteenth resembled the eighth. Then the second, ninth and sixteenth formed another family and so on. Newlands called his arrangement the *law of octaves* because each element was like the next eighth in line. The law resulted in seven families of elements with similar properties. Newlands had made a good start at classification even if several elements did not fit into it, but when he read his paper at a meeting of the British Chemical Society it brought forth mainly ridicule. Someone suggested that he try arranging the elements in alphabetical order and other inane suggestions were offered. Why it seemed so funny is hard to say. Probably, because he associated his arrangement with the musical scale and its octaves. He seems to have made no impression whatever, for when he submitted the paper to the Society's journal the editor returned it as unsuitable for publication. Newlands became discouraged and confined his future activities to industrial chemistry. However, the Royal Society gave him a medal twenty years later, after two other chemists showed that he had the right idea about his octaves.

Mendeleev, a Russian chemist, and Julius Lothar Meyer (1830–1895), a chemistry professor at Karlsruhe, soon succeeded in making a good classification after the general plan of Newlands. Mendeleev published his paper in March 1869 and Meyer in December of the same year. Their classifications were much alike, but Mendeleev developed his more fully and, for this reason and the fact of earlier publication, his name is generally given to the system.

DMITRI MENDELEEV

Dmitri Ivanovich Mendeleev (1834–1907) was born in the country town of Tobolsk in western Siberia. He was the youngest of fourteen children. His father was director of the high school, but he became blind and died while Dmitri was still very young. His mother was left with a small pension but not enough to support her family. Being a woman of resources she reopened a glass factory that some of her family had established in Tobolsk, but which had been closed. Before Dmitri was twenty, the glass factory burned down and Mrs. Mendeleev moved to Moscow where she hoped to get her youngest and favorite son into the university, but she did not succeed and moved on to St. Petersburg. There Dmitri entered the Pedagogical Institute, which was an institution for training high-school teachers. He studied mathematics, physics and chemistry and graduated at the head of his class.

Mendeleev's health was poor and after graduation he went to the milder climate of southern Russia to teach school. But the Crimean War broke out in 1854 and he returned to St. Petersburg for a time and then went to Europe for further study of chemistry and physics. In Paris he studied with Professor Regnault and then moved on to Heidelberg, Germany, where he worked for a year. There he was associated with two prominent German chemists, Bunsen and Kirchhoff.

After attending the Karlsruhe Congress Mendeleev returned to Russia. He was no dawdler. In less than three years he earned the doctor's degree, married, became professor of chemistry at the University of St. Petersburg, wrote a big textbook on organic chemistry and settled down to make a classification of the elements. Neither did he waste any time in a barber shop—he had his hair cut just once a year.

Instead of the law of octaves, Mendeleev called his classification the *periodic law*. As it turned out, the periods were not all octaves. The first two were eight in length, but the next two were eighteen. The law avoided the issue of length and simply said that when the elements are arranged in order of increasing atomic weights there is a periodic recurrence of properties. One difficulty was the fact that there were some elements that had not been discovered, and where the first was missing the classification would be wrong from that point on. Mendeleev solved this problem very simply. He was a great student of the properties of the elements and when he came to an element that did not belong in its apparent family he left a blank and tried it in the next family. This worked very well and so he went on to the end of the list of known elements.

Mendeleev's periodic table, even with the later improvements and additions, had two main defects and some minor ones. There was no place for hydrogen. This element seems to be a bachelor with no close relatives, for it still defies classification. Some chemists put it in the first family with sodium and potassium, and others put it with chlorine and fluorine just to have a place to put it.

The second defect was the failure of the system to classify fourteen metals called the *rare earths*. These metals resemble each other more than they resemble the metals of any of the families. Nobody has ever succeeded in classifying them but, as their name indicates, they were not very common and chemists have not worried very much about their lack of family connection. Before the Second World War the only member of this group that had been found useful was cerium. An alloy containing 70 per cent cerium and 30 per cent iron gives off sparks when it is scratched and has been used in gas lighters and cigarette lighters. Also, a mixture of 99 per cent thorium oxide and 1 per cent cerium oxide gives a brilliant white light when it is heated and was the material used to make gas mantles in the gaslight age. In connection with the development of atomic energy the rare earths have been more fully investigated and uses have been found for some of them. Moreover, new sources have been discovered and the rare earths are not as rare as they were once thought to be. But they are still much alike and still defy classification.

Before the work of Mendeleev, chemists had no idea how many elements there might be. Dalton had said that atoms of different elements have different weights and so nobody expected to find two elements with the same weight, but there were a lot of weights that did not belong to any element. For example, the first three elements were hydrogen, 1; lithium, 7; and beryllium, 9. Where were the elements with weights, 2, 3,

4, 5, 6, and 8? And there were many more weights below the heaviest that did not belong to any element. The periodic law and the table made from it indicated that the number of missing elements was small, because there were very few gaps in the table. This was the first inkling chemists had as to how many elements there might be, but it took another forty years to settle the matter.

Mendeleev's table made the discovery of the unknown elements easier because the families in which they occurred indicated what to look for and where to look. Mendeleev predicted the properties of three of the unknown elements and named them *eka-boron*, *eka-aluminum* and *eka-silicon*. These predictions were soon verified. National pride ran high in the 1870s and left its stamp on the names of these three elements. Eka-aluminum was discovered by the French chemist Paul Émile Lecoq de Boisbaudran (1838–1912) and named *gallium* for the ancient name of his country. Eka-boron was found by the Swedish chemist Lars Fredrik Nilson (1840–1899), who settled for the whole of Scandinavia, whence the name *scandium*. The last of the three, eka-silicon, was discovered in 1886 by the German chemist Clemens Winkler (1838–1904) and called *germanium*.

Mendeleev's success in predicting the properties of these unknown elements is shown very clearly by his prediction for eka-silicon:

	EKA-SILICON	GERMANIUM
Atomic weight	72	72.00
Specific gravity	5.5	6.36
Specific heat	0.073	0.076
Valence	4	4
Specific gravity of oxide	4.7	4.70
Specific gravity of chloride	1.9	1.887
Boiling point of chloride	Below 100° C	86° C

He also predicted the color, hardness and some other qualitative properties of the element.

One whole group of elements escaped prediction by Mendeleev because none of its members was known. These are the inert gases. Cavendish had found that about 1 per cent of the air is neither oxygen nor nitrogen, but had not investigated the gas any further. A century later Lord Rayleigh (1842–1919) and Sir William Ramsay (1852–1916) identified this gas as a new element and named it *argon*. Then they discovered that there were traces of other elements mixed with it and continued the investigation until they found other members of the family: helium, neon, argon, krypton and xenon. These elements had escaped discovery for so long because they are colorless gases that occur in very small amounts in the atmosphere and do not combine with the other elements under any ordinary conditions. After their discovery a new family was added to the periodic table as the zero group. They made each period of the periodic law one element longer.

The prediction of the properties of the elements was the most spectacular feature of the periodic table, but the table also showed that some of the atomic weights were wrong and it simplified the study of chemistry by grouping the large number of elements in a few families with all the members having similar properties.

Mendeleev published a slight revision of his table in 1871 and since then hundreds of chemists have tried to improve it, but it is still fundamentally the same as the original. The modern table includes the elements discovered since the original was made. In each group there are two families, marked A and B. A few of these families have been given names such as the inert gases (O), the alkali metals (IA), the alkaline earths (IIA) and the halogens (VIIB). Most of the families, however, are known by the name of the most prominent member such as the oxygen and nitrogen families. The following few families illustrate the nature of the periodic table:

GROUP I		GROUP VI	GROUP VII
A	B	B	B
Lithium		Oxygen	Fluorine
Li 6.9		O 16	F 19
Sodium		Sulfur	Chlorine
Na 23		S 32	Cl 35.5
Potassium	Copper	Selenium	Bromine
K 39.1	Cu 63.5	Se 78.9	Br 79.9
Rubidium	Silver	Tellurium	Iodine
Rb 85.5	Ag 107.8	Te 127.6	I 126.9
Cesium	Gold		
Cs 132.9	Au 196.9		

THE SPECTROSCOPE

Although the periodic table was a great help in the discovery of the unknown elements it was not the only boon to the exploring chemist. The spectroscope, which was invented in 1859, played a leading role, especially in the discovery of the inert gases. If a gas or the vapor of a liquid or solid element is heated hot enough it gives off a color, which is different for each element. This is the principle of the so-called Christmas salts, which are a mixture of salt crystals to throw into an open fire—each crystal produces a colored flame where it is vaporized. Copper salts give a green flame; sodium, orange; strontium, red; barium, yellow; and so on. Also, a gas can be sealed in a glass tube with electrodes at each end. The gas gives its characteristic color when an electric current is passed through it. This is the principle of the advertising signs where the tubes are bent into the shapes of letters and emit different colors according to the gas they contain.

Although an ordinary flame or an electric current will excite most of the elements enough to produce their characteristic colors, the temperature of the electric arc is required for some of them.

These colors differ more than they seem to. Calcium, strontium and neon all give a red color; somewhat different in hue, of course, but there are no names for the hues and, besides, with so many elements there are far from enough names of colors to go around. The problem of describing the colors was solved by the invention of the spectroscope.

When ordinary light is passed through a triangular glass prism, the light emerges as the colors of the rainbow. This is the spectrum of sunlight and consists of colors that shade gradually into each other beginning with violet, then blue, green, yellow, orange and red. Pass the light through a narrow slit and then the ribbon of light that this produces through a prism and the colors are spread out much like the leaves of an open book but still continuous hues of color from each to the next; it is impossible to tell where one color stops and the next begins. Now suppose we go into a dark room and use our slit and prism to examine a colored light. There will be a few colored lines with total darkness between them because not all the colors of sunlight are present, which leaves darkness where the colors are missing, just as though most of the leaves were torn out of the book and only one or two or half a dozen remained. The orange-yellow sodium light consists of two lines very close together. The violet potassium flame separates into two lines far apart, one red, the other blue. Likewise, all the colors produced by the heated elements are mixtures.

In 1859 Robert Bunsen (1811–1899), professor of chem-

istry, and Gustav Robert Kirchhoff (1824–1887), professor
of physics, both at the University of Heidelberg, built an
instrument they called a *spectroscope*. The first one was
made from a glass prism, a cigar box and pieces of two old
telescopes. The essential part of the instrument is the glass
prism, but there must be some way to get the light to it
and some way to view the spectrum after the prism produces
it. To get the light to the prism they used a brass tube with
a closed end containing a narrow slit to admit the light as a
very thin, narrow ribbon; the tube also contained lenses to
focus the light from the slit on the surface of the prism. The
other tube was a telescope with which to look at the spectrum.
Later models had a metal casing instead of the cigar box
around the prism to keep out the light that does not come
through the slit. This casing made it possible to use the
spectroscope in an ordinary room instead of a dark room. The
colored lines in a spectroscope are beautiful to look at, but
hard to describe; but light is a wave motion and each color
has a definite wave length and so a method was devised to
measure these wave lengths and then an accurate record
could be made of the spectrum of an element.

Many of the spectra have several lines, but no two elements
have the same combination. The two sodium lines are light
of about 589 millimicrons in wave length, but the red line
of potassium is 766 and the blue one is 404. The greater the
difference in wave length the greater the distance between
the lines. The two sodium lines are 589.5923 and 588.9953
millimicrons and it takes a good spectroscope to show that
they are not one line.

The spectroscope is very useful in chemical analysis and was
a big factor in the discovery of the elements. Helium was discovered in the atmosphere of the sun by means of the spectroscope. Bunsen discovered cesium in 1860 and rubidium in

1861. He named them from the Latin names of the colors, the bright blue line of cesium and the red lines of rubidium.

Chemists of the nineteenth century did not waste much time speculating about the nature of atoms. What was an atom like? The atoms of any one substance all had the same weight and atoms of different substances had different weights. They were probably different in size too, but what shape were they and what color? These were idle questions. Most chemists thought of elements as substances, not as atoms. Copper, silver, iron, sulfur and carbon were all very familiar substances, each with its own characteristics. If anyone had asked a chemist what an atom was like he would probably have said: "It is a little round ball—I guess."

There were signs, however, which began to indicate that atoms must have some kind of structure. One of these was Mendeleev's periodic table; why should lithium, sodium and potassium have similar properties? When the elements were lined up according to increasing atomic weights, members of families occurred at regular intervals. Why? These were good questions but there were no answers.

HUMPHRY DAVY

Another fact that indicated some kind of atomic structure was the effect of electrolysis. As soon as Volta invented his battery (p. 140), chemists began to try the effects of this galvanism on various substances. Berzelius was one of the first to study electrolysis, but two Englishmen really explored the matter. The first of these was Humphry Davy (1778–1829), the son of a wood carver in Penzance, Cornwall. After a little elementary education he was apprenticed to a physician who established a Pneumatic Institute to study the treatment of diseases with gases; Davy became his chemical assistant. Davy learned his chemistry from Lavoisier's textbook and a chemical dictionary and with this meager preparation he began to study gases. He discovered the intoxicating effect of nitrous oxide (laughing gas) and published a paper on the subject in 1800.

At this time Count Rumford was in the process of establishing the Royal Institution in London for the "promotion of science and the diffusion and extension of useful knowledge." Because of his recent paper on nitrous oxide Davy was recommended for the position of assistant in chemistry and was appointed to the post in 1801. His duties were many. In general, he was to conduct experiments and give lectures in applied chemistry. Consequently, he began to study the chemistry of tanning leather and problems in agriculture, mineralogy and metallurgy. He did not accomplish much in these fields, but his lectures were a great success and were particularly attractive to London's high society. Davy received numerous invitations to dinners and other social functions from which he rapidly acquired a social polish that his background and early education had not provided.

Davy's professional advancement was very rapid. Within a year of his appointment as an assistant he was made a professor of chemistry in the Royal Institution. He began intensive work in electrochemistry in 1806 and read papers on the subject before the Royal Society that year and the next. In 1812 he was knighted and two days later he married a rich widow and appointed a chemical assistant. By the end of that year Sir Humphry had resigned his position at the Royal Institution at his wife's request, but he retained a laboratory there and continued in an advisory capacity. Davy was a tremendous worker and on several occasions his health gave way and he was obliged to rest for a time.

Davy's best research was in electrochemistry. He had a battery built with 250 plates, which was the source of the strongest electric current known at the time. He first electrolyzed water in a gold dish and proved that the process gave hydrogen and oxygen and nothing else. Others had thought that acid and alkali were also produced, but these had come from salts in natural water or were dissolved from the glass containers. Davy purified the water before he electrolyzed it.

In 1807 Davy electrolyzed molten sodium hydroxide and was therefore the first to prepare sodium in its free form. He next got potassium by the same method. The next year he prepared calcium, strontium, barium and magnesium from the molten salts of those metals. These electrolyses also gave him chlorine in the free state. All this research together with his lectures and social activities made a very heavy schedule. The Davys made numerous trips to Europe. His last trip was made alone to Italy. On the return journey, he was taken ill and died in Geneva, where he was buried. He was fifty-one years old.

MICHAEL FARADAY

The assistant that Davy appointed in 1812 was Michael Faraday (1791–1867), another son of a poor family who became famous by way of self-education. His father was a blacksmith in London. There were three other children and the father could not afford much schooling for them. Michael attended elementary school, at thirteen became an errand boy for a bookbinder, and was later apprenticed to that trade. He was a born student and managed to read most of the books submitted for binding. When he was twenty-one a customer of his employer took him to Davy's lectures at the Royal Institution. Michael was fascinated with these lectures and took voluminous notes, which he illustrated with drawings of the apparatus. In December 1812 he sent these notes to Davy along with an application for a job as assistant. He got the job. On October 13, 1813, he was on his way to France as assistant, secretary and valet to Sir Humphry. The tour lasted eight months.

After his return from the tour with Davy, Faraday worked pretty much alone in his laboratory at the Royal Institution. At first he did research on alloy steel, optical glass and organic compounds, but he is best known for his later work in electricity. He was made Superintendent of Laboratories in 1821 and was married that year. The Faradays lived in rooms at the Royal Institution for over thirty years. In 1824 he was elected to the Royal Society although Davy, who was president at the time, opposed it. In 1833 he became professor of chemistry at the Institution.

Faraday is best known to chemists for his *laws of electrolysis*. Although he knew very little mathematics he did the first quantitative work in electrolysis and discovered two laws. The first law said that the amount of an element set free by electrolysis is directly proportional to the amount of electricity used—twice as much electricity, twice as much element. The second law was more specific, more surprising and more useful. Electricity is measured in coulombs and Faraday found that 96,500 coulombs set free one gram-equivalent of an element. The equivalent weight (combining weight) of copper is 31.75, and of silver, 108; consequently 96,500 coulombs of electricity set free 31.75 grams of copper or 108 grams of silver. This law made it evident that there is a definite quantitative relation between the atom and electricity. The laws were announced in 1833, but I regret to say that chemists did not unravel the relationship for nearly a century.

One reason for the delay in connecting electricity and the atom was the primitive state of electrical knowledge.

There were two kinds of electricity produced by friction, one by rubbing glass and the other by rubbing a resin. These were called vitreous and resinous electricity until Benjamin Franklin named them positive and negative respectively. Machines were made to produce this electricity, which was called frictional or static electricity. Then Volta invented his battery and the electricity from it was called galvanism after the Italian physiologist, Luigi Galvani, who had first noticed one of the effects of this electricity. In 1831 Faraday showed that galvanism and static electricity are the same thing, but they were treated separately in books published as late as 1848. With all this work on electricity Faraday needed some new names and, with the help of the classical scholar William Whewell, invented *electrode, anode, cathode, anion,* and *cation*—all terms that are still used. Faraday was no theorizer and although he put electricity on a firm basis experimentally, he made no attempt to explain what electricity is except to call it a form of energy.

Although Davy and Faraday made many discoveries in electrochemistry neither of them made any contribution to chemical theory. In fact, both of them were skeptical of the atomic theory. Davy, for example, was considerably less than enthusiastic when, as president of the Royal Society, he had to present Dalton with the royal medal in 1826.

The question that bothered chemists almost from the beginning of their work with the elements was: Which elements will combine with each other and what holds them together so tightly that they have lost all their original properties? For example, oxygen does not combine with gold at all, but it combines with iron readily to form an oxide that is totally unlike either iron or oxygen and, furthermore, to decompose the oxide is almost an impossibility. In 1814 Berzelius proposed an explanation that proved to be partly right. He had done some of the early experiments on electrolysis by passing an electric current from a battery through solutions of compounds in water and noticed that some of them were separated into their elements.

To a physicist, one pole of a battery is positive and the other negative. Strips of platinum, or other metal, attached to these poles by wires are positive and negative electrodes, or anode and cathode respectively. If copper chloride is dissolved in water in a glass or porcelain dish and the two electrodes dipped into the solution, the current passes through the solution from one electrode to the other and copper is deposited on the negative electrode while chlorine gas bubbles off at the positive. Positive charges of electricity attract negative and vice versa. It seems obvious then that copper must be positively charged and chlorine negatively charged. Several experiments of this kind led Berzelius to the conclusion that all the elements can be classified as positive or negative and that it was these unlike charges that held the atoms together. He did not consider his conclusion to be a law but to be a theory to explain why elements combine as they do and how they are held together.

From his own results and those of Davy, Berzelius developed his theory of chemical combination, which has become known as the *dualistic theory*. The theory was very simple: *Some elements have a positive charge of electricity and some a negative charge and it is the attraction of these opposite charges that holds the atoms together*. Although this explained combination and why certain elements do not combine, further elaboration was necessary to explain some additional experimental facts. For example, the metals were all positive and since most of them combine with oxygen and sulfur those two elements must be negative. But sulfur and oxygen combine with each other. Berzelius explained this by saying that some elements are more positive than others. That is, sulfur is more positive than oxygen and so will combine with it, but the metals are more positive still, which enables them to combine with both oxygen and sulfur. The theory explained these facts and many others that were known in the early nineteenth century; consequently, the dualistic theory was widely accepted and served to explain chemical combination for about fifty years.

By 1860 Cannizzaro had established the fact that some of the common gaseous elements are diatomic, such as H_2, O_2 and Cl_2. Also, after 1828, chemists made more and more compounds of carbon, and the dualistic theory did not explain either the diatomic elements or the carbon combinations, of which very few could be electrolyzed. Although it was obvious that the dualistic theory did not explain all chemical combinations, a century passed before a more comprehensive theory was forthcoming and, in fact, there is still no theory that explains all chemical union.

Scientific theories in general have a habit of becoming outmoded by the discovery of experimental facts that were unknown at the time the theory was proposed; any theory is just the best explanation at the moment. The concept of positive and negative elements has persisted and chemists still write the positive element first in a formula, thus H_2O and not OH_2, HCl and not ClH. Such formulas as $NaCl$, CaO, H_2S and $MgCl_2$ all have the positive element first and it serves as the first name of the compound: sodium chloride, calcium oxide, hydrogen sulfide and magnesium chloride. However, oxygen is always written last even though the other element is not known to be positive, as in CO_2, SO_2 and N_2O.

VALENCE

In addition to the question of what holds atoms together, a related question became important by 1850: How many atoms of an element will combine with one of another and is there any limit? In 1852 Edward Frankland (1825–1899), professor of chemistry at Owens College in Manchester, decided from all the experimental evidence that elements have a definite combining capacity, or power. These combining capacities were obtained from formulas, and in 1852 many formulas were uncertain, so it was not until after the Karlsruhe Congress that they were definitely established. By 1868 the formulas were finally settled and Johannes Wislicenus, a Geneva chemist, gave the combining capacities the name of *valence*. The measurement of anything requires a standard and so the valence of the hydrogen atom was taken as 1 and the valence of the atom of an element became the number of hydrogen atoms the atom would combine with or replace. For example, the formula of water is H_2O, which shows that one atom of oxygen combines with two atoms of hydrogen, and so the valence of oxygen is 2. Magnesium oxide is MgO and since the atom of magnesium takes the place of the two hydrogen atoms of water its valence is 2. Since electrolysis shows that the hydrogen atom is positive in many compounds, all the elements that replace it, such as magnesium, are also positive while oxygen and all the others that combine with hydrogen are negative. For this reason valences are often indicated by plus or minus signs: H^+, Mg^{++}, O^{--}, Cl^-, and so forth.

The valence numbers of elements are chiefly an aid to writing and remembering formulas although they have some other uses. The use of valence is an exercise in very simple arithmetic. From the valences Li^+, Ca^{++}, Al^{+++}, Br^-, S^{--}, and PO_4^{---} we can easily write the formulas LiBr, $CaBr_2$, $AlBr_3$, Li_2S, CaS, $AlPO_4$ and many others. The chemist can use valence to write the formula for a compound that is quite unknown and then undertake to make the compound and study its properties. The new compound may be of some use and if it is not, the method of preparation and properties are published anyway so that another chemist need not do the same work again. Years later, perhaps, someone may find a use for the compound, possibly a use that did not exist at the time the compound was first made. Ammonia was known long before it was used in electric refrigeration and chromium was discovered long before there were any automobile bumpers to plate.

Most of the compounds that are easily predicted from valences have been made and their properties recorded and so the use of valence is less important in research than it was in the nineteenth century, but it is still very useful to the student who is learning chemistry. It enables him to learn formulas easily, and the formula is the basis of many calculations that the chemist must make. For example, sulfuric acid is H_2SO_4, and it is manufactured in large quantity from sulfur. From the formula and the atomic weights it is evident that the acid contains 2 parts of hydrogen, 32 of sulfur and 64 of oxygen, a total of 98. Therefore, 32 tons of sulfur should make 98 tons of acid. If the manufacturer gets much less than that he knows that there is something wrong and tries to locate the trouble and correct it.

Valence raises a question of atomic structure. Why should an atom of iron combine with three atoms of chlorine, an atom of copper with two and an atom of silver with only one? There must be some difference in the structure of the atoms to account for these differences in $FeCl_3$, $CuCl_2$ and AgCl, but nobody had any explanation to offer.

PROPERTIES AND USES OF
SOME COMMON ELEMENTS

Our discussion of the elements has been limited mainly
to the discovery, properties and classification of them, but a
few words need to be said about the nature and importance
of some of the more common ones. Obviously, estimates of
the amounts of the various elements in existence cannot be
very accurate. Such estimates are made from the known
composition of the earth's crust including the atmosphere,
the lakes and seas and the rocks to the depths of wells and
mines. The following table shows the relative abundance of
the elements as they are thought to exist in the surface layer
of the earth:

Oxygen	46.5%	Titanium	0.63%
Silicon	27.8	Phosphorus	0.13
Aluminum	8.1	Hydrogen	0.13
Iron	5.1	Manganese	0.10
Calcium	3.6	Fluorine	0.08
Sodium	2.9	Chlorine	0.06
Potassium	2.6	Sulfur	0.05
Magnesium	2.1	Barium	0.05

No other element exceeds 0.04 per cent and only six others
exceed 0.01 per cent.

Clean, dry country air is about 78 per cent nitrogen, 21 per
cent oxygen, 1 per cent argon and 0.03 per cent carbon
dioxide by volume. Neon is only 0.002 per cent of the air
and the other inert gases much less. Although nitrogen constitutes 78 per cent of the air and is present in all living
organisms, both vegetable and animal, there is not much of
it anywhere else and so it does not appear in the table. It is

a rather inert gas and reacts with other elements only under very special conditions.

The difference between a gas and a liquid is a matter of temperature. For example, 18 ounces of water, or a little over a pint at room temperature, becomes more than 30 cubic feet of gas at a temperature just above 100° C. On the other hand, air is a mixture of gases at room temperature, but when it is compressed and cooled to a very low temperature it condenses to a liquid, or rather to a mixture of liquids. This mixture can then be distilled like any other mixture of liquids and the elements separated, because liquid oxygen boils at −183° C, argon at −185° C and nitrogen at −195° C. It takes a complicated apparatus to liquefy and distill air because of the high pressure and low temperature required, and also because the three boiling points are so close together. But these problems were solved long ago. Air was first liquefied in France in 1873 and the first industrial plant was built in this country in 1907.

Over 150 billion cubic feet of oxygen was manufactured in the United States in 1964 by liquefaction and distillation of air. The oxygen is used to make other chemicals and to produce high temperatures or more rapid reactions. The body uses the oxygen of the air to produce energy. The oxygen reacts with the products of the digestion of the food to produce heat and energy to keep us going. In case the lungs or the heart become diseased the breathing of pure oxygen makes it easier for the diseased organ to function and so a large amount of oxygen finds its way into hospitals. Some new hospitals lead the oxygen to the various rooms by pipes just as they do water or steam heat. Pure oxygen is also used in the steel industry to burn impurities out of the iron—carbon, sulfur and phosphorus are the main victims. In the use of steel in building and other fabricating processes oxygen is used in torches with acetylene as a fuel. One kind of torch that burns this mixture of acetylene and oxygen produces a very hot flame and is used to weld pieces of steel together. Another type of torch, which burns the same mixture, supplies extra oxygen and when the steel is heated with this torch it burns like so much wood. The two gases come from steel cylinders where they are under great pressure and so the torch gives a long, narrow flame, which burns its way through a steel beam or plate much faster than the steel could be sawed and with much less effort on the part of the operator. In the past few years the energetic burning of fuels in oxygen, which Scheele, Priestley and Lavoisier all noticed, has been used to furnish high-power fuels for missiles.

Aside from the gases of the air it is difficult to say which of the free elements are the most common. With three meals a day we see a lot of silver and with all the jewelry and watches gold is not exactly rare. Chromium is common in any parking lot. Iron, mainly in the form of steel, is abundant all around us, but we seldom see it. It does show up in penknives, screwdrivers, hammers and other tools, but steel beams are covered with a coat of paint, and such common items as nails, wire, garbage cans and sprinkling cans are galvanized; that is, they have the steel covered with zinc. Even the common tin can is made of steel covered with a thin coat of tin; the steel holds the food while the tin keeps the steel from rusting and lends its name to the invention. Sometimes we see copper in the form of wire or a teapot, but most of it is alloyed with other metals to form brass or bronze.

Metals find their various uses because of their specific properties such as strength (steel), resistance to corrosion (gold, platinum, chromium, tin, zinc), or the ease with which they can be worked into shapes such as sheet, wire or the more complicated forms of gold and silver jewelry.

Among the nonmetallic elements that we meet now and then, besides the gases of the air, are carbon and sulfur. We occasionally see a huge pile of yellow sulfur outside an acid factory, and a fine, yellow powder called "flowers of sulfur" is used to dust fruit trees to kill pests and also occurs in drugstores. The elderly will remember the sulfur and molasses given to children in springtime on general principles and not because it was a cure for anything in particular.

Carbon is an unusual element because it exists in three very different forms in the free state: diamond, graphite and amorphous carbon. Diamond and graphite are both crystalline forms but very different. The diamond is transparent and the graphite opaque; the diamond is the hardest natural substance, but graphite is very soft. Graphite is a black, solid substance with a slight metallic luster, which led the early chemists to consider it a kind of lead and to call it *plumbago* from the Latin name of lead. Graphite occurs naturally and is also manufactured from coke. Its most popular use is in the lead of a lead pencil. A lead pencil contains no lead, but graphite mixed with clay to produce the different degrees of hardness.

The most obvious kinds of carbon are the noncrystalline or amorphous forms. Among them are anthracite coal, charcoal, coke, carbon black and soot. Soot is often the most frequently seen, for it appears as a black cloud issuing from a chimney or a smokestack and settles impartially on the ground, the porch swing or a new straw hat. Free carbon plays an enormous role in the affairs of humanity. Coke, charcoal and anthracite coal are widely used as fuel, for separating metals from their ores and for a host of other purposes. Carbon black not only constitutes the greater part of an automobile tire, but also makes its contribution to culture as the pigment of dark paint and printer's ink. Graphite figures up our bills and the income tax, and the role of the diamond in human affairs is too complex for a chemist to unravel.

Platinum, gold, carbon, sulfur, oxygen, nitrogen and the inert gases all occur free in nature, but most of the elements occur combined with others. Common salt, NaCl, is the most common compound of both its elements, and the free elements are obtained by melting and electrolyzing it. Chlorine is a greenish-yellow, poisonous gas with the strong, penetrating odor of laundry bleach. It is widely used in industry to make compounds that contain it, such as chloroform, but the most familiar uses are the bleaching of cloth and the purification of water. The natural cotton and linen fibers are a pale yellow color; in the eighteenth century, textiles were spread out in the fields to bleach in the sun, and the process sometimes took several months. Chlorine bleaching became practical around 1799 when a Scottish manufacturer made a bleaching powder by treating lime with chlorine. The powder was more easily handled and shipped than the gas was. The bleacher added the powder to a little dilute acid, which set free the chlorine and bleached the cloth very quickly. Nowadays, chlorine gas, shipped from the factory in steel cylinders, is more convenient than bleaching powder, for bleaching paper and textiles, but chlorine bleaching compounds are sold in the grocery stores for home use.

Chlorine was first used to purify water in 1905 during a typhoid epidemic in London. Typhoid fever is one of the water-borne diseases and it has become rare since the use of chlorine to purify water supplies has become general. Although the gas is poisonous and was used in World War I to kill soldiers, that which is used to purify water does not poison anybody for two reasons: it is used in very small amounts and it reacts with the water to form acids.

$$Cl_2 + H_2O \longrightarrow HCl + HClO$$

The hypochlorous acid, $HClO$, is the effective substance in both bleaching and water purification and in these operations it gives up its oxygen and becomes HCl. In the treatment of a water supply the acid formed is neutralized with calcium hydroxide or ammonium hydroxide, which converts the acid into a salt so that it will not dissolve the iron pipes used in the plumbing. The equation for the reaction with the calcium hydroxide is

$$Ca(OH)_2 + 2\,HCl \longrightarrow CaCl_2 + 2\,H_2O$$

By the time the water reaches the customer the chlorine has become either calcium chloride, $CaCl_2$, or ammonium chloride, NH_4Cl, neither of them toxic.

There are thousands of natural compounds of the various elements and the chemist has a problem when he needs to get an element in free form, that is, separated from the others with which it is combined. The term *ore* is used by industry to mean any natural compound of an element from which that element can be separated by an economical process. The word is therefore not a chemical term, but belongs to the mining industry. The meaning of the word is usually stretched to include rock that has some valuable element mixed with it. Gold ore is likely to be sandstone or even sand with particles of gold scattered through it.

The most common ores of metals are oxides, sulfides and carbonates. The common ores of iron are the two oxides Fe_2O_3 and Fe_3O_4. The main ore of aluminum is Al_2O_3.

Common ores of zinc are zinc sulfide, ZnS, and zinc carbonate, $ZnCO_3$.

METALLURGY

The separation of a metal from its ore is called *metallurgy*, and metallurgical processes are of three kinds. In the case of metals that occur free the problem is to separate the metal from the rock with which it is mixed. Solid rocks are first crushed and ground fine. The miners of the famous California and Alaska gold rushes separated the gold from loose sand by stirring the ore with water in a pan and so the process was called *panning*. The specific gravity of gold is 19.3 and that of sand is 2.6. Since the gold is more than seven times as heavy as the sand, it settles to the bottom of the pan much more quickly and most of the sand can be poured out with the water. Any pebbles and pieces of gold can then be picked out by hand. These miners had no facilities for crushing hard rock and they also lost a good deal of gold in the form of very fine particles or dust. Large mining companies now treat the sand or ground rock with a water solution of sodium cyanide. The sodium cyanide reacts with the gold to form a soluble compound, and the solution is drained off the sand. The gold is then set free by replacement with iron or some other metal that has a greater preference for the cyanide than the gold has.

Many metals do not occur in the free state and so the most widely used metallurgical process is the reduction of the oxide of the metal with carbon. The chemical reaction is simple, but the process involves many problems on the industrial scale. For hematite, the equation for the reaction is

$$Fe_2O_3 + 3\,C \longrightarrow 2\,Fe + 3\,CO$$

The hematite and the coke are ground fine and thoroughly mixed. The mixture is transferred to a special kind of furnace called a blast furnace because a blast of air is blown into it to get a higher temperature, just as the old-fashioned blacksmith used a bellows to blow his fire and make it hotter.

Iron melts at 1275° C and so at the temperature of the blast furnace the iron is liquid and is drawn off at the bottom of the furnace and cast into bars, called *pigs*, that weigh about a hundred pounds each. The process is continuous unless the furnace breaks down or the owner runs out of customers.

The metallurgical process used for iron is also used for copper, lead, tin and some other metals. In each case there is some difference in the details of the furnace and procedure, but the chemistry of the process is the same. In each case the oxide reacts with coke or charcoal to give the free metal and carbon monoxide.

The carbonates and the sulfides are easily converted into the oxide and this must be done before the carbon will free the metal. The carbonate is simply heated and decomposes to the oxide and carbon dioxide.

$$ZnCO_3 \longrightarrow ZnO + CO_2$$

If the ore is the sulfide it is heated in a current of air (roasted) and burns to the oxide of the metal and sulfur dioxide.

$$2\,CuS + 3\,O_2 \longrightarrow 2\,CuO + 2\,SO_2$$

Some metals do not give up their oxygen to carbon, and some of them, such as sodium, potassium and magnesium, occur in nature as the chloride. To get the metals from these chlorides the ore is melted and electrolyzed.

$$MgCl_2 \longrightarrow Mg + Cl_2$$

Aluminum is a special case. Its principal ore is bauxite, which is the oxide Al_2O_3, but the metal cannot be freed from the oxygen by heating with carbon because the aluminum combines with the carbon to form the carbide, Al_4C_3. The invention of the metallurgy of aluminum is a story that involves two young men. It has been told many times, but briefly it is this. Charles Martin Hall (1863–1914) was a student at Oberlin College in Ohio. In a lecture his professor of chemistry dropped a side remark, as professors often do, to the effect that whoever discovered an economical method for the metallurgy of aluminum would make his fortune. Thereupon, young Hall decided that he would be that inventor and proceeded to work on the problem in a laboratory that he set up at home. Aluminum had been prepared by a chemical process (p. 198) that was very expensive and so only a few pounds had ever been made and that at a cost of over four hundred dollars a pound, an outrageous price for the most abundant metal in the earth's crust.

Hall undertook to separate the aluminum by the electrolysis of some of its compounds, but he ran into many difficulties. In order to electrolyze anything it must be in liquid form either in solution or molten. Hall tried aluminum compounds in water, and he got hydrogen at the negative electrode but no aluminum. Bauxite does not dissolve in any common liquid and has a very high melting point, 2050° C. Moreover, the molten oxide does not conduct a current, but Hall was not easily discouraged; he persisted until he found the answer. Cryolite, Na_3AlF_6, a natural compound of aluminum, melts at 1000° C. Hall found that if he melted the cryolite the bauxite dissolved in it. The solution did conduct an electric current, which electrolyzed the aluminum oxide to aluminum and oxygen.

After Hall had perfected the process he migrated to Pittsburgh where he found financial backing for his process. The metallurgy of aluminum was carried on in Pittsburgh for a time, but it did not prove to be an economical arrangement. There was no bauxite in the area and electricity was expensive.

The chief source of bauxite in the United States is the Ozark Mountains. The crude ore was mined there, but it contained impurities that had to be removed before it could be electrolyzed and so it was shipped to a plant in East Saint Louis, Illinois, for the preparation of the pure aluminum oxide. The oxide then went to Niagara Falls, New York, where electricity was cheap because of the water power. Such was the procedure that brought aluminum into economical production.

Once the metal was available in quantity and at a reasonable price the big question was what to do with it. The company built a plant at New Kensington, a few miles north of Pittsburgh, for the fabrication of useful products. For several years the chief use of aluminum was for cooking utensils that were sold from door to door. Many of the agents were college students working during vacation.

Hall made his fortune, but now the patents on the process have long since expired and several companies manufacture aluminum in many localities. The Ozark mines are no longer adequate and the American companies go to Jamaica, Surinam or British Guiana for the bauxite. Three million tons of aluminum were smelted in 1966 and about a third of it went into new houses as window frames, doors, siding and nails. New automobiles took over 300,000 tons. A lot of it went to make foil or cans for food packaging and the rest went for a great variety of uses.

A strange coincidence in the story of the metallurgy of aluminum is the fact that while Hall was inventing it, a young Frenchman, Paul Héroult (1863–1914), invented the same process in the same year, 1886. The coincidence caused some patent difficulties. And by way of further coincidence these two young inventors were born in the same year and both died in the first year of the First World War.

CLASSES OF CHEMICAL COMPOUNDS

Several other elements are used extensively, some in the free state and others as compounds. Only eighty-eight of the elements are found in nature, but there are over 2,500,000 compounds now known and over two hundred new ones added each day—according to *Chemical Abstracts* the number is 285 for each working day. With so many compounds, classification is necessary if we are to learn much about them. The public solves the classification problem by calling everything either a chemical or an acid, but the chemist has six main classes of chemical compounds: oxides, acids, bases, salts, organic compounds and some nondescript leftovers that do not have enough similarities to be a class. Most of the members of this miscellaneous group are compounds of nonmetals other than oxygen. Their number is very small.

The oxides are simple compounds that contain oxygen and one other element. Nearly all elements form oxides. Common and useful oxides are calcium oxide, CaO, which is lime; silicon dioxide, SiO_2, which is quartz or sand; zinc oxide, ZnO, and titanium dioxide, TiO_2, both of which are common white pigments used in paints, plastics and white automobile tires; an iron oxide, Fe_2O_3, common in red barn paints; and lead oxides, PbO and Pb_3O_4, both pigments; the latter is the red pigment of the paint used on steel. Carbon dioxide, CO_2, is manufactured and used in fire extinguishers, in soft drinks since the days of Priestley and in solid form for refrigeration under the trade name of "Dry Ice."

The acids are compounds that contain hydrogen and one or more nonmetals. If there are three or more elements in an acid one of them is generally oxygen. One common acid is hydrochloric, HCl, which is present in the gastric juice and aids the digestion of food in the stomach. It is also manufactured and widely used in industry, sometimes under the old name, *muriatic acid*. Also common is hydrosulfuric acid, H_2S, the malodorous gas of rotten eggs and white sulfur water. It is extremely poisonous, but because of its disagreeable odor and taste it has been popularly thought to have medicinal value since ancient times. There are still "health spas" at white sulfur springs throughout the world.

Most of the acids are soluble in water and the solution is colorless and tastes sour. However, tasting an acid is a hazardous venture for many of them are caustic and affect the tongue like a red-hot iron. The sour taste of foods is the taste of an acid that is present. Vinegar contains acetic acid, $HC_2H_3O_2$, grapefruit and other citrus fruits contain citric acid, $H_3C_6H_5O_7$, grapes contain tartaric acid, $H_2C_4H_4O_6$. Citric and tartaric are the principal acids of fruits in general although there are some others that occur in smaller amounts, notably ascorbic acid, also known as vitamin C. The principal acids of the chemical industry and the extent of their use is indicated by the United States production in 1964: sulfuric, H_2SO_4, 22,923,508 tons; nitric, HNO_3, 4,594,117 tons; phosphoric, H_3PO_4, 3,262,763 tons; and hydrochloric, HCL, 1,228,068 tons. All the numbers refer to short tons of two thousand pounds. The manufacture of sulfuric acid is greater than that of any other industrial chemical. One of its main uses is to make other acids.

Bases are compounds that contain a metal or other positive

radical and the OH group. The bases that dissolve in water are called *alkalies*. The most common alkalies are sodium, potassium and ammonium hydroxides, NaOH, KOH and NH_4OH respectively. The names of the bases are just the name of the metal and hydroxide: calcium hydroxide, aluminum hydroxide, sodium hydroxide and so on.

The reaction between acids and bases adds such words as *neutral* and *neutralization* to the vocabulary of the chemist. Water, alcohol, ether and many other liquids are neutral; the word means that the liquid is neither an acid nor a base. A solution of sodium hydroxide colors the dye litmus, blue, and hydrochloric acid turns it red. If one of these solutions is slowly added to the other and the mixture well stirred there comes a point where neither red nor blue litmus is affected. The solution is then neutral and the process is neutralization—the neutralization of the acid by the base or vice versa. The solution now contains table salt and water.

$$NaOH + HCl \longrightarrow NaCl + H_2O$$

Sodium bicarbonate is a mild alkali, which is often used to neutralize an acid stomach, that is, one that is too acid for comfort.

$$NaHCO_3 + HCl \longrightarrow NaCl + CO_2 + H_2O$$

The druggist will also sell you tablets of magnesium hydroxide, $Mg(OH)_2$, for the acid stomach or he will supply you with a suspension of this base in water, which he calls milk of magnesia.

Salts are harder to define than acids and bases, and they differ more from each other than either the acids or bases do. They are solids and are usually crystalline. If common salt is examined with a magnifying glass it is seen to consist of small, transparent cubes. Other salts may also be cubes, but they are more often a more complicated geometrical figure. It is difficult to find a large crystal of a salt for inspection, but when the chemist sees the sharp edges and flat faces he knows that the substance is crystalline.

A salt is a compound of a metal and one or more non-metals, although the NH_4, or ammonium radical, functions as a metal just as it does in the bases. Many salts can be made by the action of an acid on a metal, an oxide or a base. For example, zinc sulfate can be made by any of the reactions shown in the following equations:

$$Zn + H_2SO_4 \longrightarrow ZnSO_4 + H_2$$
$$ZnO + H_2SO_4 \longrightarrow ZnSO_4 + H_2O$$
$$Zn(OH)_2 + H_2SO_4 \longrightarrow ZnSO_4 + 2\,H_2O$$

Some salts occur naturally, such as sodium chloride, potassium chloride, calcium carbonate and calcium phosphate, $Ca_3(PO_4)_2$, which is the mineral matter of bones and the rock phosphate of the Florida mines. In fact, most of the estimated two thousand minerals are either salts or oxides. There are thousands of salts; many are used in pharmacy, in industry, on the farm or in the home and many others find uses only in the chemical laboratory or sit on the shelf waiting for somebody to find a use for them.

Most salts are white, but copper salts are blue or green; nickel salts are green; cobalt salts are red; and iron salts are pale green or brown. Although there are several colored salts very few of them are of any use because of that property. Cadmium sulfide, CdS, and lead chromate, $PbCrO_4$, are bright yellow, insoluble salts used as paint pigments. Dark blue glass is colored by cobalt silicate and the familiar pale green color of glass bottles is the color of iron silicate. The glass itself is a mixture of colorless silicates in which calcium silicate predominates. If the glass is colored there is generally a colored silicate present, but not always. Red glass was formerly made by adding finely divided gold and the red glass so familiar to the driver of an automobile is made with the free element selenium, which is much cheaper than gold.

Organic compounds are compounds of carbon and they will be discussed in Chapter Eight.

The miscellaneous group is a small one and hardly to be considered a class of compounds, but largely a dumping ground for compounds that do not belong in the other five classes. Ammonia is the most common member of the group and the others are seldom met outside the laboratory.

And so we see that nature provides eighty-eight elements that form an endless number of compounds either in nature or in the laboratory. No chemist knows even a few properties of all these substances. Where these substances are found or how they are made and what their properties are, is all recorded in books and journals in libraries throughout the world.

The two strangest elements are mercury and gallium. Both are silver-white metals, but, curiously enough, both are liquids. Mercury melts at −39° C and boils at 357° C. Gallium melts on a hot day—at 30° C, to be specific—and does not boil until the temperature reaches 1700° C. Why should these two metals be liquids while all the others are solids? It is a good question, but, as Dalton said, atoms of different substances are different and that is about as close as we can come to an answer.

CHAPTER EIGHT

The Strange Behavior of Carbon

AT THE BEGINNING of the nineteenth century, chemists recognized three kinds of matter. First there were the elements, about thirty of them. The compound substances that made up the crust of the earth, such as water, soil and rocks, were a second kind of matter. Then there was a third kind, the substances of animal and vegetable chemistry. Some of them, such as sugar, alcohol, the acid of vinegar, turpentine, vegetable oils and indigo, had been known since ancient times and the number of such compounds was greatly increased by the discoveries of the eighteenth-century chemists. Scheele, of oxygen fame, had separated tartaric acid from grapes, citric acid from lemons, malic acid from apples and lactic acid from sour milk. In 1773 Hilaire Marin Rouelle, professor of chemistry at the Jardin du Roi in Paris, isolated urea from urine. (Rouelle was the younger brother, and successor at the Jardin, of Guillaume François Rouelle (1703–1770), the teacher of Lavoisier.) By 1820 morphine, quinine, strychnine and some related drugs from plant sources were common. This growing group of plant and animal products was peculiar in that only four of the thirty known elements were found in them. These elements were carbon, hydrogen, oxygen and nitrogen. In fact, not many of them contained nitrogen, which left the great majority to be composed of just three elements. By 1807 Berzelius, the great analyst and neologist, decided this group of substances should have a name and in forthright fashion he gave it one. He called them *organic* compounds since they were produced by living organisms. From that date the mineral substances have been *inorganic* compounds or elements. In other words, substances were either organic or they were not because *in*- means not. Chemists are still content with these names.

When Berzelius named the organic compounds he also pointed out the impossibility of making them in the laboratory. The explanation of this supposed monopoly of the organisms in the production of these compounds was the deadly result of the philosophical doctrine of vitalism. Everybody believed that there was a vital force necessary for the production of organic substances—that such substances were tied up with the life processes of the organism. Some mysterious force enabled the beet to make sugar or the dog to make urea. These ideas prevailed until 1828 when they first began to be questioned, and they were thereafter gradually abandoned. However, even though chemists have made thousands of organic compounds, how the organism makes them is still a mystery.

FRIEDRICH WÖHLER

Making a compound from its elements or from simpler compounds is called *synthesis*. Organic syntheses in the laboratory began in 1828 when the German chemist Friedrich Wöhler (1800–1882) performed an experiment that cast the first doubt on the vitalistic theory. In order to understand what Wöhler did and why he did it we must know what led up to the event.

With so many compounds composed of the same three or four elements it is not strange that two or more are found that contain the same elements in the same ratio; analysis showed this to be true. In 1833 Gay-Lussac, who was editor of *Annales de chimie*, noticed in papers that were submitted for publication that cyanic and fulminic acids have the same composition and correctly attributed the phenomenon to different ways in which the atoms were attached to each other. We now distinguish between these two acids by writing the formula for cyanic acid HCNO and that of fulminic acid, HNCO.

In 1825 Faraday found that ethylene and butylene have the same composition as indicated by the formula CH_2. Then in 1830 Berzelius discovered that racemic and tartaric acids have the same composition. Berzelius thought that the phenomenon of two substances with the same composition deserved a name, whereupon he coined the word *isomerism* from the Greek words *isos*, "the same," and *meros*, "parts." Compounds with the same percentage of the same elements are called *isomers*. Organic chemists still use Berzelius' terminology for the thousands of isomers that have been discovered.

Now back to Wöhler. He was born in the village of Eschersheim near Frankfurt and when he was twelve years old the family moved into the city where young Wöhler received his early education and somehow acquired an interest in chemistry. In 1820 he went to Marburg to study medicine, but the university had no chemistry laboratory and so he carried on chemical experiments in his room. He was not very popular with the landlady, for he worked with cyanogen compounds, which are a bit smelly. He became a doctor in 1823 with a dissertation on urine from which he had separated a sample of urea, the compound that Rouelle had discovered fifty years before.

Wöhler did not care for the practice of medicine and in the fall of 1823 he went to Stockholm to spend a year studying

chemistry with Berzelius. The city of Berlin had just established a technical school and in 1824 Wöhler returned to
Germany and got a job on the faculty of the new school.
He was an enthusiastic chemist and in addition to his teaching he did research on any problem that attracted his attention. By 1827 he had prepared metallic aluminum by
heating aluminum chloride with metallic potassium and the
next year he used a similar method to prepare free beryllium
and yttrium. But he also continued with the cyanogen compounds of his school days. He prepared silver cyanate, which
was an isomer of the silver fulminate that his friend Justus
von Liebig (1803–1873) had prepared as a student in Gay-
Lussac's laboratory. This new idea of isomerism intrigued
Wöhler and he felt that the cyanates deserved further investigation. In the course of this work he evaporated a solution of ammonium cyanate and to his astonishment he got
crystals of urea instead of the ammonium cyanate crystals that
he expected. Ammonium cyanate is an inorganic salt, and
when it was converted into urea by heating a solution of it,
there was no longer any need for a vital force to produce
the organic urea.

Wöhler's discovery did not settle the matter of vitalism at
once, of course, and Wöhler himself seems to have had some
doubts on the subject because the ammonium cyanate had
been prepared from ammonium hydroxide and cyanic acid,
both of them made from organic material. However, he did
write to Berzelius that he had made urea without the use of
a kidney. The equation for Wöhler's synthesis is

$$NH_4CNO \xrightarrow{\text{heated}} CO(NH_2)_2$$

This reaction is not a very common type. It is a molecular
rearrangement, that is, the molecule of ammonium cyanate

and that of urea are isomers; each contains two atoms of nitrogen, one of carbon, one of oxygen and four of hydrogen. But in the ammonium cyanate they are in the combination of one ammonium radical, NH_4, and one cyanate radical, CNO, whereas the urea has one CO radical and two NH_2 radicals. The atoms in the one molecule have rearranged themselves and are now attached in a different manner to make a different molecule, as Gay-Lussac had suspected. The structural formula of urea shown in the equation was not known in 1828, but the properties of urea were well known to Wöhler, who repeated his experiment many times to make sure that his synthetic compound was the same as the natural urea.

Wöhler's work was the first break in the defenses of the vitalistic theory and it inspired chemists to attempt the synthesis of other compounds with the result that a new branch of chemistry was created. The branch has grown into a tree. How many compounds of carbon have been synthesized nobody knows, but the number exceeds two million. No other element forms more than a minute fraction of that number except hydrogen which nearly always tags along with the carbon.

Many of the organic compounds that were first obtained as natural products are now synthesized, some of them on a huge scale. Urea, for example, is now produced commercially in the United States, Japan, Germany and twenty-five other countries. The total annual production is over five million tons. Vitalism has nothing to do with the process, for the raw materials are undoubtedly inorganic; coke is burned to carbon dioxide, ammonia is made from atmospheric nitrogen and its hydrogen comes from water. Then the ammonia and carbon dioxide are heated under high pressure to form the urea. The urea is used to make plastics, drugs and other organic compounds and a lot of it is used in fertilizer to supply the nitrogen needed for the growth of plants.

About one-third of the chemists in the American Chemical Society are organic chemists—some thirty thousand of them. They and their counterparts in other countries continue to synthesize new compounds, study their properties and find uses for them if they can.

Organic research over the last century has generally followed one plan: (1) Isolate a compound from a plant or animal source or synthesize it in the laboratory. (2) Purify the compound, for it is sure to be mixed with other substances regardless of its source. (3) Analyze the pure compound for the percentage of each element in it. (4) Determine the molecular weight and calculate the formula. (5) Determine and record its physical and chemical properties. (6) Try to figure out how the atoms are attached to each other.

How to tell when a substance is pure is one of the problems of the organic chemist, for the analysis of a mixture is useless. The method used to determine the purity of a solid was devised by that patriarch of chemists, Michel Eugène Chevreul (1786–1889), who held several positions in Paris, among them professor of chemistry at the Jardin des Plantes. Chevreul published papers on a wide variety of topics in organic chemistry over a period of eighty years, and the purification of organic compounds was always one of his problems, but one which he solved to the satisfaction of all the organic chemists that have succeeded him.

If the compound was a solid, Chevreul first determined the temperature at which it melted. He then dissolved it in warm water, alcohol or other solvent and cooled the solution or evaporated part of it until he got a good crop of crystals. Some of his solid and most of the impurities remained in solution and so he filtered out the crystals, dried them and took the melting point again. If the crystallization had not changed the melting point he decided that the solid was pure. If the second melting point was higher than the first, he knew that he had increased the purity of his compound, but he still did not know whether he had removed all the impurities. Therefore, he repeated the crystallizations and melting-point determinations until the last two melting points were the same. The idea that impurities lower the melting point of a solid and that all pure samples of a substance have the same melting point has been used to determine the purity of solids since the days of Chevreul.

All samples of the same liquid boil at the same temperature if the liquid is pure. To isolate a pure liquid from a mixture is a long and tedious process, but it can generally be done by repeated distillations, and the boiling point can be observed by the use of a thermometer during the distillation.

There is no general method for the purification of gases; each is a separate problem. They could, of course, be liquefied and distilled, but that requires very special and expensive equipment.

ORGANIC ANALYSIS

The analysis of an organic compound for the percentage of carbon and hydrogen is a long, hard job. Lavoisier and later Berzelius invented the method that is used: burn the compound to carbon dioxide and water and then collect and weigh these two substances. Several chemists have improved the original method; some have improved the method of getting oxygen for the combustion and some have improved the design of the apparatus. Dalton and Berthollet tried their hands at improving the method and in 1811 Gay-Lussac introduced potassium chlorate as a source of oxygen and mixed the sample with it. But potassium chlorate and organic substances are extremely explosive and after a few unfortunate experiences within the course of the next four years the intrepid Frenchman changed to copper oxide as a source of oxygen, which was a great improvement.

Gay-Lussac's student Justus von Liebig studied the method of carbon and hydrogen determination thoroughly and improved the apparatus so much that his method was used for years. In fact, only a few changes have been made in it. A stream of pure oxygen has been substituted for the copper oxide, the charcoal furnace was replaced by a gas furnace and after 1900 by an electric furnace with which the temperature is more easily controlled than with either of the other two. Also, in recent years, the method has been adapted to the analysis of very small samples, because in organic chemical research the chemist often has only a few milligrams of his product after many days' work.

In the modern method of organic analysis a weighed sample is introduced into a horizontal glass tube and burned in a stream of pure oxygen by heating the tube in an electric furnace of special design. The gases from the combustion are led through specially designed absorption bulbs, one of which contains concentrated sulfuric acid or other drying material to absorb the water; the other contains potassium hydroxide to absorb the carbon dioxide. The bulbs are each weighed before and after the combustion and the increase in weight of one is the weight of the water and the increase in the other is the weight of the carbon dioxide. The calculation of the analysis is simple. From the formulas H_2O and CO_2 and the atomic weights of the three elements—1, 16 and 12—it is apparent that the water is $\frac{2}{18}$ hydrogen and the carbon dioxide is $\frac{12}{44}$ carbon. If the percentages of C and H do not add up to 100 per cent the difference is assumed to be oxygen for, until recently, there was no method for the direct determination of oxygen in a compound. This determination of oxygen by difference made it necessary to test for nitrogen, sulfur, phosphorus and the halogens because they do occur in organic compounds now and then. Of course, in the case of synthetic compounds the chemist would know whether one or more of these elements might be present from the substances he had used in the synthesis.

JEAN BAPTISTE DUMAS

Compounds that contain nitrogen require a separate analysis for that element. The most common method was devised by Jean Baptiste André Dumas (1800–1884). Dumas was born at Arles in the south of France. For his higher education he went first to Geneva and then to Paris where he completed his education and was soon made a professor at the Athenaeum, the first of several professorships in Paris. He became the most famous French chemist of his time because of his teaching, his research, his personality and his thinking. Among his research activities he determined about thirty atomic weights, undertook to revive the ideas of Avogadro and Ampère and tried his hand at classifying the elements. Dumas was one of the first organic chemists and devised methods for weighing a gas accurately and for the determination of nitrogen in an organic compound.

Dumas burned the compound under conditions that set the nitrogen free, collected it and measured its volume. The weight of the nitrogen is easily calculated from the fact that 22.4 liters of it weigh 28 grams under standard conditions.

In both the determination of carbon and hydrogen and that of nitrogen the combustions must be carried out with the utmost care to ensure complete combustion of the sample and also to avoid losing some of the gases or gaining others from the air by leakage of the apparatus. However, despite the hard work and the necessary care required, these combustions have been used since the early nineteenth century without much change.

Ethane is a gas with the analysis 80 per cent C and 20 per cent H. From the atomic weights of 12 and 1, the calculated formula is CH_3. This is the *empirical* formula and merely shows the relative number of the atoms present. The actual formula could be C_2H_6, C_3H_9 or any other multiple of CH_3 because they are all 80 per cent C and 20 per cent H. In 1860 Cannizzaro pointed out a method for finding the molecular weight of a gas: weigh some of it and calculate the weight of 22.4 liters under standard conditions. In the case of ethane this weight turns out to be 30 grams, which means that the molecular weight is 30. The weight of a CH_3 molecule would be 15 and so the *molecular* formula of ethane is C_2H_6.

Molecular weight determinations by the organic chemist follow analyses as day follows night—always. For gases and volatile liquids this vapor density method is generally used; in fact, Dumas devised a method for the determination of the molecular weight of volatile liquids. However, sugars, starches and many other organic compounds decompose when they are heated and so cannot be vaporized; such compounds require a different method for the molecular weight determination. The first suitable method was devised in 1884 (p. 304) and so the general use of molecular formulas is less than a century old.

With the solution of one problem another always seems to arise. Once the molecular formulas of the organic compounds were settled the chemist's problem became valence. Organic compounds seldom conduct an electric current and are not separated into their elements by electrolysis; furthermore, in 1837 Dumas showed that chlorine, bromine and iodine, which were all negative, could be substituted for the hydrogen in

organic compounds although hydrogen was considered positive. Consequently the elements cannot be positive and negative as they are in the inorganic compounds. Worse still,
the valence numbers are not indicated by the formulas.
Consider the formulas CH_4, C_2H_6, C_3H_8 and C_4H_{10}. The
valence of H is 1 and so in these formulas the valance of
carbon is 4, 3, 2.66 and 2.5 in that order. This doesn't make
sense; there are no fractions of atoms. What then is the
valence of carbon? Obviously it cannot be obtained from the
formulas of the carbon compounds as the valence numbers
are determined for the other elements.

THE STRUCTURAL THEORY

Chemists are people and this valence problem was first
solved by one of the most tragic figures in the history of
chemistry. Archibald Scott Couper (1831–1892) was born
in Scotland, the son of the owner of a textile mill. His health
was never good and he received his early education from
tutors in his home. Later he went to the University of Glasgow and then to Edinburgh. In these universities he studied
philosophy, logic and languages, but during and after his
university years he spent considerable time in Germany where
he became interested in chemistry. He began to study the
subject in laboratories there and in 1856 went to Paris to
study with Charles Adolphe Wurtz (1817–1884), who had
been one of Dumas' students and had succeeded him in
some of his professorships after Dumas became active in the
Ministry of Education about 1848.

Couper was a brilliant thinker and experimenter and on
June 7, 1858, his first paper was read before the French
Academy. (He had prepared another paper several months
earlier entitled "On a New Theory of Chemistry.") In this
paper he proposed that carbon always has a valence of 4 and

that its atoms may use one or more of these valence bonds to attach themselves to other atoms of carbon and thus form a chain. He included several formulas in his paper and used lines, or dashes, to indicate the valence bonds that connected the atoms, a method that organic chemists have used ever since. In short, he originated the structural theory of organic chemistry.

Couper asked Wurtz to present his paper to the Academy, but Wurtz was not a member and did not exert himself to find someone who could read the paper. In May 1858, Friedrich August Kekulé (1829–1896), who had studied in Paris and was now at the University of Heidelberg, published much the same ideas in a German journal. Couper complained to Wurtz about the delay in presenting his paper and Wurtz expelled him from his laboratory. Dumas, who was no longer active in research, read the paper before the Academy on June 14, 1858, but the damage was done and Kekulé had priority.

Couper returned to the University of Edinburgh as an assistant in chemistry, but soon had a nervous breakdown, which his associates attributed to his treatment by Wurtz. After a few months in a mental institution Couper recovered. Then he went fishing and had a sunstroke, which left him an invalid for the last thirty-four of his sixty-one years.

Kekulé's prior publication and Couper's disappearance from the chemical scene resulted in Kekulé getting sole credit for the structural theory. He and Wurtz made fun of Couper's protest and Wurtz used Couper's formulas without bothering to mention their source. The story has a strange end. Kekulé went to the University of Ghent in 1858 as a professor of chemistry and was there nine years when he transferred to Bonn and taught there until his death in 1896. He was succeeded at Bonn by Professor Richard Anschütz who became interested in the reason for the disappearance of Couper and, with considerable difficulty, succeeded in ferreting out the story. So, after more than half a century and after his death Couper got credit for his part in devising the structural theory of organic compounds—got it through the efforts of his rival's successor.

Couper and Kekulé decided independently that carbon always has the valence 4 and that atoms of carbon combine with each other to form chains. Chains of from fifteen to twenty carbon atoms are common and many are known that are much longer. This carbon chain idea led to another type of formula called a *structural* or *graphic* formula. Ever since the publication of the theory organic chemists have used the graphic formulas almost exclusively because they show, not only what atoms are present, but also how they are attached to each other. For example, the compounds just mentioned in connection with valence have the graphic formulas,

$$
\begin{array}{cc}
& H \\
& | \\
H-\!\!\!\!&C-H \\
& | \\
& H
\end{array}
\qquad
\begin{array}{cc}
H & H \\
| & | \\
H-C-&C-H \\
| & | \\
H & H
\end{array}
\qquad
\begin{array}{ccc}
H & H & H \\
| & | & | \\
H-C-&C-&C-H \\
| & | & | \\
H & H & H
\end{array}
$$

Methane   Ethane   Propane

$$
\begin{array}{cccc}
H & H & H & H \\
| & | & | & | \\
H-C-&C-&C-&C-H \\
| & | & | & | \\
H & H & H & H
\end{array}
$$

Butane

Each line to a symbol indicates a valence bond—1 to each H and 4 to each C. These compounds are not decomposed by electricity and so the nature of the force that holds them together was not known and was ignored for over fifty years. This did not bother the organic chemist because the valence numbers served his purpose very well and they were the same as those used for carbon and hydrogen in the inorganic compounds such as CO_2 and HCl.

Once the molecular formula of a compound is known, writing the graphic formula can be just like solving a puzzle. This practice is very useful in predicting how many isomers there are with the same molecular formula, or in deciding which are the correct formulas when there are known to be two or more isomers. For example, how many butanes are there? The molecular formula of butane is C_4H_{10}. Let us take C with a valence of 4 and H with a valence of 1 and see how many different ways they can be put together. Obviously the four carbon atoms must be joined together, for hydrogen with its one bond cannot very well tie two atoms together. The solution of the puzzle gives us

Butane   and   Isobutane

There are these two possibilities and no other; therefore, there should be two butanes and no more if the structural theory is correct. This speculation proves to be correct: two butanes and only two are known. They are both colorless gases, but they have different boiling points, densities and chemical reactions and so they are undoubtedly two different substances. Only the graphic formulas can show the difference.

There was one common compound that did not fit into this structural theory. It was benzene, which Faraday had discovered in 1825. It is a colorless, volatile liquid of pleasant odor, which he found to be present in the tar formed when illuminating gas is made from coal. An analysis gave benzene the formula CH and the molecular weight proved to be 78. Since CH would have a molecular weight of only 13 the molecular formula must be C_6H_6. Try the puzzle method on this one and you will find yourself six hydrogen atoms short. This is too many to be a mistake in either the analysis or the molecular weight determination. There must be some other explanation. Kekulé solved the problem by extending his theory. He put the six carbon atoms in a ring and attached one hydrogen atom to each carbon. This gave carbon a valence of only 3 and so Kekulé went further and connected every other pair of carbon atoms by two valence bonds. This gave the formula,

Kekulé also investigated the chemical reactions of benzene and found that they could be explained very well by his graphic formula. Benzene has come in for years of attention since Kekulé's time by hundreds of chemists, but his formula still survives. In the meantime a host of other compounds have been discovered that have this benzene ring as part of their structure.

The organic chemist is confident that if he can write a graphic formula according to the rules it will represent a real compound whether it has ever been discovered or not. To date he has been correct and many a new compound has been made from such a prediction.

If two or more isomers of a compound are known the chemist still has a problem. For example, there are two compounds with the molecular formula C_2H_6O. Here the puzzler comes up with:

$$
\begin{array}{ccccc}
& H & H & & H \qquad\qquad H \\
& | & | & & | \qquad\qquad | \\
H-&C&-C-O-H & \text{and} & H-C-O-C-H \\
& | & | & & | \qquad\qquad | \\
& H & H & & H \qquad\qquad H
\end{array}
$$

I.   II.

One of these compounds is the alcohol of beer, wine and whiskey. The other is a laboratory product that is a gas until the temperature falls below $-24°$ C, whereas alcohol is a liquid that boils at $78°$ C. Their other properties are also different—they are definitely different substances. The question is: which is the formula for which? Here the chemist gives up puzzles and does some work. He adds metallic sodium, perhaps, to each of the substances. It does not react at all with the gas, but the alcohol gives off hydrogen gas and when the reaction will not go any further there is a solid substance left. Purification and analysis of this substance shows that it has the formula C_2H_5ONa. From these results it is apparent that an atom of sodium has replaced one atom of hydrogen in the alcohol; therefore, one of the hydrogen atoms of the alcohol must be different from the other five. This leads to the conclusion that alcohol has the formula I, for in that formula one atom of hydrogen is attached to oxygen and the other five to carbon, while in formula II, all six of the hydrogen atoms are attached to carbon.

If the chemist feels that he needs more proof of his formulas he carries out other reactions of one or both of the substances to get more evidence. At the stage of the work just described he has some proof of the structure of the alcohol, but that of the other compound depends entirely on structural theory. Both of these formulas have long since been established from their chemical properties; the one is grain alcohol and the other belongs to a class of substances called ethers.

If the molecular formula of a compound is large, there are so many possible structures that the puzzle method is of little use. In such cases the chemist makes a *derivative*, that is, he makes another compound from his new one, and then identifies the derivative either by its properties, if the derivative is a known compound, or by analyzing and deriving its formula if it is new. At times the chemist must make several derivatives and then, in good detective fashion, try to solve the structure of his compound from the evidence the derivatives provide. In the above example the C_2H_5ONa is a derivative of the alcohol and it alone is a good clue to the structure of that substance.

Once the structure of a substance is established the chemist may attempt to synthesize it, for synthesis is considered the final proof of the structure of an organic compound. In brief, the chemist first takes the compound apart and then puts it together again.

In the latter half of the nineteenth century thousands of chemists were busy making organic compounds, and this rapid increase in the number of such compounds brought on the problem of naming them. The alchemists and the early chemists had named each substance as it was discovered. The French had named alcohol *eau de vie*, which means water of life, although it might have been better to call it water of liveliness. Other names of the early days indicated some outstanding property of the substance such as sugar "sweet" and acetic acid "sour." Some were named from their source: urea from urine and marsh gas for the gas that bubbles up from swamp water. The general system of nomenclature devised by Lavoisier and his colleagues did not include the organic substances, for at that time there were not enough of them to be a problem.

As structural formulas became more common it was obvious that there were a great many groups of atoms that occurred in the formulas of several different substances: such groups as CH_3-, -OH, -CO, -NH_2 and several others. These were called *radicals*. The idea had been current in Lavoisier's day, for there are inorganic radicals too, but their use in organic chemistry did not get under way until toward the middle of the nineteenth century when they soon became the basis of organic nomenclature. The formula for alcohol given above contains the -OH, or hydroxyl, radical. It was soon noticed that there are a lot of compounds that contain this group, and so the entire lot were called *alcohols*. The -OH group is usually referred to as the functional group of the alcohols because it gives them their characteristic chemical properties. For instance, all of them react with sodium to give hydrogen. As soon as a chemist learns that a compound is an alcohol he knows that it contains an -OH group in its formula and that it reacts with sodium and several other substances that he knows about. The physical properties of a compound depend largely on its molecular weight and the arrangement of the carbon atoms in the molecule, but the chemical properties depend on the functional group or groups present. Although the word *alcohol* means any one of hundreds of compounds that contain the -OH group, the word is also used to designate the original alcohol. The word is used in this sense when the doctor says: "Lay off alcohol," or the label on a wine bottle indicates 18 per cent alcohol. This use of the same word with two different meanings in the same science is not very scientific, but it is very common and seldom causes confusion. The words *salt* and *ether* are other examples of the same usage, but when the chemist is writing he is usually specific and writes sodium chloride or diethyl ether, which leaves no doubt about what he means.

There are fewer classes of organic compounds than one might expect. The main general classes are *hydrocarbons, halides, alcohols, ethers, ketones, aldehydes, acids, amines* and *amides*. Each of these classes has subdivisions and many compounds belong to two or more of these main classes. Citric acid, for example, is both alcohol and acid, and a large group of important compounds are both acids and amines.

HYDROCARBONS

The hydrocarbons are the simplest class: they contain carbon and hydrogen only; consequently, the simplest formula of all is methane, CH_4. Bubbles of methane can be seen rising from pools of stagnant water on any warm day. It is also the gas dreaded as an explosive in coal mines and it is the main component of natural gas. Natural gas and petroleum together contain a whole long series of compounds related to methane. The second member of the series is ethane, C_2H_6, and then propane, C_3H_8, followed by butane, C_4H_{10}. All four of these gases are common fuels; the first two in natural gas and the other two in "bottled gas," which is now on sale in most communities.

The series of hydrocarbons from petroleum continues with pentane, hexane and so on continuously by increases of CH_2 to $C_{36}H_{74}$, and there are even scattered members above that. There are two butanes, as we mentioned earlier, and as the number of carbon atoms increases the number of isomers becomes so much greater that there are thousands of these hydrocarbons. The commercial fractions of petroleum such as dry-cleaner's fluid, gasoline, kerosine and lubricating oils are each mixtures of many of these hydrocarbons. The higher members of the series are solids and are found in petrolatum and paraffin. The entire series is called the *paraffin* series of hydrocarbons because its members react with very few substances. Chlorine will replace hydrogen, but burning is the paraffins' best chemical activity. The name paraffin comes from two Latin words *parvum*, little, and *affinis*, affinity or attraction.

As individual members of the paraffin series of hydrocarbons were identified it became necessary to invent names for them. The first four were called by the arbitrary names, methane, ethane, propane and butane, but it soon became evident that a different name for each hydrocarbon would make too many names to remember and so a more systematic method was devised: pentane, C_5H_{12}, hexane, C_6H_{14}, heptane, C_7H_{16}, and so on. All the compounds in the series have similar chemical properties and so all the names were given the same suffix, *-ane*, but the compounds all needed individual names and so the prefixes were taken from the Greek names of the numbers just as in geometry we have pentagon, hexagon, etc. In chemistry the prefixes refer to the number of carbon atoms. Since the series goes all the way up to C_{36} the reader may wonder about the name of that member, but so do chemists who usually solve the problem by calling it $C_{36}H_{74}$. When anyone wishes to appear scholarly he looks up the Greek name of the number. I am sure there is one, but I have never seen it.

The names of many of the radicals come from the names of these hydrocarbons. If we drop one H from methane we have CH_3. This is a radical for it has a free bond where the H came off. A radical may be formed from any other hydrocarbon in the same way and is named by replacing the *-ane* of the name of the hydrocarbon with *-yl*: methyl, ethyl, propyl and so on. This plan gives us the names of compounds such as methyl chloride, CH_3Cl, ethyl alcohol, C_2H_5OH, and propylamine, $C_3H_7NH_2$.

This was a simple, systematic method of nomenclature —it is called the *radical method*—and it worked very well until it broke down for lack of names for the radicals. In the case of propane there are two places from which to remove the H to form the radical:

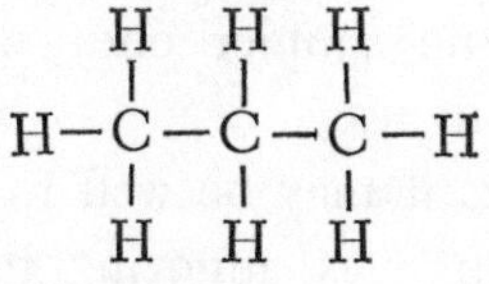

Propane

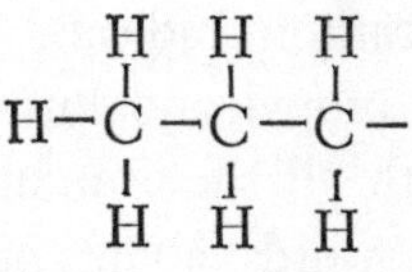

n-Propyl

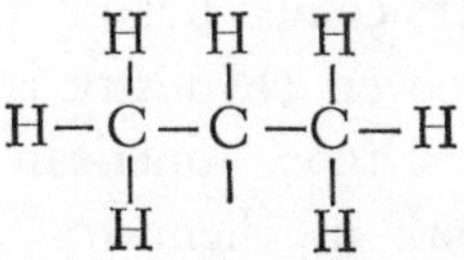

Isopropyl

The six hydrogen atoms on the two end carbons all bear the
same relation to the whole molecule, and likewise the two
hydrogen atoms on the middle carbon atom bear the same
relation to the whole molecule; consequently, there are only
two different positions for the removal of the hydrogen atom;
it can be removed from either an end carbon or from the
middle carbon. Both these radicals are from propane and so
we have two propyls. To distinguish between them the one
with the free bond at the end of the chain is called *normal*
propyl and is indicated in writing by an *n-* before the name.
Both radicals have the molecular formula C_3H_7, and are
therefore isomers; consequently the second radical is called
isopropyl.

This system was fine as far as it went, but it did not go
very far. There are two butanes and between them there are
four different positions from which the H can be removed.
This results in four different butyl radicals and each of them
must have a name. There are five pentanes, which give eight
pentyls; and when we get to decane, $C_{10}H_{22}$, there are
seventy-five of them and each supplies several decyls. It is
easy to see why the chemist soon ran out of names for the
hydrocarbon radicals. However, the simpler ones—methyl,
ethyl, propyl and butyl—are still in use.

With all these unfamiliar names it may be well to insert
a few words about pronunciation; it is annoying to read
words one cannot pronounce. In this case there is no reason
to worry; chemists do not know what to call them either.
When the words were coined nobody thought to include the
pronunciation. Moreover, chemistry is an international science and, until about 1900, American students who wished
to do advanced work in chemistry studied in France or
Germany. Consequently, many American college professors
spoke chemical English with a strong foreign accent. I have
had teachers who were trained in England, Scotland, France,

Germany and the United States. Sometimes the pronunciation was such that only formulas or other writing on a blackboard revealed the subject under discussion. Even in England "laboratory" is la-BOR-a-tory while here we call it LAB-O-ra-tory. Also, the radical C_2H_5 is e-THYLE (like *mile*) in England, but here it is just like the girl's name, Ethel.

Several years ago the American Chemical Society became concerned about the pronunciation by members who read papers at the meetings and, naturally, appointed a committee. The committee compiled a list of about two hundred words with the various pronunciations indicated. Several hundred of these lists were sent to teachers and other chemists for them to check the pronunciation they preferred—on the democratic principle that the majority is right. In some cases there were as many as four different pronunciations and in a few cases some of us preferred a pronunciation the committee had not even thought of. When these questionnaires were returned to the committee they made up a list of the major preferences. In some cases the preference was so evenly divided that two pronunciations were included in the compiled list. The Society published the list in one of its journals and sold reprints at ten cents a copy. Many teachers used the list in their teaching and there has been some uniformity of pronunciation, but attendance at a meeting still discloses considerable variation. There is good agreement on some words, of course; nobody misses alcohol, AL-de-hyde is easy and hydrocarbon is like hydro anything else—hydrogen, hydroplane, hydrophobia, etc., but amine may be am-EEN, or AM-in and amide can be any combination of *am* or *aim* and *id* or *ide* with the accent either fore or aft. The committee is still in existence and now deals with spelling and nomenclature as well as pronunciation, but there is no law against anyone pronouncing the words any way he likes.

The ever increasing complexity of organic compounds soon

required a new and more comprehensive system of nomenclature and in 1892 chemists from several countries met in
Geneva, Switzerland, to devise a new system. They produced
the *Geneva system*, which was used for some forty years.
Then it began to show shortcomings, whereupon the International Union of Pure and Applied Chemistry, when it met
at Liége, Belgium, in 1930, overhauled the Geneva system.
They did not change it fundamentally but extended it,
simplified it and made it more specific. The system is now
called by the name of the society that devised it rather than
the name of the city where it originated, but to save space in
writing and breath in speaking it is called the IUC *system*.

The chief characteristic of the IUC system is the use of
numbers for the carbon atoms and numerical prefixes to indicate the number of radicals attached to the carbon chain.
A few simple examples will show the nature of the system.

2,3-Dichlorobutane   2,2-Dimethylbutane

2-Pentanol

Dichloro and *dimethyl* tell how many of these groups are
present, the 2,3 and 2,2 tell where the groups are attached

to the butane chain. In the third example, the *ol* is the last syllable of alcohol, the 2 indicates the carbon to which the OH is attached and the pent is the number of atoms in the chain.

Benzene, C_6H_6, is often abbreviated by a hexagon to save writing the full structure, which is given on p. 209. If one H is removed from the benzene we have C_6H_5, and for some mysterious reason this radical was, and still is, called *phenyl* and not *benzyl* as we might expect. This explanation of benzene and its radical enables us to present a rather complicated substance and its IUC name.

This is 1, 1, 1-trichloro-2,2-bis (*p*-chlorophenyl) ethane, or less accurately, dichlorodiphenyltrichloroethane. The name considers the compound to be ethane that has had the three hydrogen atoms on the first carbon replaced by chlorine atoms, hence the 1,1,1-trichloro. Then the 2,2 indicates that two substitutions have been made on the second carbon of the ethane. *Bis* is always used to denote two complex radicals. The hexagon represents the benzene ring with four hydrogen atoms at the corners where nothing else is shown. The corner opposite the one attached to the ethane chain is the *para* position, which is indicated by the *p*. The position is occupied by chlorine and so the radical is called parachlorophenyl;

there are two of them. This substance with a long name is a common insecticide, but it is hard to imagine an advertisement of it or a customer asking for it under such a name. Among friends in and out of chemistry it is DDT.

A *series* is any number of organic compounds with similar properties and whose members differ in formula by CH_2. For example, CH_3Br, C_2H_5Br, C_3H_7Br, etc., is a series of organic bromides.

The Ethylene Series. There are several series of hydrocarbons, but none of them has as many members as the paraffin series; some of them have very few. In the ethylene series, two carbon atoms in each member use two of their valence bonds to hold themselves together. This means that the simplest member must have two carbon atoms. This member is ethylene, C_2H_4. The ethyl part of the name tells us that it has two carbon atoms like ethane and the *ene* says that the compound has at least one double bond because all such compounds have similar properties. The graphic formulas of the first three members of the series are:

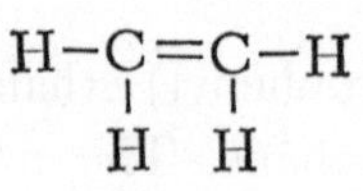

Ethylene
Ethene

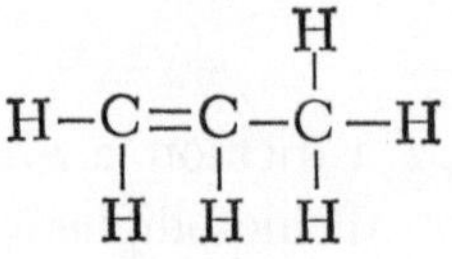

Propylene
Propene

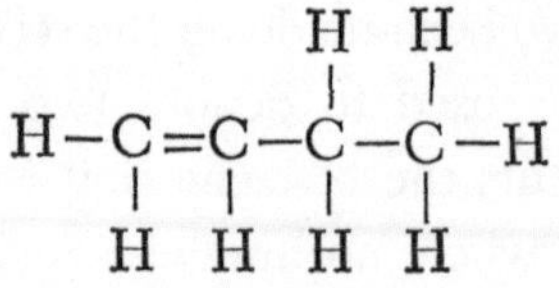

Butylene
1-Butene

All three of these hydrocarbons are made from petroleum, and ethylene and propylene are among the top eight manufactured organic compounds. The annual production of ethylene in this country is 7.5 billion pounds and that of propylene is 3.2 billion.

Ethylene and propylene are older names of these hydrocarbons and are still in common use, but the IUC name omits the *yl* and so the newer names are ethene and propene. From butene on it is necessary to use a number to locate the double bond. In the above example the bond is between carbon atoms 1 and 2, but only the smaller number is necessary to locate it. The other isomer is 2-butene.

The chief chemical property of the ethylene hydrocarbons is their unsaturation—they form other compounds simply by the addition of other substances; one of the two bonds between the carbon atoms lets loose to form two and these combine with other substances:

$$\text{H}-\text{C}=\text{C}-\text{H} \longrightarrow \text{H}-\underset{\underset{\text{H}}{|}}{\overset{\overset{|}{}}{\text{C}}}-\underset{\underset{\text{H}}{|}}{\overset{\overset{|}{}}{\text{C}}}-\text{H} \; + \; \text{Br}_2 \longrightarrow \text{H}-\underset{\underset{\text{H}}{|}}{\overset{\overset{\text{Br}}{|}}{\text{C}}}-\underset{\underset{\text{H}}{|}}{\overset{\overset{\text{Br}}{|}}{\text{C}}}-\text{H}$$

Many other substances will combine with the hydrocarbons of this series just as the bromine does.

The Acetylene Series. The acetylene series begins with the gas acetylene, which uses three of its bonds to unite its two carbon atoms.

$$\text{H}-\text{C}\equiv\text{C}-\text{H} \; + \; 2\text{Br}_2 \longrightarrow \text{H}-\underset{\underset{\text{Br}}{|}}{\overset{\overset{\text{Br}}{|}}{\text{C}}}-\underset{\underset{\text{Br}}{|}}{\overset{\overset{\text{Br}}{|}}{\text{C}}}-\text{H}$$

Acetylene   Tetrabromoethane

Acetylene is made from calcium carbide and water. It was formerly used as a gas to light houses and later, automobiles. It is now used as a fuel in torches for cutting and welding metals because it burns in oxygen to produce a very hot flame. It is also used to make many organic compounds because it reacts with so many different substances.

These unsaturated hydrocarbons not only add bromine, chlorine, sulfuric acid and a host of other substances, but they also add to each other. When Faraday discovered that ethylene and butylene have the same empirical formula, CH_2, they appeared to be isomers, but a few years later when the gases were weighed it was found that the molecular weight of ethylene is 28 and that of butylene is 56, which means that the molecular formulas are C_2H_4 and C_4H_8 respectively. At this point Berzelius rose to the occasion as usual and proposed a name for this new situation; he called it *polymerism*. That is the name we still give to the existence of compounds of which the formula of one is a multiple of the formula of the other. Butylene is a polymer of ethylene; and benzene, C_6H_6, is a polymer of acetylene, C_2H_2. The meanings in this family of words—polymer, monomer, dimer, polymerize and so on—have been liberalized in recent years to include cases in which the higher polymer is not exactly a multiple of the monomers from which it is made. There are very high polymers in which the multiple may be in the hundreds or even in the thousands. Some of these high polymers are made from two different simple compounds and in that case the weight of the high polymer cannot be a multiple of either of the simple compounds. Such compounds are called copolymers and are similar in their formation to those that are made from a single substance.

A simple case of polymerization is that of butene (butylene) in the presence of sulfuric acid to form an octene:

$$CH_3-\underset{\underset{CH_3}{|}}{C}=CH_2 \ + \ CH_3-\underset{\underset{CH_3}{|}}{C}=CH_2 \longrightarrow$$

Isobutene

$$CH_3-\underset{\underset{CH_3}{|}}{\overset{\overset{CH_3}{|}}{C}}-CH_2-\underset{\underset{CH_3}{|}}{C}=CH_2$$

2,2,4-Trimethylpentene
(an octene)

If a polymer is small it is called a dimer, trimer, etc., to indicate that the multiple is 2, 3, etc., but if the number is very large or unknown it is simply called a polymer.

Under different conditions molecules of butene can add to each other in a very different fashion:

$$x\left(\underset{\underset{CH_3}{|}}{\overset{\overset{CH_3}{|}}{C}}=CH_2\right) \longrightarrow x\left(-\underset{\underset{CH_3}{|}}{\overset{\overset{CH_3}{|}}{C}}-CH_2-\right) \longrightarrow$$

$$-\underset{\underset{CH_3}{|}}{\overset{\overset{CH_3}{|}}{C}}-CH_2-\underset{\underset{CH_3}{|}}{\overset{\overset{CH_3}{|}}{C}}-CH_2-\underset{\underset{CH_3}{|}}{\overset{\overset{CH_3}{|}}{C}}-CH_2-$$

In this case a large number of molecules of isobutene add to each other to form a long chain. Only three are shown in the equation, but the free bond at each end of the polymer chain can add another molecule any time it feels like it. To stop the chain formation at any particular length is generally a bit difficult, but that is why there are polymer specialists—first, to make unsaturated compounds add, and then to make them stop adding. The polybutylene indicated above is a synthetic rubber. Natural rubber is a polymer of isoprene, a five-carbon hydrocarbon with two double bonds and therefore of the *diethylene* series.

$$CH_2 = C - CH = CH_2$$
$$\mid$$
$$CH_3$$

Isoprene

Only one double bond of the isoprene takes part in the polymerization by the rubber tree, so the rubber hydrocarbon is still unsaturated. Many high polymers are among our daily contacts. Besides natural rubber there are starch, proteins, cellulose (wood, paper) and also the synthetic rubbers, bakelite, nylon, lucite, polyethylene (around carrots and such at the supermarket) and several other plastics and textiles. Bakelite is a copolymer of phenol, C_6H_5OH, and formaldehyde, $HCHO$. In fact, many of the common plastics are copolymers.

The Benzene Series. The benzene series of hydrocarbons is a very important series of hydrocarbons with very few members. It begins with benzene, the ring compound of six carbon atoms and a hydrogen attached to each carbon (p. 209). It was discovered by Faraday in coal tar and that was the only source of it until recent years. Large quantities are made from petroleum; the total production in this country is about 4.7 billion pounds annually. Phenol is hydroxybenzene, C_6H_5OH, with a hydroxyl group replacing one of the six hydrogen atoms. Phenol is not an alcohol as one might expect but a crystalline, acidic compound that is very caustic; it is the carbolic acid of the drugstore, where it has been liquefied by the addition of a little water or alcohol.

The second member of the benzene series is generally known by its old name of *toluene*; it is methylbenzene, that is, it has a methyl group instead of one of the hydrogen atoms of benzene. It comes from the same sources as the benzene and is manufactured here to the extent of about 2.9 billion pounds a year.

There are four isomers of the third member of the series; three of them are the xylenes, or dimethylbenzenes, and the fourth is ethylbenzene. The combined annual production of the three xylenes is about 2.46 billion pounds and that of ethylbenzene is nearly the same. The members of this series are the starting compounds for the manufacture of hundreds of drugs, dyes, plastics and other compounds. The main use of ethylbenzene is the manufacture of one kind of synthetic rubber.

The Alcohol Series. The alcohols contain the OH group attached to a carbon atom of a carbon chain. The simplest alcohol is CH_3OH, which may be pictured as methane with one hydrogen atom replaced with the OH radical and which gives rise to the name of methyl alcohol or, in the IUC system, *methanol*. It was known as wood alcohol for centuries because it was made by heating wood in a furnace or oven; the alcohol was in the vapors that came off and were condensed. It is now made in large quantity from carbon monoxide and hydrogen and finds many uses. It is a solvent in spirit varnishes and the common source of the methyl group for anyone who needs one. It is very poisonous: small quantities cause blindness, and large quantities, death. During prohibition days the manufacturers and users of wood alcohol changed over to the name methanol, which did not sound so much like something to drink.

This alcohol series continues with many other alcohols related to the other hydrocarbons of the paraffin series as methanol is related to methane. They are ethanol, C_2H_5OH; propanol, C_3H_7OH; butanol, C_4H_9OH; and so on. The lower ones are still widely called by their older names such as ethyl alcohol, propyl alcohol and butyl alcohol. A chemist uses whichever name comes to mind first as you may notice from the usage in this book.

Ethanol is the active component of alcoholic beverages. In addition to its importance in these potions it is used to make ether and a host of other compounds. It is also used as a solvent in perfumery, cosmetics, flavoring extracts and drugs. A tincture is a drug dissolved in alcohol—the most familiar is tincture of iodine. Iodine is a dark gray, crystalline solid that for some unknown reason dissolves in alcohol to give a brown solution. Alcohol is used as the solvent for iodine because water does not dissolve it very well and also because the alcoholic solution is a much better antiseptic. We make over four billion pounds of alcohol in this country annually.

Industrial alcohol is made from petroleum or molasses, but beverage alcohol is made from grains or from fruit. Corn, barley, rye, wheat and rice all contribute to the alcohol supply according to their cost and availability. The grain is ground and cooked with water until the starch becomes a thin paste. An enzyme, usually malt, is added to change the starch to sugar. Yeast is added next and changes the sugar to alcohol, but it does not produce a very strong solution: if the alcohol gets up to 13–14 per cent it kills the yeast and the fermentation stops. Sugar is expensive and so the manufacturer takes care that there is not enough sugar present to make 13 per cent alcohol. The label of a bottle of table wine discloses the fact that the alcohol content is about 13 per cent by volume. If there is excess sugar in the grapes the wine is sweet; if it has all fermented the wine is dry. Why *dry* I do not know, but the word sour is reserved for wine that is on its way to vinegar.

Brandy is made by distilling wines and some of it is added to natural wines to produce the port, sherry, muscatel and other fortified wines that contain from 18 per cent to 21 per cent alcohol. Rum is made from fermented molasses, cane juice or a mixture of the two by distillation to concentrate the alcohol. Whiskey, gin, beer, and a small amount of industrial alcohol are made from grains. Before molasses and petroleum got into the business all the industrial alcohol was made from grain and was called grain alcohol.

Pure alcohol boils at 78° C and water at 100° C; therefore, when a dilute solution, say 5–10 per cent alcohol, is boiled the alcohol distills faster than the water. A peculiarity of alcohol is that a 95 per cent solution boils at a slightly lower temperature than pure alcohol, which accounts for the fact that industrial alcohol is 95 per cent alcohol and not 100 per cent as might be expected. When distillation begins, the first vapor to enter the condenser may be close to 95 per cent alcohol but, as time goes on, the condensed vapor contains increasing amounts of water; eventually all the alcohol has boiled away and the vapors are all water. If he is making a beverage (whiskey), the distiller's problem is to tell when he has the proper concentration of alcohol. In the old days and even today in remote areas, I hear, distilling establishments are small and cannot afford a chemist. So, the distiller puts some of his product into a bottle and shakes it. When he has about the right amount of alcohol, bubbles that look like glass beads gather on the surface of the liquid. This concentration of alcohol came to be called *bead* whiskey or *proof* whiskey. When chemists finally got around to the matter they found that proof whiskey contained about 50 per cent alcohol by volume. This is a convenient figure and so when standards were set, 50 per cent by volume was designated as 100 proof for tax purposes and trade regulations. Wines and beer have their alcoholic content expressed as percentages, but the distilled liquors are usually 80, 86, 90 or 100 proof and there are rums as high as 160 proof. The percentage of alcohol is obviously half the proof figure.

Alcohol can be made from anything that contains either starch or sugar, and this fact, together with the many uses of alcohol and its euphoric property, tends to defeat prohibition laws.

Several of the higher alcohols of this series and some of other series are abundant and useful, but space does not permit their discussion here. Glycol, $HOCH_2CH_2OH$, or dihydroxyethane, for example, is the nearly universal antifreeze for the cooling systems of automobile and airplane engines.

ALIPHATIC ACIDS

The acids related to the paraffin series of hydrocarbons are called *aliphatic* acids because so many of them are found in fats. They all have the functional group, -COOH. The first member of the series is formic acid, which the ant injects to make her sting more effective. Acetic, the next in order, is the acid of vinegar. These acids have the following structures:

$$H-C=O \atop \quad\; O-H$$

$$H-\overset{\displaystyle H}{\underset{\displaystyle H}{C}}-C=O \atop \qquad\qquad O-H$$

Formic acid   Acetic acid

The members of this series that occur in fats begin with butyric, C_3H_7COOH, and go to stearic, $C_{17}H_{35}COOH$, and one or two higher ones, which are found in a few oils. A curious feature of these acids is that only those with an even number of carbon atoms and only those with an unbranched chain, that is, the normal acids, are found in fats. Just why plants should make only the acids with these features, when there are thousands of acids with branched chains and also odd numbers of carbon atoms, is not yet satisfactorily explained.

Rancid butter contains free butyric acid, which furnishes the unpleasant odor, and a property of the next three, $C_5H_{11}COOH$, $C_7H_{15}COOH$ and $C_9H_{19}COOH$, is indicated by their names, caproic, capryllic and capric respectively. *Capra* is the Latin word for goat and the odor of these three acids is reminiscent. The conventional names of the acids are nearly always used because they apply only to the normal acids, whereas the systematic name, such as decanoic, applies to all the acids with ten carbon atoms.

THE ESTERS

Formic and acetic acids have their own sources and uses, but the others that are important are those that are constituents of the fats. Solid fats, such as lard, tallow and human fat, and the liquid fats olive oil, corn oil, cottonseed oil and castor oil are all mixtures. As Chevreul demonstrated over a century ago, the fats are mixtures of esters. An ester is a compound formed by the combination of an acid and an alcohol and is therefore related to both of them. For example, ethyl alcohol and acetic acid react to produce ethyl acetate:

$$H-\overset{\overset{\displaystyle H}{|}}{\underset{\underset{\displaystyle H}{|}}{C}}-\overset{\overset{\displaystyle H}{|}}{\underset{\underset{\displaystyle H}{|}}{C}}-O-H \; + \; H-O-\overset{}{\underset{\underset{\displaystyle O}{\|}}{C}}-\overset{\overset{\displaystyle H}{|}}{\underset{\underset{\displaystyle H}{|}}{C}}-H \longrightarrow$$

Ethyl alcohol   Acetic acid

$$H-\overset{\overset{\displaystyle H}{|}}{\underset{\underset{\displaystyle H}{|}}{C}}-\overset{\overset{\displaystyle H}{|}}{\underset{\underset{\displaystyle H}{|}}{C}}-O-\overset{}{\underset{\underset{\displaystyle O}{\|}}{C}}-\overset{\overset{\displaystyle H}{|}}{\underset{\underset{\displaystyle H}{|}}{C}}-H \; + \; H_2O$$

Ethyl acetate   Water

Wines age very slowly by reactions of this type between the alcohol and the acids of the grapes, but in the laboratory we speed up such reactions by adding sulfuric acid or some other substance that will act as a catalyst and combine with the water formed in the reaction.

The esters that make up fats are called *glycerides* because, although they may contain as many as twenty different acids, the alcohol is always glycerol, which has the structure

$$H-\overset{\overset{\displaystyle H}{|}}{\underset{\underset{\displaystyle OH}{|}}{C}}-\overset{\overset{\displaystyle H}{|}}{\underset{\underset{\displaystyle OH}{|}}{C}}-\overset{\overset{\displaystyle H}{|}}{\underset{\underset{\displaystyle OH}{|}}{C}}-H$$

Glycerol

The natural glycerides are mostly mixed glycerides because the three OH groups have reacted with two or perhaps three different acids to form the ester linkages. The fats may seem to have a complicated composition, but the plants make them from carbon dioxide and water and all of us make them from anything on the menu except salt and water.

Whether the fat is a solid or a liquid depends on the acid components of the glycerides. Palmitic acid, $C_{15}H_{31}$COOH, and stearic, $C_{17}H_{35}$COOH, are both solids and a high percentage of their esters makes a solid fat. Butyric and what are sometimes dubbed the three goats, are liquids and their esters are present in butterfat and coconut oil. There are three other acids common in fats but they all belong to different series. Oleic acid, $C_{17}H_{33}$COOH, is unsaturated with two hydrogen atoms less than stearic, which has the same number of carbon atoms; it has a double bond in the middle of the carbon chain, which relates it to the ethylene series of hydrocarbons. The other two unsaturated acids are linoleic, $C_{17}H_{31}$COOH, with two double bonds; and linolenic, $C_{17}H_{29}$COOH, with three double bonds in the carbon chain. All three of these unsaturated acids are liquids and they are the predominating acids in the vegetable oils. They have recently gained publicity in connection with unsaturated fats and cholesterol in the blood vessels, a matter that has not yet been settled to the satisfaction of everyone. The two paint oils linseed and tung contain high percentages of linolenic acid ester, which is the most unsaturated and which combines with the oxygen of the air to form the tough film that holds the pigment to the painted surface.

THE AMINES AND AMIDES

Of the other series of organic compounds we have space to mention only two, the *amines* and the *amides*. These are compounds that contain nitrogen. The amines are related structurally to the alcohols and ammonia; they have a hydrocarbon radical attached to the -NH₂ group, such as CH₃NH₂, C₂H₅NH₂, etc. They are named methylamine, ethylamine and so on. We seldom meet the simple amines outside the laboratory although traces of them do supply the odor of aging fish. Some of the higher ones related to other series of hydrocarbons are used to make drugs and dyes, and acids that contain the amine group constitute the proteins.

The amides bear the same relation to the acids that the amines do to the alcohols: they have the -NH₂ group instead of the -OH of the acid. For example,

$$
\begin{matrix}
& H & & & & H & \\
& | & & & & | & \\
H-C & -C & -O-H & \qquad & H-C & -C & -N-H \\
& | \quad || & & & | \quad || \quad | & \\
& H \quad O & & & H \quad O \quad H &
\end{matrix}
$$

Acetic acid　　　　　　　　Acetamide

The amides all take their names from the related acids. Urea is carbonamide, the amide of carbonic acid:

$$
\begin{matrix}
H-O-C-O-H & \qquad & H-N-C-N-H \\
|| & & | \quad || \quad | \\
O & & H \quad O \quad H
\end{matrix}
$$

Carbonic acid　　　　　　　Urea

In his search for the composition of matter the chemist has found many substances with two or more functional groups. The common fruit acids, citric, malic and tartaric, are both alcohol and acid. The two sugars, glucose of fruits and lactose of milk, are both alcohols and aldehydes. Sucrose, the sugar of cane and beet, is a complicated alcohol with the molecular formula $C_{12}H_{22}O_{11}$. It is the organic compound supreme, leading all others in production with 10 billion pounds annually in the United States and over 100 billion pounds throughout the world. The white, crystalline granulated sugar from the grocery store is a practically pure organic chemical and that is unusual in commercial products.

THE DEVELOPMENT OF DYES

The dye industry has an interesting history. From the most ancient times colored extracts from plants have been used to dye cloth. Indigo was one of these extracts and it is still an important dye used to color blue suitings for men including many uniforms. Alizarin is a bright red dye extracted from the madder plant and was used to dye the uniforms of French soldiers in former years. The royal purple of the Romans came from a Mediterranean shellfish, but the animal supplies very little dye and so the color was scarce and expensive. The Romans confined its use to royalty, which is the origin of the expression "born to the purple."

Strange as it may seem, the first synthetic dye was made by a boy of eighteen, an English student. William Henry Perkin (1838–1907) entered the Royal College of Science in London at the age of fifteen and at seventeen became an assistant in chemistry to Professor A. W. von Hofmann. He was an ambitious student and set up a laboratory in his home where he could work in his spare time, and in this laboratory he undertook to make quinine. He did not succeed in that project, but ended up with a black, gummy mass instead. However, Perkin was not discouraged by the failure of his experiment and so he tried to make quinine from aniline, $C_6H_5NH_2$, which is an amine related to benzene and a simpler substance than the one he had used before. Again he got a black mass and when he tried to extract the quinine he got a colored substance instead. Perkin had a practical mind and he knew that there is more to a dye than color;

the colored substance must adhere firmly to the textile so that it will not wash out and also it must not fade in sunlight. Consequently, he sent a sample of his colored compound to a cloth dyer who reported it as "promising" if not too expensive. This report persuaded Perkin to postpone his further education and go into industry.

Perkin and his father consulted Professor von Hofmann as to the advisability of manufacturing the new dye and he advised against it, but the Perkins treated the free advice in the usual manner. The family raised the capital and in June 1857 they began to build a factory. Perkin was just nineteen years old and knew nothing about business; he had never been inside a chemical factory and his father knew nothing about chemistry.

Perkin and his brother hunted all over England before they found a supply of benzene, which was to be their starting material. At that time benzene was produced only as a by-product of the gasworks. The boys finally found a supply at $1.25 a gallon, but it was not pure enough. Consequently, their first operation was the distillation of the benzene to improve its purity. This, of course, increased the cost, because of the work and heat required, and also because of the loss in volume caused by the removal of the impurities.

The first step in the manufacture of the dye was the conversion of benzene to nitrobenzene, $C_6H_5NO_2$, which was accomplished by treatment with strong nitric acid. But there was no suitable nitric acid on the market and so they devised and installed equipment to make that. The second step converts the nitrobenzene to aniline, the substance Perkin had made the dye from in the laboratory. He soon devised a method for making the aniline and equipment with which to make it. Finally, the aniline was oxidized to the dye by a chromate salt, which was available on the market. The weight of the dye he obtained was less than 5 per cent of the weight of the benzene used because of the losses at the various stages of the process. The reactions of organic substances rarely if ever give the weights of the substances shown by the equation.

Once the dye was made the next problem was to persuade dyers to use it. But teen-agers with a purpose are hard to discourage and before the end of the year 1857 the dye was in use in at least one dye house under the name of "aniline purple." The color of the cloth was a pink hue that could not be obtained with any other dye known at the time. It did not catch on quickly with British dyers, but despite its cost it became very popular with the French, who named it *mauve* because of the similarity in color to the flower of the mallow, which the French call *mauve*.

Perkin's synthesis of mauve was the beginning of the coal-tar dye industry. As usual, once a new idea is introduced its expansion follows by the aid of many hands—many chemists began to synthesize dyes. This was particularly true in Germany, which soon led in both synthesis and manufacture. Before 1918 very few dyes were made in the United States and the shortage caused by the war in 1914 resulted in clothes of very few colors. One musical show had all the costumes in black and white and soldiers returning from Europe after the war saw so many dark blue dresses with white collars on the streets of New York that they thought all the women were in uniform.

After World War I the American chemical industry entered the dye business in a big way and their research laboratories began to make new dyes while the factories turned out both new and old ones. Although manufacture did not get under way until 1920, the speed with which it grew is indicated by the fact that by 1929 we imported 6,437,147 pounds of dyes, but manufactured 111,421,505 pounds. Some five hundred different dyes were manufactured here by fifty-four companies. Since 1929 thousands of new dyes have been made in the United States and elsewhere—many of them have found a use and many of them have proved useless. The introduction of rayon, nylon, dacron and other new textile materials offered a challenge to the dye chemist because a dye that is very good on one textile may be worthless on another.

DRUGS

The synthesis of drugs has been one of the most important activities of organic chemists. An illustration of how chemists sometimes work is the discovery and development of the sulfa drugs, which have done so much to overcome infections inside the human body. In 1932 a German chemical company made the following dye:

$$H_2N - \bigcirc \overset{\overset{\displaystyle NH_2}{|}}{-} N = N - \bigcirc - SO_2NH_2$$

4-Sulfonamido-2′,4′-diaminoazobenzene

This dye combined very firmly with textiles that are protein in nature—silk and wool. Bacteria are also protein and so it occurred to some of the research staff to try the effect of the dye on these organisms; it was found to combine with the bacteria and kill them. Thereupon, the dye became a drug and was patented under the name of "Prontosil." A German physician used it in 1933 to cure a child of a blood infection and the next year another physician showed that it was effective in killing *streptococcus* and *staphylococcus* bacteria, both of which cause serious infections.

In 1933 biochemists at the Pasteur Institute in Paris were trying to find out what happens to Prontosil when it is injected into the human body. They found that the physiological processes break it down to the simpler compound p-aminobenzene sulfonamide:

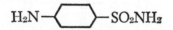

p-Aminobenzene sulfonamide

Further investigation showed that this compound is just as effective a drug as the Prontosil. As in many other cases of organic compounds the name was a little long for general use and so the compound was named sulfanilamide and by this name it is still known to chemists, doctors, pharmacists and those of the general public who can remember it.

The effectiveness of sulfanilamide against certain infections was established in 1935, and immediately organic chemists everywhere began to synthesize other compounds of similar structure with the hope of finding a drug with some advantage over sulfanilamide. Within five years over a thousand compounds had been made and tested. There is no way to predict physiological properties and so each compound had to be tested; most of them proved to be useless, but a few were not. Among the useful ones were sulfapyridine, sulfathiazole and sulfaguanidine. These differ by having the complex pyridine, thiazole or guanidine substituted for one of the H atoms of the -SO_2NH_2 group in the original sulfanilamide. Here is the formula of the simplest of these three compounds:

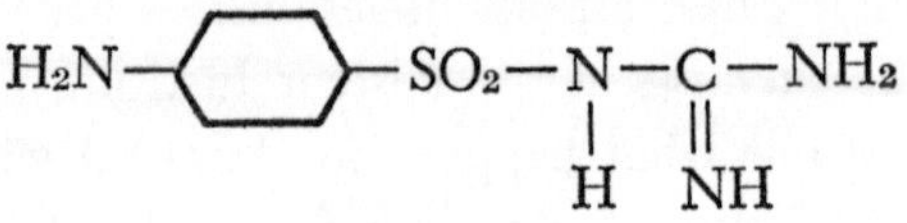

$$H_2N-\bigcirc-SO_2-\underset{\underset{H}{|}}{N}-\underset{\underset{NH}{\|}}{C}-NH_2$$

Sulfaguanidine

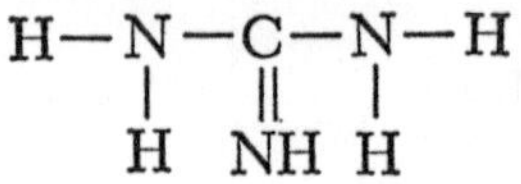

$$H-\underset{\underset{H}{|}}{N}-\underset{\underset{NH}{\|}}{C}-\underset{\underset{H}{|}}{N}-H$$

Guanidine

OTHER PROBLEMS

An important duty of many organic chemists is to find new uses for old products or uses for by-products. During the First World War there was a great demand for acetone for use as a solvent in the manufacture of gunpowder. Acetone was then produced as a by-product of the charcoal industry. The vapors from the charring wood contain acetone along with wood alcohol and acetic acid, but the process took a lot of work and a lot of wood and so chemists began to look about for a better source of acetone. A method was soon devised that consisted of the fermentation of sugar with a kind of bacteria. However, the process not only made acetone but also butyl alcohol. Up to then butyl alcohol had been a laboratory curiosity. There was no commercial use for it and it began to accumulate. The chemists tried to find some use for the alcohol, but not until the end of the war did they discover that if they combined it with acetic acid to make butyl acetate, they had a very useful solvent; it dissolved both resins and nitrocellulose. Such solutions with some pigments added to provide color made excellent paint for automobiles. The paint could be sprayed on the cars, which lowered the cost of manufacture, made mass production possible and thus created traffic problems. Every time a problem is solved another is generally created. When the war was over chemists had to look for some more uses for the acetone.

The dye and the drug industries and, more recently, the production of plastics and of organic chemicals from petroleum, have been great spurs to the science of organic chemistry, but not all work in the field has had such spectacular results. The applied chemists in these industries owe a huge debt to those who have worked mainly or solely in pure chemistry, to the Coupers, the Kekulés and all the other chemists who have worked for the increase of knowledge without any thought of its practical application. Priestley, Dalton, Lavoisier, Cannizzaro, Wöhler and most of the other chemists mentioned in these pages are remembered for the work they did in pure chemistry; most of them did practical work too, but it has long been forgotten.

The organic chemist today has problems both harder and easier than those studied in the nineteenth century. Easier because apparatus has been improved, many new kinds have been invented and chemical supply houses now stand ready to deliver thousands of kinds of apparatus on demand and to make new pieces if the chemist can explain exactly what he wants. The manufacture of apparatus and instruments has done as much to advance the knowledge of chemistry as the invention of printing. The problems are also easier because there are now many tests for the functional groups and so many compounds have been identified that a derivative is likely to be some well-known compound easily recognized by its properties without a long, tedious analysis.

The problems are now harder because most of the substances with small molecules have been made and as the size of the molecule increases the number of possible isomers increases enormously. Of the hydrocarbon C_3H_8 there is only 1 possible structure, for C_6H_{14} there are 5 and for $C_{14}H_{30}$ there are 1858. If additional elements are present the number of isomers becomes astronomical.

The real victim of the great mass of organic chemistry is the teacher of the subject, who must maintain a fair knowledge of the entire field and the progress that goes on. In his spare time he undertakes research to extend the subject and thus help to keep his colleagues more fully occupied; all such colleagues, of course, are doing the same thing.

CHAPTER NINE

The Analyst Answers Questions

ANALYTICAL CHEMISTRY is the father of all chemical science and by far the most important field—without it there would be no other kind of chemistry. The entire field of analytical chemistry consists of two problems. The first and oldest is the identification of the different kinds of matter. Is this gold? Is this sulfur? Is this a diamond? Such problems are as old as the chemical arts, but they are still with us in a much expanded form. There are not only more than two million single substances to be identified, but there is also a long list of natural and manufactured mixtures such as corn syrup, linseed oil, turpentine and thousands of others.

The second problem of the analyst is the determination of the composition of matter. There is no record that anyone ever tried to determine the composition of matter in terms of the four elements of the ancient Greeks, but after Boyle suggested that some substances are elements and all the others composed of two or more of these elements, composition became a problem to be solved. Progress was slow for the first hundred years after Boyle made his suggestion and it was not until the time of Lavoisier that the idea of elements was firmly established. With Proust's law of the constant composition, analysis was off and going. Berzelius alone made over two thousand analyses. Before the year

1800, rocks and minerals were identified mainly by their physical properties: color, density, hardness, crystal structure, effect of heat and any other useful property the mineral might have. Beginning with the work of Proust, chemists began to analyze these natural substances for the elements they contain and how much of each element is present.

A chemical formula is calculated from the results of an analysis and so any compound for which there is a formula has been analyzed at least once and many of them several times.

Analytical chemistry of the eighteenth century and early nineteenth would probably come under the head of research. The chemist not only had to devise methods of analysis, but those were the days when chemistry was fulfilling its original purpose, namely, explaining the composition of matter. Those were also the days of the most active discovery of new elements, and each element discovered meant a new method of analysis to be devised.

As the nineteenth century progressed, analytical problems developed in agriculture, industry and commerce. Many of these problems were simple elementary analysis. How much phosphorus in this fertilizer? How much nitrogen in this soil? How much carbon in this steel? And then came problems that were much more complicated. Is this butter? Is this maple syrup? What is the composition of this paint? Such questions as these belong to a different kind of analysis called *proximate*. Its purpose is to measure the amount of one or more compounds in a mixture or to identify a mixture, such as how much alcohol there is in a bottle of beer, how much fat in a sample of milk, or whether this is olive oil. Commerce provides many problems because of differences in prices—for example, the difference in cost between butter and margarine or between olive oil and cottonseed oil.

An analysis is always made to answer one or more questions. The possible questions are legion. The properties of brass, bronze or any other alloy depend on the metals in it and their relative proportions. Both the manufacturer and the user of the alloy need to know exactly what its composition is. A fertilizer is mainly a source of nitrogen, phosphorus and potassium and most of the states require the percentage of each of these elements to be stated on the label so the farmer will know what he is buying. Therefore, the manufacturer must have an analysis of every batch of fertilizer that he makes and each state needs an analysis to check compliance with its law. The federal government, the states and some of the large cities regulate the composition of various commodities sold within their jurisdiction. Foods, drugs, cosmetics, pesticides and fertilizers all come in for regulation. In all such cases the government agencies need hundreds of analytical chemists to see that the products on the market comply with the regulations, and the manufacturer or the vendor also needs analyses to avoid violating the regulations by accident or neglect.

In addition to the composition of its commodities commerce is often concerned with their identity. For example, olive oil costs about twice as much as the other edible oils because it is especially prized for its flavor. Its higher price offers a temptation to the producer, importer or dealer to mix a cheaper oil with it or substitute a cheaper oil altogether. Here the chemist is required to identify a natural product. This is usually not very difficult, but it is very time-consuming. A much more difficult problem is the verification of a label that says that the oil is a salad oil containing 20 per cent olive oil; this is especially difficult if the other oils in the mixture are unknown.

The federal government permits the use of a small number

of dyes in foods and cosmetics and specifies which ones may be used, because many dyes are toxic. Chemists are often required to determine whether a dye that has been used in a food is on the permitted list. The Food and Drug Administration of the federal government has many such problems of both composition and identity. In a recent year the chemists for that agency made over forty thousand food analyses and several thousand more of drugs, cosmetics, cattle feeds, pesticides and other regulated products.

QUALITATIVE ANALYSIS

Now that we have an idea of what an analytical chemist does and why he does it, the next question is: How does he go about doing it? One of the simplest problems is the identification of an unknown substance. Every pure substance has its own characteristic set of properties. Whether the unknown is a piece of metal, an inorganic salt or an organic compound, the chemist determines its properties and compares them with those on record. Chemists have always hoped to find a good supply of spot tests that are specific, that is, the test to be a property of one substance and no other. Alas for his hopes! Very few such tests have ever been found. Only four come to mind at the moment: a glowing splint thrust into a bottle of oxygen bursts into flame; a sodium compound heated in a colorless flame gives it an orange color; hydrogen mixed with air in a glass test tube explodes when it is ignited with a sound like the bark of a small dog; and a drop of an iodine solution makes a blue spot on starch. There are undoubtedly other spot tests of a general nature and they are sometimes useful, but they do not go very far toward identifying over two million substances.

Just what a chemist now does to identify a sample depends on his experience and what he already knows about the sample. If it is totally unknown, which is rare, the chemist tries to burn a little of it to see whether it leaves an ash. If it does he knows that it is not purely organic because organic substances burn completely to gases if they burn at all. Substances that contain metals always leave an ash just as wood and coal do. If there is no ash, therefore, the analyst has eliminated all the metals with one simple test. If the substance proves to be organic the chemist proceeds to measure its physical properties, such as its boiling or melting point, density or index of refraction, and to determine some of its chemical properties according to a systematic procedure. For eliminating purposes the most important physical property is the compound's solubility in alcohol, water and ether. For example, if it does not dissolve in water it cannot be a sugar. In any case the chemist continues with his plan of procedure until he has enough evidence to identify the substance beyond any doubt; and he can never predict ahead of time how many properties he will need to investigate.

If the sample does not burn at all, it is probably inorganic and the chemist undertakes a qualitative analysis for the elements present. For this purpose he has a routine procedure. He dissolves the sample in water if possible. If it does not dissolve in water he tries dilute nitric acid. If that fails he resorts to more complicated procedures, but whatever it takes, he gets it into solution. The chemist is familiar with the solubility of many substances and so the dissolving process itself tells him something about the sample. If it dissolves in water without any coaxing it could be one of several salts but not an oxide nor a silicate nor any one of several salts the chemist knows to be insoluble in water. If it dissolves and the solution is colorless the sample is not a copper compound because solutions of copper compounds are blue or green, and, also, compounds of cobalt, nickel, chromium and iron all give colored solutions.

Once the chemist gets the sample into solution he begins to add reagents. These reagents are solutions of compounds that he knows to have certain effects, and he always adds them in the same order unless something about the solution process tells him that some of them are unnecessary. His scheme may start with hydrochloric acid, HCl. If a white solid, which he calls a precipitate, forms and settles to the bottom when he adds the HCl to the solution of his unknown he knows there is either silver or lead present or both. If the sample has dissolved in water it may also contain mercury, but of all the metals only these three form precipitates when HCl is added to their solutions. On the other hand, if there is no precipitate, lead and silver are absent and he can add the next reagent to test for some of the other metals. But if a precipitate formed he filters it out of the solution by pouring the mixture through a porous paper fitted to a funnel. He has then separated silver and lead from any other metals there may be in the solution. He now examines both the solid and the solution until he has identified all the metals present.

If he wishes to identify the negative elements he takes another portion of his sample and follows a procedure designed for the purpose. If lead is the only metal present and the sample dissolved in water it is probably either lead acetate or lead nitrate and spot tests for these two radicals will settle the question.

QUANTITATIVE ANALYSIS

In quantitative analysis the procedures are somewhat different; the element to be measured must first be separated from any others that may interfere with the procedure to be used. Suppose the chemist has a piece of metal and wants to know whether it contains silver and if so how much. He cuts or files off a little of the metal and dissolves it in nitric acid. Most metals react with this acid to form their nitrates, which are all soluble in water. The dilute nitric acid contains water and the chemist may add some more water if he thinks it a good idea. He now adds hydrochloric acid to the solution and if it remains clear there is no silver present and the analysis is finished, for that is what he wanted to know. But if there is a white precipitate he knows that he has silver or lead or both. To settle this point he filters out the precipitate and washes it well with hot water. Lead chloride dissolves in hot water but silver chloride does not. When the washing is finished or sooner, he tests the wash water for lead. Since lead is the only metal that could be in solution a simple spot test will do the trick. He adds a solution of potassium chromate, K_2CrO_4, and if there is lead present it forms a beautiful yellow precipitate of lead chromate, $PbCrO_4$. If there is no lead nothing happens.

If lead is present he begins again, for it is extremely difficult to wash all the lead chloride out of a mixture with silver chloride. He now cuts or files another sample and weighs it. Suppose it weighs 0.2 g. He uses a very small sample because it uses less reagents and takes less time; it dissolves more quickly, filters more quickly and so on. He dissolves his weighed sample in dilute nitric acid as before, but since he now knows there is lead present he changes the procedure at this point. He adds sulfuric acid, which forms insoluble lead sulfate, $PbSO_4$, but does not react with the silver. When he filters the mixture he removes the lead sulfate and the silver nitrate remains in solution. Now that the lead has been removed he adds the hydrochloric acid and precipitates silver chloride, $AgCl$. He filters the precipitate from the solution, dries it and weighs it. Suppose it weighs 0.15 g. The atomic weight of silver is 107.87 and that of chlorine is 35.453 and so the silver chloride has the molecular weight 143.323. Therefore,

$$\frac{107.87}{143.323} \times 0.15 \text{ g is 0.1129 g of silver in 0.2 g of the metal,}$$

or

$$\frac{0.1129}{0.2} \times 100 \text{ per cent, or 56.45 per cent silver in the sample.}$$

In order to avoid possible blunders or accidents the chemist usually makes two or more analyses of the same sample; that is, he does the analysis in duplicate, in triplicate, etc. The results will not be exactly the same, but they should not be very different. No measurement of any kind can be made exactly. In this analysis a drop of solution may splash out of the beaker, a little solid may be lost in the washing, the silver chloride may not be completely dry when it is weighed or some other procedure may not have been carried out perfectly. If the chemist did the analysis in triplicate and got 56.42 per cent, 56.40 per cent and 56.49 per cent he would have very good results and would report the average of these three values. If the results were 56.42 per cent, 56.50 per cent and 57.04 per cent he is not much of an analyst. It has taken considerable time to describe this simple analysis; it would take much longer to do it.

Some analyses, that of an alloy for example, give percentages that add up to about 100 per cent. In many practical analyses, however, no attempt is made to determine everything present. A fertilizer is analyzed for nitrogen, phosphorus and potassium, which are the main elements required by plants. Special fertilizers also contain small amounts of iron, copper and a few other elements that are required by plants in very small amounts, and such fertilizers may be analyzed for these elements also; but even then the total would be far short of 100 per cent. The phosphorus is present as $CaHPO_4$ and related compounds, and neither the hydrogen nor the oxygen is ever determined. The potassium is probably present as KCl, which is only slightly more than half potassium, and the nitrogen may be sodium nitrate, $NaNO_3$, ammonium sulfate, $(NH_4)_2SO_4$, or urea, $CO(NH_2)_2$, and of all these elements only the nitrogen, phosphorus and potassium are determined.

Oxygen is a component of rocks, glass, porcelain, cement and other inorganic materials. Since chemists have never found a method for the determination of oxygen in an inorganic compound the analysis of such material necessarily gives less than 100 per cent. However, in order to see whether the analysis has determined all the principal components, the chemist assumes that the metals are present as the oxides. Suppose he analyzes a blast furnace slag, which is mainly calcium silicate. He determines calcium and silicon and even if the slag were pure he would not have 100 per cent, but if he calculates the calcium as the oxide, CaO, and the silicon as the oxide, SiO_2, the results on a pure sample would add up to 100 per cent because CaO and SiO_2 add up to calcium silicate:

$$CaO + SiO_2 \longrightarrow CaSiO_3$$

It is customary to report such analyses as the oxides; it has the advantage that if the percentages total much less than 100 per cent the analyst knows that either he has made a mistake or that there is an element present that he has not determined and a thorough qualitative analysis may be in order.

PROXIMATE ANALYSIS

Proximate analysis encounters very different problems from those of the elementary analysis, which I have just discussed. What appears to be one of the simplest of these problems is the determination of the amount of water present in some commodity, flour for instance. The chemist uses a small flat-bottom metal dish with a cover that fits tightly. He dries both the dish and the cover and weighs them, adds some flour to the dish, adjusts the cover and weighs again. The increase in weight is the weight of the flour sample. Now he removes the cover and places both it and the dish in a drying oven heated to just above 100° C. After an hour or so he removes the dish, covers it, cools it and weighs again. The loss in weight is the weight of the water in the flour. His notebook might look like this:

Wt of dish, cover and flour	20.576 g	
Wt of dish and cover	15.265	
Wt of flour	5.311 g	

After drying:

Wt of dish, cover and flour before drying	20.576 g
Wt of dish, cover and flour after drying	19.818
Wt of water	0.758 g

From these data we see that 5.311 grams of flour lost 0.758 gram of water and so the flour contained

$$\frac{0.758}{5.311} \times 100\% \text{ or } 14.3\% \text{ water.}$$

Both the method and the calculation are simple, but if the
oven is not hot enough the water will not all evaporate, and
if it is too hot the flour will char and lose weight. If the
sample is too big, an hour will not be long enough to dry it,
and in all these cases the analysis will be wrong. An official
method for this analysis specifies a sample of 2 g in an oven
at 130° C for 1 hour. Flour usually contains about 14 per cent
moisture and the exact amount is often important; flour is
sold by the pound, and also if the moisture is too high the
flour does not keep well. Then again, flour is often bought
on specifications, one of which might be not over 14 per cent
moisture. In such cases it is important to have an official
method so the chemist for the mill and the one representing
the buyer can get the same analysis of the same flour.

Another very common proximate analysis is the determination of the percentage of fat in a mixture. Fat is one of the
nutrients in foods. Also, some foods, such as dairy products,
have legal requirements for the fat content. By federal regulation butter must contain at least 80 per cent milk fat. Milk
must contain 3 per cent fat in some states and 3.5 per cent
in others. Several kinds of cheese must contain 50 per cent
fat on the dry basis, that is, 50 per cent of what is left after
the water has been removed must be fat.

To illustrate a common method for the measurement of
the amount of fat in a commodity let us take a cheese
analysis. A portion of cheese is ground in a meat chopper or
some such gadget and a 5 g sample is dried and weighed
in the same manner as that used for flour. The chemist
determines the water first because the legal requirement is
based on the dry weight and also because he may need to
know the water content for other reasons. He next extracts
the dried sample with ether, for ether dissolves fat but not the
sugar, salt and protein of the cheese. He must filter the ether

extract to remove any solid particles of the dried cheese that may be floating in it. He catches the filtrate in a weighed dish. The ether evaporates very rapidly, so it soon leaves and the fat is left alone in the dish. Another weighing and a subtraction gives the weight of the fat and from this weight and the weight of the sample it is easy to calculate the percentage of fat. This is a very common method for the determination of fat in foods and other materials.

A more difficult type of proximate analysis is the identification of a natural or a manufactured product. Because of their peculiar properties olive, linseed, tung and castor oils are more expensive than cottonseed oil, soybean oil and many others. Buyers of these special oils want to be sure they get what they pay for. Even if there were no difference in price, cottonseed or soybean oil would be a poor substitute for linseed oil in the manufacture of a paint, nor would they have the flavor of olive oil in a salad dressing.

To identify an oil a chemist determines what he calls *constants*. These are properties that he can measure quantitatively such as specific gravity, refractive index, the amount of iodine the oil will combine with or the amount of alkali required to convert it into soap. The values of these constants have been determined on samples of known identity at some time in the past. Some chemist with a curiosity has gotten some cottonseed, olives, peanuts or what not, removed the oil and determined its constants. He may have had several lots of his material from different sources to see whether all samples of the oil have the same constants. Such work has been done by many chemists over many years and the results have been published. Societies, government agencies and energetic individuals have collected these widely scattered results and published them in handbooks. These compilers have found that genuine samples of an oil do not all have the same values and so the recorded constants are not very constant, but usually fall within a rather narrow range. The specific gravity of cottonseed oil is 0.917–0.918; peanut oil, 0.917–0.926; olive oil, 0.914–0.918. This means that these oils are 0.914 to 0.926 times as heavy as water. The measurement of these specific gravities is simple but slow; the chemist uses a small bottle that holds about 2 ounces and is designed for specific gravity work. He weighs it, fills it with water and weighs it again, which gives him the weight of the water the bottle holds. He then empties the bottle, dries it, fills it with oil and weighs it again. This gives him the weight of the oil that has the same volume as the water he weighed and the one divided by the other is the specific gravity of the oil. If several determinations are to be made with the same bottle, the bottle and water need be weighed only once. All bottles used for this purpose look alike but do not weigh the same and, furthermore, glass dissolves slowly in water and so the chemist must check the weight of his bottle now and then; it may have lost weight or somebody may have traded bottles with him.

From the specific gravities reported above it is obvious that the determination of specific gravity alone will not serve to identify an oil, and so the chemist looks further. The *iodine number* is the number of grams of iodine that will combine with 100 grams of the oil. Measurement of this constant is too long and involved for description here, but some of the values are cottonseed oil, 111–115; almond oil, 93–103; olive oil, 86–90. Here the values do not overlap and if there were only these three possibilities the iodine number alone would settle the question. But there are dozens of fatty oils in commerce, and if the sample is totally unknown the chemist must keep on determining constants until he has a set that could apply to one oil only.

It may occur to the reader that the unknown oil might be an uncommon one for which there are no constants in the book. This has happened. Several years ago government officials discovered that teaseed oil was being imported into the United States but none was being sold. This aroused some curiosity among the officials and the government chemists found that the constants for the teaseed oil are very close to those of olive oil and that the teaseed oil was being used to adulterate olive oil. They began at once to hunt for a method for the identification of teaseed oil and soon found one. This sort of thing could happen again because the seeds of many tropical plants are rich in oil and at any time some enterprising individual may decide to manufacture and market a seed oil that has not been commercialized before. The various oils imported into this country pay different duties. Consequently, chemists for the customs service must identify every shipment of oil that comes in so as to know what duty should be imposed. An oil is generally shipped under its own name and so a new one would be recognized, but if someone had the bright idea of shipping a new oil under the name of an old one, or mixed with an old one, the chemists would have a problem.

There are actually thousands of vegetable oils. Almost any seed contains considerable oil, but comparatively few are in commerce. Who has heard of oil of acorns, almond, avocado, black walnut, Brazil nut, cherry seed, date seed, hazelnut or peach kernel? Once in a blue moon a chemist may encounter one of these oils or even a less common one, and so the oil chemist must keep up with commercial developments if he is to do a good job of identification. If he is dealing with a tank car full of oil he knows that it is not hazelnut oil because hazelnuts are scarce and expensive. If he has only a half-pint sample the possibilities are unlimited.

The determination of water and fat and the identification of an oil indicate the nature of the work done by the proximate analyst. There are also proteins, sugars, starches, vitamins and other substances that must be measured to answer questions that plague the food industries, not to mention the problems in patent medicines, soaps, paints and other commercial mixtures.

SAMPLING

There is one big problem that faces every analytical chemist: How to get a sample? The word "sample" has two different meanings to a chemist. It refers to all the material available to the chemist for analysis—a cubic centimeter of blood, a quart of milk, a 5-pound bag of flour or a carload of coal. The chemist usually refers to this as the original sample. Then he weighs 2 g for the determination of water, 1 g for another determination, 0.2 g for a third and so on. These are analytical samples. An industrial chemist may be confronted with all the ore from the mine, a barge full of limestone or a carload of coal, flour, lard or any other commodity that is shipped in large quantity. An analysis is supposed to be representative of the entire lot and very few samples used for a determination are larger than 5 grams. When we recall that an ounce is just over 28 grams we can see how small a fraction of a commercial lot is used to represent the composition of the whole. It is somewhat like determining the result of a presidential election from a poll of a few thousand voters.

Even a quart of milk presents a problem. When milk remains undisturbed for some time the cream rises to the top; all the fat is in this layer, and even before the cream line can be distinguished there is a higher percentage of fat in the upper half of the bottle than in the lower half. The chemist overcomes this difficulty by pouring the milk from one vessel to another several times and then removing his small analytical samples before the milk has time to separate again. If he needs another sample a half-hour later he goes through the pouring act again.

Liquids can usually be made uniform by mixing, but it is almost impossible to be sure that a sample of a solid is representative of the whole lot. The analyst usually uses a method of sampling that has been designed for the commodity in question and adopted as official by some organization or government agency related to the industry involved. The official method for sampling flour, wheat or other small grains in bags consists in passing a long, slender, specially designed tube through the bag in a specified manner and thus removing a small portion of the cereal. The number of bags sampled must be the square root of the number in the lot but not less than ten. If there were 25 bags in the lot, 10 would be sampled; if there were 400 bags, 20 would be sampled. The several tubefuls of cereal are emptied into a jar with an airtight cover and mixed in a manner specified in the directions. This sample may contain from 1 to 10 pounds and must be so well mixed that 1-gram to 5-gram samples will represent the jarful.

OFFICIAL METHODS

There are many analyses that concern two or more people, companies or government agencies. In the food field nearly every processed human food or animal feed is bought, sold or legally regulated by specifications of some kind; consequently, dependable and uniform methods of analysis are necessary. The Association of Official Agricultural Chemists was organized September 9, 1884. To quote their own description of their society: "Membership in the Association is institutional and includes the State Departments of Agriculture, the State Agricultural Colleges and Experiment Stations, the Federal Department of Agriculture, and the Federal, State and City offices charged with the enforcement of food, feed, drug, fertilizer, insecticide and fungicide control law."

All the chemists that work for these institutions belong to the Association because of their employment—there are no dues. The Association originally concerned itself with methods of analysis of agricultural commodities; however, drugs came under government control in 1906, and in 1938, cosmetics joined the list of commodities that official chemists may have to analyze. The main purpose of the Association is to devise methods of sampling and analysis. The first methods adopted were for the analysis of fertilizers; next came methods for cattle feeds. The first methods for the analysis of foods were for dairy products. Then the passage of the first general food law, the Food and Drugs Act of June 30, 1906, boosted the need for methods of analysis for both foods and drugs. In 1920 the Association published a book of methods, and it has been revised every five years since that time. It also publishes a journal in which new methods appear between editions of the book.

The procedure used by the Association to establish an official method is a long and involved process and may take several years unless an emergency demands quick action. In the meantime the chemist who must make the analysis uses any method he can find. The reason for the delay is that the members are all busy with their analytical duties and the work on a new method is done whenever they can find the time. The president of the Association appoints a committee for each limited field, such as dairy products, fertilizers or vitamins. In the broader fields there are subcommittees: for butter, cheese, market milk and so on in the area of dairy chemistry, for example. The members of a committee (usually the chairman, of course) collect all the methods they can find in the literature for the analysis under consideration. They then study these methods for the time they take, how well duplicate analyses agree with each other and other features agreed upon by the committee. Methods that are poor in some respect are abandoned; sometimes none remains and so the committee undertakes to devise a method of its own. Once a promising method is found it is tested by the members of the committee and by any others who will volunteer for the job. The tests consist of replicate analyses of a sample the chairman sends out—a portion of the same sample to each chemist who will cooperate. Each chemist analyzes the sample by the method proposed and sends his results along with any comments he may have to the chairman of the committee. The chairman writes a report, including the analytical results, and sends it to all the members of his committee. If the results are good and the members are satisfied, the method is presented at the annual meeting of the Association. That body may adopt the method, reject it, or send it back to the committee for further study. If the method is adopted it is published in the *Journal* and then in the next edition of the book of methods.

The Food, Drug and Cosmetic Act of 1938 was the first to include cosmetics. This created an emergency for the official chemists because there were no official methods for the analysis of cosmetics—not even a committee on the subject. Needless to say, there soon was one.

The book of methods is officially known by the lengthy title of *Official Methods of Analysis of the Association of Official Agricultural Chemists* and called the AOAC methods for short. A chemist for a food processor may or may not use these methods, but if he is concerned with products subject to legal regulation he generally uses them—because in case his product happens to become the subject of court action, an independent method will not have as much standing in court. The chemist may think he knows a better method, but it is very hard to convince a judge or jury to that effect. Drugs and cosmetics are not exactly agricultural and so the Association has changed its name to the Association of Official Analytical Chemists, which still leaves it the AOAC.

The American Pharmaceutical Association and a related group of pharmacists publish two volumes similar to the *Methods* of the AOAC. These are the *United States Pharmacopoeia* and the *National Formulary*, which contain standards of composition and methods of analysis for drugs. The methods are used in the drug industry and in some cases the Food, Drug and Cosmetic Act specifies that these standards and methods are official under the law.

There are several other organizations that devise methods of analysis. The American Association of Cereal Chemists and the American Oil Chemists Society each have compiled methods of analysis; the former for flour, bread and other products of the milling and baking industries, the latter for fats, oils, soaps, cottonseeds and other products or raw materials of these industries. The American Public Health Association and several other groups have books of methods for use in their respective fields of analysis.

From this brief discussion of official methods of analysis it is obvious that the consulting analyst, who may do analytical work in many fields, needs a large library because nobody pretends to remember the details of even one of these hundreds of methods unless he is making the same analysis daily. He must also have journals to keep up with the newer methods. There is the *Journal of Analytical Chemistry* in this country and similar journals abroad that publish methods of analysis that may have no connection with any industry or any legal control. These methods are devised by college professors, research chemists or others and may be for some substance that recently has become important, such as uranium, or the method may introduce a new principle to be used in analysis. Sometimes a new method is the thesis of some student representing the research he did for the master's or doctor's degree. There is a great variety of motives for publishing a new analytical method—sometimes one wonders just what the motive was.

These methods that are not connected with any society or industry are by no means useless. A chemist never knows what analysis he may be called on to make next unless he is a control chemist who spends all his time analyzing batches of steel, sugar or some other commodity that his employer manufactures. A consulting laboratory with which I was once connected received about a pint of an organic liquid for the determination of the amount of water in it. When the client was asked how much he thought there was he replied that there was a fraction of 1 per cent, but that he had to know the exact amount. Fortunately, he was a regular client and did not ask about the cost. None of us had ever made such an analysis and had no idea how much work was involved. As soon as the client left, the three of us most concerned with the reputation and income of the laboratory inquired of each other how to go about the job. None of us had ever seen a method for such an analysis and we all had visions of having to invent one. But first, a look at the literature is always indicated. The *Journal of Analytical Chemistry* was at hand and has an annual index. The three chemists began to search these indices and within fifteen minutes found a method.

It proved to be as good as the author claimed it to be and the sample was analyzed promptly and at no great cost.

THE ''ROQUEFORT CHEESE'' CASE

A problem that came to my attention was a lot more bother. Roquefort cheese is made from sheep's milk and ripened by the growth of the blue mold *Penicillium roquefortii*. Sheep give very little milk and so the cheese is expensive, which had led to the development of a process for the manufacture of a similar blue-mold cheese made from cow's milk. This cheese is manufactured in large quantities in France, Denmark, the United States and several other countries. It is simply called *blue cheese* and costs about a third less than the Roquefort; the loaves are also the same size as the Roquefort. The situation led to the practice on the part of unscrupulous dealers of cutting blue cheese in the familiar wedges and wrapping them in tin foil labeled *Roquefort*. In fact, the Roquefort producers were furnishing the foil, which is how they came to discover the substitution— they were selling more foil than cheese. At that time the difference in price was about fifteen cents a pound at wholesale. Damage suits had been undertaken by the Roquefort producers, but the only method they had to distinguish between the two kinds of cheese was the taste of it. In court one "expert" would testify that a sample was Roquefort and another that it was not. The substitution was illegal under the food laws, but the problem was new to government chemists and they had no method for distinguishing between the two kinds of cheese, and did not consider the violation serious enough to justify the time necessary to devise one. The Roquefort producers, however, took a different view of the matter and offered a prize to encourage some chemist to invent a method.

The problem seemed to me to be an interesting one and I began to investigate it. The first step was obvious to any research chemist with any experience in proximate analysis—read what dairy chemists have to say about the milk from different animals. Anybody who begins to read about a subject of which he is totally ignorant is always amazed to learn how much somebody else knows about it. An available library had a recent book on dairy science and in it were excellent descriptions of different kinds of milk. Of course, I was looking for some difference between cow's milk and sheep's milk that could be used analytically. The book did not mention analytical methods, but it stated that the fat of sheep's milk contains more caproic and caprylic acids than that of cow's milk. This fact impressed me, for I knew that a fat constant called the *Polenske number* is to some extent a measure of the content of these acids. The next step was simple logic—get an authentic sample of each kind of cheese, separate the fat and measure the Polenske number. The Roquefort sample proved to have a value of 3.5 and the blue cheese 2.8. These results supported the statement in the book and the Roquefort representative in New York was asked whether he would like further tests of the method. He saw that a lot of work was necessary, but he was quite excited at the prospect for they had already lost thousands of dollars by the substitution, and he began to scour this country, Canada and Europe for samples of different kinds of cheese. He rounded up over two hundred samples of cheese and some of milk and butter from both sheep and cows. A laboratory with which I was associated at the time did most of the analyses, but both the laboratory and I had other problems and besides it took some time to collect the samples.

Consequently, it was over a year before everybody was satisfied with the conclusion that the Roquefort fat always gave a Polenske value of 3 or more and that the fat from the cow's milk was always under 3.

In the course of this analytical work we began to notice that the sheep's milk fat was much whiter than that from cow's milk. A return trip to the book on dairy science revealed something I should have noticed before. All chemists know that grass and other forage crops contain the yellow pigment carotene, and the author of the book on dairy science also knew that the cow stores this pigment in the fat but that the sheep does not. The chemists then lined up their little bottles of fat samples, which had been extracted from the cheese for analysis. The yellow color of the cow's milk fat in contrast to the sheep's milk could be seen across the room.

Everybody concerned thought that the two differences were sufficient to distinguish definitely between the two kinds of cheese, whereupon officials of the city of New York raided the cutting room of a dealer and a warehouse where cheese was stored. Samples were seized and analyses showed that plenty of the wedges of blue cheese were labeled *Roquefort*, and a court action followed. The trial was before three judges of a New York court. Polenske values were a bit technical, but seemed to be convincing, especially since one of the judges had been a chemist in his younger days. Then when the fat samples were displayed, the difference in color settled the matter. The cutters were convicted and fined. This episode occurred in the 1930s and for many years cheese cutters were shy about selling blue cheese as Roquefort, but "Roquefort cheese" spreads and salad dressings began to spring up and many of them were made from blue cheese. In recent years this practice brought legal action against a restaurant. Asked if they have a Roquefort salad dressing, the more cautious waiters are now likely to say that they have a blue cheese dressing. The analytical methods seems to have solved the problem as far as Roquefort cheese is concerned.

The chemists who work for a manufacturer of drugs or other chemicals are continually devising methods because of new problems that constantly confront them. Most of these methods are published—analytical procedures are seldom secrets.

NEW ANALYTICAL INSTRUMENTS

We have emphasized the time required for chemical analyses of various types, but several inventions through the years have shortened many analyses or improved them. Faraday discovered the laws of electrolysis about 1835, but it was a generation before anyone applied the electrolytic principle to analysis. In 1864 Oliver Wolcott Gibbs (1822–1908), a professor of chemistry at Harvard University, published an analytical method for the quantitative determination of copper and nickel. He weighed a platinum crucible, poured his solution of copper or nickel into it and suspended a heavy platinum wire in the solution. He then connected the wire to the positive pole of an electric battery and the crucible to the negative pole. In three hours or less the inner wall of the crucible was plated with copper (or nickel) and none remained in the solution. He then emptied the crucible, washed, dried and weighed it. The increase in weight was the weight of the metal to be determined, and no calculation was required from the atomic weights. Copper and nickel both dissolve in nitric acid but platinum does not; consequently, the plated metal could be removed in a few minutes and the crucible was ready to be used again. Platinum electrodes of different design from those used by Gibbs are now widely used for the determination of several of the metals.

The middle years of the nineteenth century saw the introduction of three instruments that have proved invaluable in analytical chemistry. These are the refractometer, the polarimeter and the spectrometer. All of them use the properties of light. When light passes from one transparent substance to another its direction is changed. This is called *refraction* and is the explanation of why a straight stick partly immersed in water seems to be broken at the surface of the water. Some transparent substances change the direction of light more than others. The instruments used to measure the extent of this refraction are called *refractometers* and the scale on the instrument indicates the result in a calculated form called the *index of refraction*. This value for water is 1.333; alcohol, 1.361; benzene, 1.501. A common handbook lists the indices of refraction for about three thousand liquids and a large number of transparent solids. The diamond has a very high value, 2.419, hence the sparkle. These values are very useful for the identification of minerals, pure liquids, fats, fatty oils and essential oils. There are also tables that enable the chemist to determine the percentage of some of these substances in solution; among them are alcohol, glycerine and sugar. The reading of the refractometer takes only a few seconds and is sometimes all that is needed for an analysis. However, such an instrument may cost several hundred dollars.

Light consists of a wave motion. Think of a ray of light as a wire that has been bent into waves, all the waves in the same plane so the wire would lie flat on the floor. Now, a beam of light, such as that from the headlight of an automobile or the tiny one that comes in through a hole in a window shade, is made up of millions of these rays, each with its own plane of vibration as though a multitude of wavy wires were strung between two points without regard for the angles of the planes; some would be vertical, some horizontal and others at all possible angles. Several devices comb out these vibrations so that those that emerge are all parallel. Such light is said to be *polarized*. Reflected light is somewhat polarized and certain prisms will completely polarize it. One of the most common devices is "Polaroid," which is a plastic material used in spectacles to cut down the amount of reflected light. The polarimeter is an instrument with a prism, to polarize a beam of light, mounted in a metal tube to exclude light that does not pass through the prism. At the other end of the tube a second prism is mounted so it can be rotated. With the two prisms in the zero position the light passes through both of them with maximum brightness, but as the second prism is rotated less light passes until at an angle of 90° there is no light at all. This is known as the position of *extinction*.

The distance between the two prisms of the polarimeter is about ten inches to make room for the sample to be examined. If the prism is set at extinction and then a tube with glass covers at the ends is filled with a sugar solution and placed between the prisms, light again emerges. The number of degrees through which the prism must be rotated to get extinction again is the measure of the rotation of the sugar solution. Such is the nature of the polarimeter at a cost of several hundred dollars again.

Substances that rotate polarized light are said to be *optically active*. All the optically active compounds are natural products. They include the sugars, alkaloids and essential oils. The polarimeter is most useful in the analysis of these substances. It is an absolute requirement in the laboratories of the sugar manufacturer and refiner.

The spectroscope has grown in the last hundred years to the *spectrometer* for measuring spectra and the *spectrograph* for recording the results as they are measured. It has also grown in price from hundreds to thousands of dollars. There are now many types of instruments for measuring both the emission spectra of the elements and the absorption spectra of the molecules. The result of all this development is an analytical tool for determining the structure of organic compounds and for the detection and identification of both elements and compounds, even in small amounts.

The *chromatograph,* another aid to the analyst, has appeared in the past twenty years as an outgrowth of the work of Michael Tswett (1872–1919). Tswett was born in Asti, Italy, of a Russian father and an Italian mother. While he was still young the family moved to Switzerland where the boy was educated. He studied botany, physics and chemistry at the University of Geneva, and after he finished his studies there he taught botany in various universities in Poland, Russia and Estonia. The vicissitudes of war and no fault of his own kept him on the move, but during his fifteen years in Warsaw he managed to do some research. He investigated the pigments from the leaves of plants and discovered that if he filtered a solution of these pigments through a glass tube filled with powdered calcium carbonate, the pigments stuck to the powder and the different pigments appeared as colored bands at different places along the tube and were thus separated from each other. He called these colored bands a *chromatogram* and suggested that the method could be used to separate colorless substances also. These results and suggestions appeared in a paper that Tswett published in 1900, but possibly because he was a botanist, chemists paid very little attention to his work, except a few who criticized it. Perhaps the method was too easy for the chemists, who were accustomed to long extractions, crystallizations or distillations for their separations.

Tswett died in 1919 and it was thirty years later that chemists rediscovered his work, and then papers on chromatography began to appear from here, there and everywhere. Scarcely a chemical journal appears today without at least one paper on chromatography. Absorbing powders other than calcium carbonate have been discovered, paper has been used for a wide variety of chromatograms and apparatus has even been invented for the separation of gases. Among analytical chemists this is the chromatographic age—the chromatograph separates substances, the spectroscope identifies them. An enthusiast at a recent chemists' meeting announced, on the basis of chromatographic studies, that the essential oil from orange skin contains twenty-seven substances, but he had not identified many of them.

ANALYTICAL PROBLEMS

Other equipment has been invented for the benefit of the analytical chemist, but many analyses, especially the quantitative variety, are still made by the same kind of method used a century ago. The airplane has been invented, but some must still go by train and some must walk—there is no other way to get there.

There are times when the object in view can be accomplished without a long and costly analysis. A young man came to a consulting laboratory and presented a small bottle of a pale yellow powder for analysis. In answer to the usual questions he said it was a powder used in embossing and he wanted to go into the embossing ink business. He wanted to duplicate the powder, which someone else was using. He asked what the analysis would cost and to the consternation of one of the partners the other said twenty-five dollars. After the client left, the shaken partner inquired of the other how he proposed to analyze that stuff for twenty-five dollars. "That is simple," he said, and sprinkled a pinch on a nearby hot plate. A smoke arose of strong, strange odor. This chemist had worked for a shellac company, recognized the powder and verified his opinion by the odor. He then telephoned a shellac dealer and asked if he sold the grade of shellac used in embossing. The reply was affirmative and the chemist ordered a pound of it. When the client returned he got a report on the result of the identification, a pound of the powder and the address of one source of it—more than many a client has received from a more elaborate and costly project.

Another problem had some comic aspects. A small manufacturer packed his product in fiberboard cases for shipment. Girls sealed these cases with gummed paper, but water did not wet the gum readily and it took the girls some time to spread the water over the paper. Someone sold the boss a liquid that wet the paper evenly and quickly. The liquid cost five dollars a gallon, but five gallons cost only ten dollars. The superintendent thought this was an enormous reduction in price for such a small increase in quantity, and asked the chemist to analyze this magic liquid. It seemed obvious to the chemist that the liquid was water with a wetting agent in it. Soap is the most common wetting agent. Water may stand in drops on glassware, dishes or the skin, but if there is soap present the water wets the surface and spreads out evenly. There are several wetting agents that are better than soap. The chemist took a measured sample of the liquid and evaporated it. Sure enough it was 99 per cent water and 1 per cent of some wetting agent. At this point the chemist ended the analysis and wrote a letter to a company that advertised wetting agents and asked for samples. He received two. One of them worked fine and cost nineteen cents a pound—enough for twelve gallons of the liquid.

Many a chemist has been presented with a bottle—usually a very small one—of bootleg liquor, a pill, a stone or something else and asked to analyze it. The donor usually expects a free analysis. For example, a middle-aged widow sat down to lunch with a group of us at a cafeteria. For some reason no longer remembered, we began to talk about investments and, naturally, each of us had his own ideas on the subject. The widow favored gold mines, but the rest of us did not—we thought they were too risky. It then developed that she had invested a considerable part of her wealth in a gold mine somewhere in the West. When we seemed to doubt the wisdom of her investment she offered to bring me (the only chemist in the group) a piece of ore from the mine so I could analyze it. That afternoon she made good the offer and brought me a stone of about two ounces. I think it was a piece of fairly rich gold ore because the mine promoter had given it to her. However, I pointed out that an analysis was useless because she had no proof that the ore had come from her mine and even if it did she had no idea how much of it the mine could produce. The worst fears of the pessimists among us were realized; the mine turned out to be a fraudulent promotion. The next morning the *New York Times* had an article on the subject and ended it by saying that the police of a California city were looking for the promoter—the district attorney wanted to see him.

An experienced chemist has learned how to discourage the freeloaders who may be personal friends with a curiosity, or casual business acquaintances who feel that the work would add to the chemist's prestige—and incidentally to his own profit. A more difficult situation is the client who is able and willing to pay for the work, but does not know what he wants.

Chemists have a code of ethics to which most of them subscribe, and they will not do work for a client if they think the results will be of no use to him. An unscrupulous chemist could run up an enormous bill and not get any information useful to the client. Perhaps the client presents a pint jar containing something that looks as though it might be soap, paint, a face cream or a salad dressing and asks to have it analyzed. The chemist at once suspects that the client does not know just what he wants and so he begins to ask questions. The first question always is, "What is this?" The second, "Why do you want it analyzed?" Suppose it turns out to be a salad dressing; the client can surely tell him that much. Sometimes the questions reveal that the client can be quite definite as to why he wants an analysis. The sample may be a competitor's product that is better than his own and he wants to duplicate it. On the other hand, it may be his own product, which has been spoiling on the shelf and he wants to know why. In the latter case the chemist will ask him what is in it and how he puts it together. He may also ask for samples of the raw materials. In any event the chemist gets all the information he can. He then has some idea of how much work is involved and can quote an approximate cost. If the object is to duplicate a competitor's product, the chemist must know exactly what it is that he wants duplicated—the flavor, the texture or the exact composition.

The analytical chemist, like the lawyer and the doctor, soon learns not to be surprised by anything. A small manufacturer of a proprietary product did a business of about five million dollars a year, and was very anxious to maintain the secrecy of the composition of his product. After his death, it became known that he had paid two different laboratories over one thousand dollars each to analyze his product—he just wanted to see if they could do it. One of them could.

Anything for analysis?

CHAPTER TEN

How Matter Behaves

Most of the natural philosophers of the eighteenth century were both chemists and physicists, but as the years of the nineteenth century advanced, physics and chemistry began to drift apart. The work of Lavoisier, Proust, Dalton and Wöhler encouraged the chemically minded to discover new elements, determine their properties and atomic weights, analyze natural substances or synthesize new ones and determine their properties. These main projects furnished plenty of problems to keep any chemist busy without his worrying about questions that seemed to have little or nothing to do with the composition of matter.

The physicists, on the other hand, turned their attention to such matters as the nature and properties of heat, sound and light, and to simple machines, such as levers and pulleys, for increasing the power of man. Other subjects that occupied the physicists were the applications of energy to the production of work, such as the use of a steam engine to pump water out of a mine. Physics also took over completely the study of electricity and its production as well as its conversion into light, heat or mechanical energy.

By the middle of the nineteenth century the two sciences had separated almost completely. No scholar pretended to be both chemist and physicist. A great many teachers taught both sciences but that was merely a practical arrangement, for they considered them to be separate subjects just as though they were teaching both history and mathematics.

PHYSICAL CHEMISTRY

By the time physics and chemistry had achieved complete separation the chemists had learned how to determine atomic weights and the search for new elements had lost its glamour. They had analyzed hosts of natural substances and synthesized thousands of new ones. Consequently, the more imaginative chemists began to look about for new fields to conquer —the result: the birth of physical chemistry.

Descriptive chemistry simply states the results of observation and experiment. Gold is a yellow metal. Alcohol is a colorless liquid that boils at 78° C. Yeast makes alcohol out of sugar. Heat decomposes red oxide of mercury into the metal and oxygen, but it does not decompose lime into calcium and oxygen. These and all other such observations we call descriptive chemistry. By contrast, physical chemistry is concerned with the laws of chemistry, how to predict and control chemical action and why matter behaves the way it does. In short, *physical chemistry* deals with the laws and theories of chemistry.

Lavoisier launched the law of the conservation of mass and Proust the law of constant composition in the last quarter of the eighteenth century. At the very beginning of the nineteenth century came Dalton's law of multiple proportions and his atomic hypothesis. These three laws and the hypothesis are the most fundamental concepts of chemistry, for they apply to all kinds of matter. Only one law and one theory advanced since then can compete in breadth of application; these are the law of the conservation of energy and the electron theory, both to be discussed later.

Each law and theory has its own peculiar usefulness. The law of the conservation of mass tells the chemist that he cannot get more matter out of a reaction than he puts into it, nor does any less result. If he heats 2 g of copper with 1 g of sulfur he should get 3 g of something out of it and if he gets only 2.5 g he knows that there is something wrong and begins to look for the trouble. Without the law he would not know that there is an error and would probably advance a hypothesis to explain why copper sulfide weighs less than the elements from which it is made. If he did it would not take long for some other chemist to make him look silly by showing that he had lost some of the sulfur, which burns readily in air and escapes as a colorless gas.

Proust's law of constant composition has also been a great help to chemists. Water contains 11.11 per cent hydrogen and 88.88 per cent oxygen no matter where you get the sample. If a chemist had to analyze water every time he needs to know its composition, I am afraid he would turn to alcohol for purposes in which the composition does not matter.

The idea of constant composition led to interesting developments as soon as Dalton advanced his hypothesis and Berzelius hit upon his logical symbols for the chemical elements early in the nineteenth century. The physical chemists combined composition with theory and came up with chemical formulas. It took fifty years to get the correct values for the atomic weights with which to calculate the formulas and so some of the early ones were wrong, but the chemists found them useful nevertheless. The substance reposing in the saltcellar on the table has three names or, perhaps, two names and a picture: salt, sodium chloride and NaCl. The chemist much prefers the last, for the word *salt* tells him very little about the nature of the material, the name *sodium chloride* tells him that the substance is composed of the elements sodium and chlorine and none other, but *NaCl* adds the information that it contains 60.7 per cent chlorine and 29.3 per cent sodium. How so? Well, sodium has the atomic weight 23 and chlorine 35.5, therefore,

$$\frac{35.5}{23+35.5} \times 100 \text{ per cent} = 60.7 \text{ per cent chlorine}$$

Formulas are very useful in planning experiments or manufacturing operations; they enable the chemist to calculate how much material to use to get a given amount of the product. For example, lye is sodium hydroxide and is made by passing an electric current through a solution of salt in water. The equation is

$$2\,NaCl + 2\,H_2O \longrightarrow 2\,NaOH + Cl_2 + H_2$$
$$117 \qquad 36 \qquad\quad 80 \qquad 71 \quad 2$$

The 2 placed before the first three formulas is to balance the equation so that the number of atoms of each element will be the same on each side of the arrow. The formula of a substance is fixed by its composition and that cannot be changed; consequently, if we need more atoms of an element than a compound has in its molecule, we must take another molecule—sometimes several more. Many chemists use an *equals* sign instead of the arrow, which is the origin of the word *equation* in chemistry. It is not an equation until the number of atoms on one side of the arrow is equal to the number of atoms on the other side. Once an equation is balanced it represents a reaction that complies with the law of the conservation of mass. In the above equation the weights add up to 153 on each side of the arrow. The weights are equal but the substances are different. The weights are relative, of course, and so they may be expressed in grams, pounds, tons or any other units of weight.

With the balanced equation before him the chemist has a clear picture of the reaction. From 117 pounds of salt he will get 80 pounds of lye, and whether he likes it or not he will get 71 pounds of chlorine and 2 pounds of hydrogen.

How does a chemist discover a law? By making several experiments and examining the results to see if he can draw any general conclusions. How many experiments are necessary? That depends on the nature of the experiments and the disposition of the chemist. If he is very cautious and careful of his reputation he may make several hundred if they are not too time-consuming. If he is bursting to get into print he may make two or three. He can always count on other chemists to make further experiments to prove him either right or wrong—more likely the latter. Such experiments either help to establish the law or to obliterate it. Any law that ever reaches a textbook has been tested many times since its original publication and it is this multitude of experiments and experimenters that gives the chemist confidence in his laws.

A law simply states the nature of the results of experiments in general terms, but a hypothesis, or theory, is philosophical in nature and always tries to answer a question, usually either how or why something happens. In some cases a hypothesis becomes a theory and in rare cases a fact. Lavoisier explained fire by saying that the burning material is combining with the oxygen of the air. His hypothesis soon became a theory, and so much work has been done on combustion since his day that the explanation has long since become a fact.

The atomic hypothesis at first explained only the law of constant composition and the law of multiple proportions. Then, as time went on it was found to explain the results of more and more experiments, and with all the additional support it has become the atomic theory. By the second

decade of the twentieth century, chemists learned how to use
X rays to take pictures of the shadows of atoms and so today
most chemists consider the atomic theory a simple statement
of fact.

BOYLE'S LAW

The oldest law that chemists find useful was announced
by Boyle in 1662. It is a law of physics, for it has nothing to
do with the composition of matter, but simply states that
the volume of a gas is inversely proportional to the pressure
upon it if the temperature does not change. This means that
there is an exact mathematical relationship between the
volume of a gas and the pressure upon it. When the law was
discovered (see Chapter Four), the measurement of pressure
was in inches of mercury, but scientists now use the metric
system in which 760 millimeters are the same as 30 inches
and so a pressure of 760 millimeters of mercury has become
the standard for reporting the volume of a gas.

If an experiment produces a gas and the chemist wishes to
know how much there is of it, he fills a bottle or gas-measuring
tube with water or mercury and inverts it in a pneumatic
trough containing the same liquid, after the manner of Hales
and Priestley. This gives him his gas in a bottle or measuring
tube over water or mercury in an open vessel and, therefore,
exposed to both the temperature and pressure of the atmosphere. Suppose the gas measures 500 ml and the barometer reads 750 mm. According to Boyle's law the volume of
the gas is inversely proportional to the pressure upon it and
so the volume would be less if the pressure were 760 mm. Or,
to be exact,

$$\frac{750}{760} \times 500 \text{ ml} = 494 \text{ ml}$$

Zero degrees centigrade has been adopted as the standard temperature for reporting gas volumes and so the standard conditions are now 760 mm and 0° C. Anytime a chemist mentions a gas volume without further qualification any other chemist understands it to be the volume at standard temperature and pressure, STP for short. If a gas at 0° loses ½73 of its volume for each degree it is cooled, then if it were cooled 273 degrees it would lose all its volume and there would be nothing left. Fortunately, all gases become liquids before they get that cold and so the conclusion becomes purely hypothetical, for the law does not apply to liquids. The law is used as the basis of another thermometer scale called the *absolute* or *Kelvin* temperature scale. The latter name derives from the British physicist, Lord Kelvin, who devised the scale. It is always designated by the letter K to distinguish it from the F, C, and R scales (pp. 130–132). The degrees are the same as the centigrade degrees, but the zero is the theoretical temperature at which a gas would disappear, −273° C. The Kelvin scale has the advantage that all temperatures are positive; 0° C is 273° K and −20° C is 253° K. Chemists measure their gas temperatures with the centigrade thermometer and add 273 to get the Kelvin temperature, which is used in all calculations.

CHARLES'S LAW

According to Charles's law the volume of a gas is directly proportional to the Kelvin temperature. The volume of the gas mentioned above after it was corrected for the pressure was 494 ml. If the temperature of the laboratory were 27° C when the gas was collected, its volume at 0° would be less, or, in accord with Charles's law,

$$\frac{273}{273+27} \times 494 \text{ ml} = 449.5 \text{ ml STP.}$$

The densities of gaseous elements and compounds have been determined and recorded at STP conditions. Oxygen under these conditions weighs 1.429 g per liter; therefore if the gas just mentioned were oxygen it would weigh $\frac{449.5}{1000} \times$ 1.429 g=0.642 g. The volume of a gas is easily measured, but gases are very hard to weigh and so it is a tremendous help to a chemist to be able to measure the volume of a gas and calculate its weight.

The volume of a gas can always be corrected for pressure and that result corrected to standard temperature just as I did in the above example, but for many purposes it is more convenient to have the two laws combined into one formula. Consequently, after the application of the proper mathematics the chemists came up with $PV=nRT$, which they call the equation of state for gases. P, V, and T are the pressure, volume and Kelvin temperature, n is the number of moles and R is a constant, that is, it is the same for all values of P, V, and T for 1 mole of any gas. If the pressure is expressed in atmospheres and the volume in liters, the value of R is 0.082. This formula has many uses. As an example of one of them, what is the volume of 1 g of hydrogen at 27° C and 750 mm?

One atmosphere is 760 mm; therefore we have $^{750}\!/_{760}$ of 1 atmosphere and a mole of H_2 is 2 g, so we have ½ mole and 27° C is 300° K. Substituting these values in the equation $PV=nRT$, we have

$$\frac{750}{760} V = \frac{1}{2} \times 0.082 \times 300$$

$$V = \frac{760 \times 0.082 \times 300}{750 \times 2} = 12.46 \text{ liters}$$

AVOGADRO'S NUMBER

In 1811 the Italian chemist Avogadro announced that *equal volumes of gases contain the same number of molecules if the gas volumes are measured at the same temperature and pressure.* He did not evolve the notion just to have something to publish, but to explain the laws of Boyle and Charles and more especially the law of Gay-Lussac. Like any other hypothesis this was just a guess, but the idea proved to be very useful. His reasoning explained the physical properties of gases, but it seemed to have been too subtle for his colleagues and so they paid little attention to it until forty years later when his compatriot, Cannizzaro, revived it.

From Avogadro's hypothesis came the idea of the *mole*. The atomic weight of hydrogen was 1 and since Avogadro had demonstrated that hydrogen is diatomic, the molecular weight of H_2 was 2. Atomic and therefore molecular weights are merely relative, but the chemists decided to express these weights in grams and call them *gram-atomic weights* and *gram-molecular weights*. These names were rather long and cumbersome and so they invented the word *mole* to replace them. Consequently, a mole of hydrogen gas is 2 g, a mole of oxygen is 32 g, a mole of carbon dioxide, CO_2, is 44 g, and so on; the volume of a mole of a gas is always 22.4 l at STP. Obviously, then, the determination of the molecular weight of a gas is simple in principle: weigh some of the gas and calculate the weight of 22.4 l. This fact was pointed out by Cannizzaro fifty years after Avogadro failed to get the point across to his colleagues.

The chemist thinks in terms of moles rather than in grams and liters. Consider the equation for the simplest method of preparing hydrogen:

$$Zn + H_2SO_4 \longrightarrow ZnSO_4 + H_2$$

65 g   22.4 l

The equation shows that a mole of zinc gives a mole of hydrogen, which is 2 g, but the chemist thinks of gases in terms of volume and so to him 22.4 liters of gas are produced.

Another illustration of the usefulness of the molar volume is a reaction in which two or more gases are involved:

$$2 H_2 + O_2 \longrightarrow 2 H_2O$$

2 × 22.4 l + 22.4 l   2 × 22.4 l

The balanced equation shows that 2 moles of hydrogen react with 1 mole of oxygen to give 2 moles of water vapor. An inspection of the equation reveals that the number used to balance the equation also represents the relative volumes of the gases.

The idea of molecular volume is important in many other matters. It enables a chemist to calculate the density of a gaseous element or compound. Carbon dioxide has the formula CO_2 and therefore the molecular weight is 12+ (2×16) or 44 and the mole is 44 g, or 22.4 l. The density is therefore 44 g/22.4 l, or 1.964 g/l.

No doubt many people have wondered why hydrogen is used to fill balloons; it has caused many disasters because it ignites so readily. From the discussion of molar volumes the reason for its use is apparent. Air is mainly a mixture of nitrogen and oxygen and the weight of 22.4 l is 28.9 g. Physicists learned long ago that the buoyancy of air on a balloon is the difference in weight between the weight of gas in the balloon and the weight of an equal volume of air. Hydrogen is the lightest gas; its weight of 2 g gives it a lifting power of 28.9—2 or 26.9 grams for every 22.4 liters—just about an ounce per cubic foot of balloon. The next best gas is the next heavier one, helium, which has the molecular weight 4. Its buoyancy is 28.9—4 or 24.9 g for each 22.4 liters, which is 92.5 per cent of the buoyancy of hydrogen. Helium does not burn but it is very scarce and expensive. In the 1920s when the United States government was studying dirigibles for military use several million dollars were spent to recover helium from natural gas in Kansas and Texas where the gas contains about 1 per cent helium. They got enough to fill one of the big dirigibles and then, after a few wrecks in windstorms, it occurred to someone that a balloon is not much of a competitor for an airplane over a battle-field and the big dirigible was abandoned. Helium and hydrogen have the balloon business pretty much to themselves. To be of any use at all a gas must weigh less than 28.9 g per molar volume. The next heavier elements than helium are lithium 7, beryllium 9, boron 11, carbon 12 and nitrogen 14. Lithium, beryllium and boron are solids and do not form any useful gaseous compounds, while carbon and nitrogen form only one compound each that could be of any use. These are methane, CH_4, and ammonia, NH_3, with molecular weights of 16 and 17, which gives them buoyancies of only 12.9 and 11.9 grams per mole—less than half that of hydrogen. Moreover, both of these gases are flammable too.

Although Avogadro stated that equal volumes of gases contain the same number of molecules he did not venture an opinion on what the number is. By 1870 chemists and physicists began to invent methods for counting them—indirectly, that is. There are now several quite different methods and they are all rather complicated but, strange as it may seem, they agree very closely that there are 6.023×10^{23} molecules in a mole. That this is an enormous number is obvious when we recall that 10^2 is 100, 10^3 is 1000, and so on. In fact, the smallest drop of water that the eye can see contains several billion molecules. If anyone cares to know what a molecule of water weighs he can divide 18 g by 6.023×10^{23} and get the weight in grams, but the answer will consist mostly of a decimal point and a long, long row of zeros. This vast number of molecules in a mole is named for the man who named the molecule and advanced the famous hypothesis: it is the *Avogadro number*. Now that the number of gas molecules in a gas volume can be determined experimentally, many chemists call the old hypothesis *Avogadro's law*.

Dalton, of atomic theory fame, discovered a gas law about the year 1800; it is Dalton's *law of partial pressures*. The law states that the gases in a mixture do not affect each other unless they react chemically; the nitrogen, oxygen and argon of the atmosphere do not affect each other at all. Each gas has the same pressure it would have if the others were not there. For example, normal air is mainly 78 per cent nitrogen, 21 per cent oxygen and 1 per cent argon, and so at the normal pressure of 1 atmosphere, or 760 mm, the pressure of the nitrogen is 78 per cent of 760 mm or 592.8 mm, that of the oxygen is 21 per cent of 760 mm or 159.5 mm, and the argon is 7.6 mm.

In 1801, William Henry (1774–1836), who was a doctor, the owner of chemical plants, writer of chemical textbooks and friend of Dalton, discovered that the solubility of a gas in a liquid is directly proportional to the pressure of the gas at the surface of the liquid. If 1 gram of a gas dissolves in a liter of a liquid at a pressure of 1 atmosphere then 2 g will dissolve at a pressure of 2 atmospheres, that is, it will if the temperature does not change. This is Henry's law. Fish and all other aquatic life get their energy from the use of the small amount of oxygen dissolved in the water. Land animals enjoy a 21 per cent concentration of oxygen in their atmosphere, but within all the variations of the barometer oxygen has a pressure of less than 160 mm, and so the dissolved oxygen in natural water is a mere fraction of 1 per cent.

Another qualitative application of Henry's law is the common soft drink. Carbon dioxide is dissolved in the water under pressure of about 4 atmospheres, that is 4 times 760 mm, but the carbon dioxide in the air has a pressure of less than 1 mm. When a bottle of soda water is opened the gas escapes as rapidly as it can get around to it, which rate depends on both temperature and agitation.

Thomas Graham (1805–1869) was a Scottish chemist teaching at the University of Glasgow in 1830 when he made the discovery that is now called Graham's law in his honor. The law states that the velocities with which gases diffuse are inversely proportional to the square roots of their densities—the heavier the gas molecule the slower it travels. Since the molecular weight of a gas is its density multiplied by 22.4, this law furnishes another way to get the molecular weight of a gas. The law also applies to the rates at which gases escape through a small hole, which is easily measured. If the escape of a gas of known density, such as air or oxygen, is timed and then the same vessel filled with the unknown gas at the same temperature and pressure, and its escape timed, the results are the relative velocities. From these values and the density of the standard, the density of the unknown can be calculated from the formula

$$\frac{t^2}{t_1{}^2} = \frac{D}{D_1}$$

In this formula t and t_1 are the times of diffusion of the standard and unknown gas respectively and D and D_1 are their densities. The whole operation takes much less time than the determination of density by weighing the gas.

KINETIC THEORY

It is an interesting fact that while gases follow the six laws we have just mentioned, neither solids nor liquids follow any of them. This strange situation calls for an explanation, and such a theory was perfected by the efforts of many physicists and chemists over a long stretch of years; it is called the *kinetic theory of gases*. Before Boyle announced the first law of gaseous behavior, some scientists seem to have had the idea that gases are composed of particles in motion. However, nobody calculated the effects of such particles until the Swiss physicist Daniel Bernoulli (1700–1782) did so in 1738, when he calculated the pressure of a gas caused by the motion of the particles (named molecules by Avogadro in 1811) and came up with the formula $p = \dfrac{mv^2}{3V}$ in which p is the pressure, m the mass of the molecule, v the velocity and V the volume of the gas. At this time Boyle's law was the only law that concerned the physical behavior of gases. As other laws were discovered there was more than pressure to explain, and so physicists of France, England and Germany expanded the theory over more than a century until it reached its final form in the nineteenth century. Consequently, chemists have had the kinetic theory to comfort them for over a hundred years.

There are several parts to the kinetic theory necessary to explain all the behavior of gases. The first idea is that a gas is composed of molecules that are far apart compared to their size. This theoretical statement explains why gases can be compressed so much. If oxygen under normal atmospheric pressure is compressed until it liquefies, the liquid has only one eight-hundredth the volume of the original gas. According to the kinetic theory the pressure does not change the molecules; it just pushes them closer together. This enormous contraction in volume under pressure is a characteristic of all gases, but of no liquids or solids. If we put water or a piece of iron under pressure it is not compressed at all, or at least not enough to detect unless we are prepared to use a pressure of several tons and to measure extremely small decreases in volume. For all practical purposes liquids and solids are not compressible. Their molecules are already about as close together as their nature permits.

A second provision of the kinetic theory states that the molecules of a gas are in rapid motion in straight lines and that their speed depends on the temperature. Molecules, of course, like the various heavenly bodies, attract each other more strongly the closer they are together. Let us see what these assumptions explain. In order that we may smell anything the molecules of the odorous substance must reach the nerves of the nose. Remove the stopper from a bottle of perfume or, better still, from a bottle of hydrogen sulfide gas, which has the powerful odor of rotten eggs, and very soon the odor will be noticed several feet from the bottle. The molecules have gone a long way in a hurry.

The pressure of a gas is the result of these moving molecules striking the walls of the vessel that contains them, as Bernoulli had shown. In the case of a toy balloon inflated to a certain size, if more air is added the balloon increases in size because there are now more molecules to pound against the rubber. Also if the balloon is warmed, it expands because the molecules move faster and strike the rubber more often.

In a pan of water the molecules are in motion, but they are so close together that their attractive force holds most of them down and thus maintains a definite surface—gases do not have surfaces. But despite their attraction the molecules of a liquid are still free to move. The molecules near the sur-

face that happen to be going toward it have enough energy
to break the attraction of the other molecules and escape.
We call the process evaporation. There are several ways to
speed it up. We can warm the liquid and thus increase the
speed of the molecules so that more of them will have enough
energy to escape, or we can pour the liquid into a pan of
greater diameter so there will be more surface and less depth.
Still another method is to get the molecules away from the
surface so they will not hit the molecules of the gases in
the air and bounce back into the liquid. An electric fan
directed across the surface of the liquid will take care of
that problem. Wet clothes on a line on a sunny day are in
ideal conditions for evaporation. The water is in such a thin
film that it is nearly all surface; the heat of the sun speeds
up the movement of the molecules and the breeze carries
them beyond return.

In this discussion of evaporation we have emphasized the
role of the moving molecules, but the space between the
molecules of a gas also plays a part. As the water molecules
evaporate they go off into the space between the molecules
of the gases of the air. Gases have so much room between the
molecules that all gases mix in all proportions and mix
quickly. If two gases are brought together they mix in less
time than it takes to read this sentence, but two liquids
simply left in contact may take weeks to mix even if they
mix completely when they finally get around to it.

The provisions of the kinetic theory that we have mentioned tell a chemist how to convert a gas into a liquid as well
as how to turn a liquid into a gas. There are two opposing
forces in a gas. One is the energy with which the molecules
attract each other; the other is the energy of their motion.
The energy of attraction increases with the weight of the
molecules and also as they approach each other. This energy

would bring the molecules together in a heap if it were not for the energy produced by their motion, which increases with rising temperature. Now, when a chemist wants to liquefy a gas the procedure is obvious; he compresses the gas to bring the molecules closer together and cools it to reduce the energy that keeps them apart. When the energy of motion falls below that of the attraction, the gas liquefies. All gases have been liquefied. Some of the lighter ones such as hydrogen and helium require a very low temperature because of the very slight attraction of the light molecules. Commercial gases, such as carbon dioxide, chlorine and sulfur dioxide, are liquefied and sold in steel cylinders under a pressure of several hundred pounds. The "bottled gas" that is widely sold as fuel is either liquid propane, C_3H_8, butane, C_4H_{10}, or a mixture of the two.

How fast are the molecules of a gas moving? Well, that depends on the weight of the molecule and the temperature. A molecule of hydrogen at $0°$ C travels at 1838 meters a second, which is about 4000 miles an hour. Hydrogen is the fastest of the lot because it is the lightest. At the same temperature a molecule of helium (4) does 1311 meters; oxygen (32), 461; and carbon dioxide (44), 393; the heavier the molecule, the less the speed, according to Graham's law. You cannot put a molecule on a reducing diet and so the only way to increase its speed is to increase the temperature.

It must not be supposed that once a molecule of hydrogen is released it will be a mile away at the end of a second for it strikes a molecule of oxygen, nitrogen or argon and takes off in a new direction like a ball thrown against a wall. Between bumps it travels in a straight line a very short distance indeed. These distances are not all the same and the physical chemist concerns himself with the average, which he calls the *mean free path* of the molecule. At standard pressure the mean free path is one millionth of a centimeter (1×10^{-6} cm), but at an altitude of 500 km the mean free path is about 20 kilometers (2×10^6 cm)—molecules to bump into are scarce up there. The path of a moving molecule is a zigzag affair and might even bring it back to its original neighborhood.

Still another assumption of the kinetic theory is that the molecules are perfectly elastic. This means that they do not lose any energy when they collide. If a tennis ball is dropped to the floor it bounces and falls again, several times, but it finally comes to rest. The energy with which the ball strikes the floor depends upon its weight and the height from which it was dropped. When it collides it is flattened on one side and quickly resumes its spherical shape. The energy it exerts in resuming the sphere throws the ball up, but each time this energy is less than that exerted by the ball when it last fell. If it were the same the ball would bounce to the height from which it fell and would never stop bouncing; it would be perfectly elastic. Perfect elasticity explains why a gas that is confined never settles to the bottom of the container like a room full of dust. Solids and liquids settle, gases never do.

Many interesting conclusions can be reached by applying mathematics to the provisions of the kinetic theory, and physical chemists take great delight in doing so. However, I suspect that there are those among us who find mathematics one of the lesser forms of entertainment. The mathematical formula for kinetic energy is rather harmless, however, and may be enlightening. It is

$$K.e. = \tfrac{1}{2} \; mv^2$$

Energy of any kind is the capacity to do work and kinetic energy is produced by a body in motion. In the formula *k.e.*

is the kinetic energy, m is the mass or weight of the moving body and v is the velocity or speed with which it moves. If the body is a gas molecule the energy produced by it would not be very much, but if the body is a two-ton automobile the energy is considerable. A point to notice is that the energy increases with the square of the velocity so that a car at eighty miles an hour exerts sixteen times as much energy as the car at twenty miles an hour. This is one of the reasons why a car takes so much more gasoline at high speed and also why it does so much damage when it hits something.

Hundreds of experiments with gases support the kinetic theory. The equation of state (p. 279), $PV=nRT$, is a law and was originally derived from the results of experiments, but it can also be derived mathematically from the provisions of the kinetic theory. When experiment and theory produce the same result it is usually considered good evidence that the theory is correct.

We must emphasize the fact that a law holds only within certain limits, which the chemist must know if he wishes to apply the law. The equation of state for gases applies at high temperatures and at low pressures, that is, when the molecules are far apart. Hydrogen and helium follow the law to higher pressures and lower temperatures than most gases because their molecules are so light. Heavy gases like carbon dioxide (44) and sulfur dioxide (64) do not follow the law so well and are much more easily liquefied. The kinetic theory explains why the gases depart from their laws. When a gas is under low pressures the molecules are far apart and their attraction for each other is slight or negligible, but as they are brought closer together by increased pressure there comes a time when the attraction adds considerably to the effect of the external pressure and the gas contracts more than it should for the amount of the pressure applied. Attraction is directly proportional to the product of the masses of the molecules and inversely proportional to the square of the distance between them. Obviously, two sulfur dioxide molecules of weight 64 will have a much greater attraction for each other than two helium molecules of weight 4. The relative attraction is 4×4 to 64×64, or 1 to 256. This is why sulfur dioxide is easier to liquefy than helium. Also, as the molecules approach each other there comes a place where the volume of the molecules themselves becomes an appreciable part of the volume of the gas.

Johannes Diderik van der Waals (1837–1923), a Dutch physicist, modified the equation of state in 1879 to include the effects of the size and attraction of the molecules and thus obtained a formula that is accurate over a greater range of pressure and temperature than the original equation. His equation is

$$(P + \frac{a}{V^2})\ (V - b) = RT$$

P, V, R and T are the same as those in the original equation. The values for a and b are different for each gas because a depends on the mutual attraction of the molecules and b depends on their individual volumes. The following table of a few of these values indicates their dependence on the size of the molecules:

FORMULA	MOLECULAR WEIGHT	a	b
H_2	2	0.2444	0.0266
N_2	28	1.390	0.0391
CO_2	44	3.592	0.0427

Substitution of these values in the van der Waals equation extends the range of accuracy to lower temperatures and higher pressures.

COMPOSITION AND PROPERTIES

In 1831 Professor Franz Neumann (1798–1895) of the University of Königsberg attempted to extend the law of Dulong and Petit to compounds and published a law to the effect that the molecular heats of compounds of similar composition are the same. These two laws were the earliest attempts to relate physical properties and chemical constitution.

One of the most active chemists in searching for some relationship between chemical constitution and physical properties was Professor Hermann Kopp (1817–1892) of the University of Giessen until 1863 and then at Heidelberg. Kopp is known best for his four-volume *History of Chemistry*, which was published in the years 1841 to 1847, but for over half a century, from 1838 to his death in 1892, he worked on the physical properties of substances. Several chemists had attempted to extend Neumann's law, but Kopp made a thorough study of the subject and found that although the law does apply to a limited number of compounds it is not sufficiently general to be of any use in predicting the formula of a compound from its physical properties.

One of the complications in both the law of Dulong and Petit and that of Neumann is the fact that every substance has several specific heats. (Specific heat is the heat required to raise the temperature of 1 gram of a substance 1° C.) However, the result differs with the temperature at which it is measured. For example, the specific heat of tin is 0.0541 calorie per gram if it is measured from 20° to 21° and 0.0565 when it is measured from 100° to 101°; it also has other values at other temperatures and so the dilemma is in deciding which value to use when applying the law. Although these two laws were used somewhat when they were new, they are now just history.

Kopp measured the boiling and melting points of a large number of organic compounds, and since his measurements were very precise they have been extremely useful to the analytical chemist for the identification of organic compounds. But Kopp was interested in finding a relationship between these properties and the structure of the compounds. He found none except that in a homologous series, such as methyl, ethyl, propyl and the higher alcohols, both the boiling and the melting points increased with the molecular weight. Even in this case there are two or more isomers of each alcohol from propyl up the series and the regular increase in these values applies only to the normal alcohol of each group, that is, to the one that has an unbranched carbon chain with the -OH group on the end carbon.

Professor Kopp also studied solutions to learn the effect of the presence of one substance on the extent of solubility of another. He found very little effect—none at all that was quantitative. About all he learned was that if you dissolve all you can of one substance in a given volume of water you can still dissolve a considerable amount of a second substance in the same water, but not as much as if the first substance were not present.

We have discussed the molecular volume of gases and said that the molecular weight of a gas divided by its density always gives 22.4 liters at STP. Kopp determined the densities of many liquids and solids, both compounds and elements, and calculated their atomic or molecular volumes, but he found no such relationship as that shown by gases.

Kopp was not the only chemist who studied physical properties. Others investigated the rotation of polarized light, index of refraction, absorption spectra and other properties.

Of all the work done on physical properties only optical rotation (p. 266) and absorption spectra have proved to be general in application and are still in use today. Both properties are used in establishing the formulas of organic compounds.

The study of physical properties helped the chemist very little in his efforts to predict and control chemical action, but the properties were useful as such and the work served to warn other chemists that this field of investigation is not very fertile.

While Kopp was studying physical properties other chemists were studying energy in their search for laws to correlate the diverse behavior of matter, and by 1887 enough work in physical chemistry was in progress to justify publication of a journal. In that year Professor Wilhelm Ostwald (1853–1932) of the University of Leipzig and Professor Jacobus Henricus van't Hoff (1852–1911) of the University of Amsterdam, two of the ablest chemists of the day, began publication of a journal of physical chemistry in German. This venture called the attention of chemists to the physical side of the science; many writers consider the year 1887 the beginning of physical chemistry as a special field of study.

ENERGY

To say that a man is not very energetic is meant to intimate that he is not very much inclined to work, but the physicist has no such notion in mind when he speaks of energy; since the things he works with are not alive, inclination has nothing to do with it. To him, energy means the *capacity* to do work, and work consists of a force acting through a distance. The word *work* has many different meanings, such as schoolwork, brainwork, legal work and so on, but the physicist will have none of them. Work is a very definite physical action, such as the lifting of a weight against the force of gravity. Although horizontal movement of objects does not require as much work as lifting them, it requires work, for the movement is resisted by the momentum of the object, its friction with the surface over which it is moved, and the air through which it moves. All work requires energy to do it. The energy from his metabolism takes a man upstairs, electricity operates an elevator and the heat of the sun raises water vapor high into the sky.

There are many kinds of energy. The main forms are heat, light, sound, electricity, magnetism and also molecular, chemical, mechanical and atomic energy. A magnet will pick up a needle and a big one will lift a ton of steel. Sound will cause windows to rattle and light makes a tree grow to a great height or a flower to turn toward the sun.

Energy never seems to be in the right form for either man or nature. Both are always transforming it, that is, they change it from one kind to another. Rocks, roofs, and other features of the earth's surface change sunlight to heat. The heat evaporates water that falls again as rain and then the engineers take over and, as the water runs back to the sea, they pass it through turbines hitched to dynamos and generate electricity to turn into light or run a fan to stir up the air, or perhaps to haul a train.

Units have been devised for the measurement of energy. The chemist usually measures it in the form of heat and for the purpose he uses the *calorie*, which is the amount of heat required to raise the temperature of a gram of water $1°$ C, or to be exact, from $14.5°$ C to $15.5°$ C, for the specific heat of water varies with the temperature like that of anything else. The calorie is such a small unit that to use it to measure the heat of a furnace would be like measuring the length of a race track with a foot rule. Therefore, a larger unit is made in the usual fashion of the metric system by giving a name to 1000 calories. A kilogram is 1000 grams, a kilometer is 1000 meters and a kilocalorie is 1000 calories. These kilocalories are the ones to be watched when a man's belt becomes too tight. The calorie is abbreviated to cal and the kilocalorie was formerly abbreviated by Cal, but these abbreviations were too much alike and so the abbreviation of the kilocalorie is now kcal. Either abbreviation may be found in some scientific books such as those on diet. In line with the naming of instruments in general (barometer, thermometer, etc.), an instrument used to measure heat is called a *calorimeter*.

Mechanical energy in very small amounts is measured in *ergs*. For larger amounts the *joule* is used; it is 10^7, or ten million, ergs. To lift a dime an inch requires over 5000 ergs. The fact that an erg is so small is why the joule is such a large multiple of it rather than 1000 as in the case of the calorie and some other units. The joule was named for the English brewer and amateur physicist, James Prescott Joule (1818–1889), who determined by experiment the relation between the units of mechanical energy and those of heat—1 calorie is equal to 4.185×10^7 ergs, or 4.185 joules. If this number has no other value at this point it at least indicates that a man must lift a lot of weight very high to consume the 20 kcal in the teaspoonful of sugar he just put in his coffee.

It is hard to devise a machine to turn one kind of energy into another effectively. The difficulty is the tendency of such a device to turn the energy into more than one kind when we want only one. A steam locomotive, for example, is less than 8 per cent efficient. It burns fuel to draw a train of cars, but most of the heat escapes with the smoke or the steam exhaust, while some is converted into sound and light. A diesel engine does better, but it also loses energy in the exhaust and as sound. In fact the various types of combustion engines produce so much heat that they must be cooled by circulating air or water or they get too hot to run at all, as anyone finds out when he forgets to put water in the radiator of his automobile. An engine that would turn all the chemical energy of combustion into mechanical energy to propel a vehicle would be quite an invention. The most efficient energy transformer seems to be the firefly, which is said to convert over 90 per cent chemical energy into light.

Heat, light and electricity are the most important forms of energy to the chemist. Chemical energy usually shows up in one of these three forms. Burning fuel produces heat and light; the chemical action in a voltaic cell produces electricity.

COUNT RUMFORD

Electricity was investigated by Benjamin Franklin and several European scientists of the eighteenth century and by the end of that century it was a well-recognized form of energy with many of its charactistics known. Heat and light were not so well understood. Lavoisier had included both of them in his table of elements, and the nature of heat was a matter of controversy for years. The first to champion the energy idea with experiments to back him up was that romantic gentleman, Count Rumford. Rumford was born Benjamin Thompson (1753–1814), a native of Massachusetts who left there at the time of the American Revolution, wandered over Europe and worked from time to time in different countries. The ruler of Bavaria made him a count and Thompson chose the name of his wife's native town to go with the new title. Among his many activities he founded the Royal Institution in London and, after the death of his first wife, married the widow of Lavoisier.

At one time Rumford was superintendent of the Bavarian

munition works and noticed that a lot of heat is produced in the boring of brass cannon. He was able to show that the amount of heat was related to the amount of mechanical enegy used in the boring. From these experiments he decided that heat is some kind of mechanical motion. By 1807 the idea was getting about that both heat and light are energy in the form of a wave motion. Several French and English engineers and physicists studied the vagaries of heat and by 1840 it was definitely considered not an element.

Every time matter changes its condition, energy is involved, and the amount of it is definite for that substance and that change. For example, to increase the temperature of a substance, energy must be added to it in some form—heat, electricity, light, mechanical energy. When a substance cools, an amount of heat is given off—the same amount it took to heat it.

The heat required to melt a solid is called the *heat of fusion* and is expressed in calories per gram. The heat of fusion of aluminum is 94.5; gold, 15.36; salt, 123.5; and ice, 80 calories per gram.

A liquid will change to a vapor at any temperature, and the heat required for the process is naturally called the *heat of vaporization*. Since the value is different at different temperatures it is always reported at the boiling point of the liquid unless otherwise specified. A few heats of vaporization are ether, 83.9; ethyl alcohol, 204.3; and water, 540 calories per gram.

Both physicists and chemists are concerned with these physical changes in temperature or condition, but the chemist is more involved with the energy effects of chemical changes. Here again a definite amount of heat or other energy is involved for each chemical change. Combustion has been a subject of study since the days of the phlogiston theory and so its heat was the first to be studied. Heats of combustion are large and therefore expressed in kilocalories per gram. Hexane, C_6H_{14}, a component of gasoline, produces 11.5 kcal; carbon disulfide, CS_2, 3.2; alcohol, C_2H_5OH, 7.1; and sugar, 4.1 kcal per gram.

Combustions, of course, are only one of many types of reactions, and all types involve heat. For example, the neutralization of an acid by a base produces heat.

$$HCl + NaOH \longrightarrow NaCl + H_2O + 13.7 \text{ kcal}$$

Here the amount of heat applies to molar quantities of the reagents, that is, 36.5 grams of HCl and 40 grams of NaOH.

A dry cell is a device for converting chemical energy into electricity. It is not dry: the term simply means that the cell does not have a liquid free to slop around in it. A more precise name for the device would be a damp cell, because the components of the cell must be moistened or it will not produce any electricity. It is usually a cylindrical container made of zinc and in the middle there is a rod of carbon. Between the two is the tightly packed moist mixture to react with the zinc and produce the electricity. The top of the cylinder is closed with a special sealing wax that serves two purposes; it prevents the evaporation of water and it insulates the carbon and zinc from each other electrically. When the carbon rod is connected to the zinc container by a wire, an electric current flows through the wire. As the current flows the zinc dissolves—so much zinc lost, so much electricity produced—and eventually a hole comes in the container and the cell soon dies because of the evaporation of water.

A chemical reaction that produces energy is said to be *exothermic*. The three reactions just mentioned—fire, neutralization and the dry cell—are all exothermic. A reaction that absorbs energy is *endothermic*. Although the syllable *therm* in these words indicates heat, the words apply to any kind of energy, such as the action of light in photography and electricity in electroplating, both of which are endothermic. An endothermic reaction must have a continuous supply of energy to keep it going; electroplating stops when the current is turned off, and the photographic plate is affected only during its exposure to light. An exothermic process, on the other hand, continues to the end without any application of energy. A fire once started burns until it runs out of fuel or until the air gives out. If a piece of zinc is dropped into acid it dissolves until there is none left or until the acid is all used up.

Whether a reaction is exothermic or endothermic there is an energy level below which the reaction will not start. Beginning students of chemistry usually prepare oxygen for study by heating potassium chlorate in a glass test tube by means of a flame.

$$2\,KClO_3 \longrightarrow 2\,KCl + 3\,O_2$$

But if potassium chlorate is merely warmed even as hot as the boiling point of water, it will not decompose regardless of how long it is kept at that temperature. In fact, it does not decompose until it is heated above its melting point, which is $368°\,C$. Room temperature is high enough to start the reaction of zinc and acid.

The temperature required to start some reactions depends on other conditions. For example, hydrogen burns in air if its concentration is between 4 per cent and 74 per cent. Within this range the temperature of ignition varies somewhat, but is somewhere around $580°\,C$. Natural gas, which is mostly methane, CH_4, must be present in air within the range of 5 per cent to 14 per cent to ignite, and the temperature of ignition is lower than that of hydrogen—about 350° C. The fact that the ignition temperature depends on the relative proportions of fuel gas and air in the mixture explains why it is sometimes difficult to start an automobile on a cold day; not enough gasoline evaporates to produce the required amount necessary for easy ignition and if it does not fall within a range of about 10 per cent it will not ignite at all.

LAW OF CONSTANT HEAT SUMMATION

In 1840 Germain Henri Hess (1802–1850), professor of chemistry at the University of St. Petersburg, announced the first law connecting heat and chemical processes. It is Hess's *law of constant heat summation,* and states that the heat of a chemical reaction is the same, regardless of the steps in which the reaction occurs. For example, carbon can be burned directly to carbon dioxide in one step if there is enough oxygen present:

$$C + O_2 \longrightarrow CO_2 + 94.0 \text{ kcal}$$

It can also be burned to carbon monoxide if the amount of oxygen is limited:

$$C + \frac{1}{2}O_{2_2} \longrightarrow CO + 26.4 \text{ kcal}$$

Then another half-mole of oxygen will burn the carbon monoxide to carbon dioxide:

$$CO + \frac{1}{2}O_2 \longrightarrow CO_2 + 67.6 \text{ kcal}$$

The sum of the heats of the last two reactions is equal to that of the first. In other words, when 12 grams of graphite burns to CO_2, 94 kilocalories of heat are produced by whatever stages the changes occur. Physical chemists use this law to calculate the heats of reactions that cannot be measured directly.

There are many more heat effects to occupy the attention

of chemists. Those involving gases lend themselves to many lovely mathematical calculations because they also involve work as well as heat when they change in volume. Any process that involves heat and work comes under the head of thermodynamics, one of the biggest and most important topics in modern physical chemistry.

In 1842 a German doctor, Julius Robert von Mayer (1814–1878), on a voyage to Java had occasion to notice that the blood in the veins of tropical residents was redder than that of northerners. From this observation he concluded that those who live in hot climates require less energy from their food than those from colder climates, that different kinds of energy are interchangeable and that none is lost. Five years later, another German doctor stated the idea in the more precise form in which we know it today. He was Hermann von Helmholtz (1821–1894). His statement is the *law of the conservation of energy* and simply states that energy can neither be created nor destroyed. It is the twin of the law of the conservation of matter and has been as useful as its earlier counterpart. Energy can be changed from one kind to another or to several others, but none of it is ever lost. This makes it possible to determine the efficiency of a machine. Suppose a certain amount of electricity is passed through the filament of a light bulb, and only about 4 per cent is converted into light; the remainder escapes as heat and so we say the bulb is only 4 per cent efficient.

PHYSICAL PROPERTIES OF LIQUIDS

Another topic of physical chemistry is the problem of solutions. There are four laws that apply to the effects on a liquid caused by something dissolved in it. In order to keep the discussion in order I shall number these laws.

1. *Vapor Pressure.* Every liquid has a vapor pressure that

depends only on the temperature. For water this pressure is 4.6 mm of mercury at 0° C, 17.5 mm at 20°, 31.8 mm at 30°, and 760 mm at 100°. The vapor pressure of other liquids are all different, of course; that of chloroform is 61 mm at 0° C, 159.6 mm at 20°, 246 mm at 30°, and 760 mm at 61.2° C. These vapor pressures are the pressures exerted by the molecules as they leave the surface of the liquid. If the liquid were put into a flask and the air pumped out the remaining pressures would be those listed above.

The boiling point of a liquid is the temperature at which the vapor pressure is the same as the external pressure. Since the standard atmospheric pressure is 760 mm, the normal boiling point of a liquid is the temperature at which the vapor pressure is 760 mm. From the vapor pressures just mentioned, the normal boiling points of water and chloroform turn out to be 100° C and 61.2° C, respectively. If water is put into a flask and the air pumped out, it will boil at 30° when the pressure falls to 31.8 mm, and at 0° when the pressure gets down to 4.6 mm.

The vapor pressure of a liquid depends only on the temperature. But what happens when liquids are mixed? In 1884 François Marie Raoult (1830–1901), a professor at the University of Grenoble, discovered the law that tells us the answer. The result depends on the relative number of molecules present. The molecular weight of chloroform is 119 and that of acetone is 58; therefore, there are just as many molecules (6.023×10^{23}) in 58 grams of acetone as there are in 119 grams of chloroform. The vapor pressure of acetone at 30° C is 283 mm and that of chloroform is 246 mm. Suppose we mix 238 g (2 moles) of chloroform with 174 g of acetone (3 moles) at 30°. We have 5 moles in all; the chloroform molecules are ⅖ of the total and the acetone molecules are ⅗ of the total. According to Raoult's law the vapor pressure of the chloroform is $\frac{2}{5}$ of 246 mm or 98 mm, and that of the acetone is $\frac{3}{5}$ of 283 mm, or 170 mm, and the total vapor pressure is the sum of these, or 268 mm. The law takes it for granted that the two liquids do not react with each other. If they do, the problem is complicated by the number of molecules of any new substance formed by the reaction.

The vapor pressure of a liquid is affected in the same way by a solute that has no vapor pressure. Glucose, a common sugar in grapes and other fruits, has the molecular weight 180. If 180 g of glucose are dissolved in 342 g of water (19 moles), then the water molecules are $\frac{19}{20}$ of the total and the vapor pressure of the solution is $\frac{19}{20}$ of that pure water. At 30° that is 0.95×31.8 or 30.2 mm.

2. *Boiling Point.* We have just seen that a substance with no vapor pressure lowers the vapor pressure of the liquid in which it is dissolved. At 100° C the vapor pressure of water would be less than 760 mm if there were a solid dissolved in it. Consequently such a solution must be heated above 100° before it will boil. In general, a nonvolatile substance raises the boiling point of any liquid in which it is dissolved. In the case of water, 1 mole of each solute dissolved in 1000 g of water raises the boiling point 0.51° C. A mole in 1000 g of chloroform raises its boiling point 3.63° C. Each liquid has its own boiling-point elevation constant, for a mole of any nonvolatile solute in 1000 g of the liquid. The 1000 g of liquid is taken arbitrarily as the amount to be used in reporting the value of boiling-point elevation constants.

3. *Freezing Point.* Just as the boiling point of a liquid is raised by the solute in it, the freezing point is lowered. One mole in 1000 g of water lowers the freezing point 1.86° C. Other freezing-point depression constants are: benzene, 5.12° C; acetic acid, 3.9° C; ethylene bromide, 12.5° C; and camphor, 40° C.

The physical chemist uses Raoult's laws, particularly the third one, to determine the molecular weights of solid substances. Constants are on record for a large number of liquids, and so the chemist can generally find one for which the constant is known, and which will also dissolve his unknown. If he can not find the constant for any liquid that dissolves his treasure, he can always determine the constant for some liquid that will. Suppose the unknown dissolves in benzene. He freezes a sample of benzene and records the freezing point. Then he dissolves a weighed amount of the unknown in a weighed amount of his benzene and freezes the solution. The second freezing point will be lower than the first; how much lower, he measures with a delicate thermometer. From this number of degrees, the weight of the sample and the weight of the benzene and the constant, he calculates the molecular weight of his unknown. Let us say he dissolves 5 g of the unknown in 100 g of benzene and the thermometer shows that the solution freezes 2.56° C lower than the benzene alone. Five grams in 100 g is 50 in the standard 1000 g of the solvent, and the depression of a mole in this amount of benzene is 5.12° C; then $\frac{5.12}{2.56} \times 50$, or 100, is the molecular weight of the dissolved substance.

In addition to the determination of molecular weights, the physical chemist uses this law for several practical purposes. For example, ethylene glycol, $C_2H_4(OH)_2$, mixes with water in all proportions and has a low vapor pressure, which makes it useful as an "antifreeze" for automobile radiators and some airplane motors. Its molecular weight is 62 and so 62 g in 1000 g of water will depress the freezing point 1.86° C. If the temperature is likely to go down to 0° F, which is −17.6° C, we must add $\frac{17.6}{1.86} \times 62$, or 589 g, of glycol to each 1000 g of water. Liquids are usually measured by volume, and 1000 g of water is 1000 milliliters, but glycol is heavier than water and the 589 g measures only 530 ml, and so the glycol required to depress the freezing point to the Fahrenheit zero is just a little more than half that of the water in the mixture. The gas station operator has a printed table that tells him how much glycol to use in a radiator of a given capacity to protect it against freezing at any temperature the owner specifies. Some chemist or engineer, of course, has calculated the values given in his table.

4. *Osmotic Pressure.* This is the name of the pressure caused by the tendency of a liquid to diffuse into a solution in which it is used as a solvent. It can be demonstrated by putting a solution of sugar in water in a parchment bag and then immersing the bag in pure water. If the bag is attached to a glass tube the pressure will soon force a column of the solution up the tube. If such an experiment is set up so the pressure can be measured it is found to be enormous. A mole of sugar (342 g) in a liter of water produces a pressure of over 300 pounds to the square inch. As in the case of Raoult's laws the amount of the pressure depends on the relative number of molecules of solvent and solute. Osmotic pressures are difficult to measure for two main reasons: they are very great and perfect membranes are scarce. There are several membranes, like the parchment just mentioned, which serve to show that there is a pressure, but to make a measurement the membrane must be perfect, that is, it must allow the solvent to pass, but none of the solute. The bigger the molecule the less likely it is to pass through a membrane; consequently, osmotic pressure is now used mainly to determine the molecular weights of large molecules—weights of 1000 or more.

ARRHENIUS' IONIZATION THEORY

Although these laws of solution had great practical value, all was not serene with the theorists. Raoult had established his laws from experiments with organic substances in water or organic liquids. Solutions of acids, bases and salts in water do not follow the laws, but they do conduct an electric current, and these facts resulted in the classification of substances into electrolytes and nonelectrolytes according to the conductivity of their aqueous solutions. The non-electrolytes (sugar, alcohol and many other organic substances) follow the laws of solution; the electrolytes (HCl, KOH, NaBr and other acids, bases and salts) do not. The cause of the difference needed explanation and one soon appeared. Svante Arrhenius (1859–1927) presented it as his dissertation for the doctor's degree at the University of Uppsala. The faculty seem to have awarded him the degree in spite of his thesis for they did not think much of it. He then read it before the Academy in Stockholm and they did not like it any better. Arrhenius did not give up. He sent copies of it to several German chemists. The older ones were not impressed, but van't Hoff and Ostwald liked it, and at last he had support. The thesis was first read in 1883, but it was not published until 1887. It is now known as *Arrhenius' ionization theory.*

Water and dry salts are very poor conductors of electricity, but when a salt is dissolved in water the solution conducts very well. Arrhenius explained this by saying that when an acid, base or salt dissolves in water it dissociates into two parts each of which carries an electric charge. Furthermore, the sum of the positive charges on one particle equals the sum of the negative on the other. One fragment is positive and the other negative and he had to assume the total charge is the same; otherwise there would be an electric charge on the solution—but there was not. The fragments were named *ions* and consist of single atoms in some cases and groups of atoms in others. For example, sodium chloride and potassium sulphate dissociate according to the following equations:

$$NaCl \longrightarrow Na^+ + Cl^-$$
$$K_2SO_4 \longrightarrow 2\,K^+ + SO_4^{--}$$

The sodium, potassium and chloride ions are single atoms while the sulphate ion is the familiar radical. Inorganic radicals of long standing all turned out to be ions when in solution. This is reminiscent of Berzelius' idea of positive and negative valences, but goes further and indicates that these valences are actual electric charges. Sugar, alcohol and numerous other organic compounds do not ionize when they are dissolved in water and so their solutions do not conduct a current.

I have emphasized that Raoult's laws depend on the relative number of molecules of solvent and solute. Since sodium chloride ionizes, a mole of it (58.5 g) in solution has double the number of molecules if each ion is considered a molecule; therefore, the freezing-point depression of a mole of salt should be twice as much as that of a mole of sugar. It would thus seem that we should be able to extend these laws to include the electrolytes simply by saying that if a salt ionizes to give two ions then its effect on vapor pressure, boiling point, freezing point and osmotic pressure will be twice the normal; if to three ions, like the potassium sulfate, the effect will be three times the normal; and so on. Experiment shows that the idea has some merit, but the effects are not that simple. A solution of sodium chloride does have almost twice the normal effect on freezing points, but not quite, and, furthermore, the extent of the effect changes with the concentration. Arrhenius explained this situation by saying that salts do not ionize completely except at extreme dilution. Starting with dry salt, the more water we add the more it is ionized until finally it dissociates completely. This notion explains the experimental results.

How do ions carry an electric current? The method is different from the way a wire does it. In a wire the electric charges that constitute a current are passed along from atom to atom like a collection plate along a church pew. In a solution the ions swim along in the water and hand over their charges to the electrode when they get there—the negative ions to the positive electrode and the positive ions to the negative electrode.

ELECTROLYTES

For the next quarter of a century after Arrhenius published his theory, solutions were the main topic of research by physical chemists. Twentieth-century chemists have modified and extended the theory somewhat, but it is still fundamentally correct.

Compounds whose solutions are good conductors are called *strong* electrolytes and the poor conductors are *weak* electrolytes. These are only relative terms like hot and cold; there is no division line between them. Most inorganic acids, bases and salts are strong electrolytes and the organic compounds that dissolve in water are generally nonelectrolytes or at least very weak ones.

The characteristic part of an acid is the hydrogen ion, H^+, that forms in solution. It is this ion that gives acids their sour taste, that changes the color of indicators and accounts for some other effects. Hydrochloric acid, HCl, is one of the strongest electrolytes, and if a mole of it is dissolved in enough water to make a liter of solution it dissociates completely into H^+ and Cl^- and the solution contains a mole of each of these ions. On the other hand, acetic acid, $HC_2H_3O_2$, is very weak and a mole of it in a liter of solution dissociates so little that only about 0.01 mole of H^+ is present.

However, other substances in the solution change the extent of the dissociation of the acid. Since very small concentrations of the hydrogen ion are important in biology and elsewhere, it is often important to know the exact amount of the ion in solution regardless of where it comes from or what other ions are present. There are methods for determining the concentration experimentally, but in many cases the concentration is so low that the number of moles consists mostly of zeros. For example, water itself dissociates slightly, according to the equation

$$H_2O \longrightarrow H^+ + OH^-$$

However, the dissociation is so slight that the H^+ is only 0.0000001 mole per liter. Numbers like this are a nuisance and liable to error because someone did not count the zeros correctly.

p H

In 1909 a Danish chemist, S. P. L. Sørensen (1868–1939), surmounted the difficulty by using the logarithm of the number to express the hydrogen ion concentration. It will be recalled that the common logarithm of a number is the power of 10 that equals the number. For example, 100 is 10^2 and so 2 is the logarithm of 100, 3 is likewise the logarithm of 1000, etc. The number 0.0000001 is $\frac{1}{10,000,000}$, which is $\frac{1}{10^7}$, or 10^{-7}, and its logarithm is -7; the logarithm of 0.0000002 is -6.7. Concentrations expressed in this manner are designated as pH and the minus sign is omitted because they are all fractions and therefore all the logarithms are negative. The pH of water at 25°C is 7.0, and since water is equally acidic and basic it is called neutral; that is, it dissociates equally into the H^+ characteristic of an acid and the OH^- characteristic of a base, as we indicated in the equation above. Water dissociates more as the temperature rises; the pH of neutrality at the body temperature of 37°C is 6.8. One point that must not be overlooked is that, since all these logarithms are negative, the bigger the number the less hydrogen ion concentration there is present—a pH of 6.7 is more acid than a pH of 7, and 4.5 is more acid still.

Some industrial operations and most biological processes are sensitive to slight changes in pH. The pH of water is the neutral point so that any pH less than 7 is acid and any pH greater than 7 is alkaline at 25°C. It is changes of this order that the gardener talks about when he speaks of an acid or an alkaline soil. Some plants grow best in one or the other, and hydrangeas and some other flowers are pink or blue according to the pH of the soil. Each of the various enzymes that carry on the digestion of food as it passes along the alimentary canal functions best at a specific acidity. Saliva, which starts the digestion of starch in the mouth, operates best at pH 6. Pepsin, which starts the digestion of protein in the stomach, prefers the pH 2. Both of these are in the acid range, but the enzyme in the intestine that carries on the digestion of starch is more effective on the alkaline side at pH 8. Human blood has the pH 7.4. A change to 7.3 produces acidosis; and to 7.5, alkalosis. If the pH of the blood dropped to 7 the patient would probably not recover.

The malting of barley in the manufacture of beer and whiskey requires a pH of 4.4 in order to change the starch to sugar in the least time. The growing of bacteria, yeasts and molds for laboratory study or for industrial processes needs close attention to the pH requirement of the organism concerned.

These few applications of pH are examples of the practical value of the ionization theory. There are many more in chemistry, biology and industry.

SPEED OF REACTION

Some chemical reactions occur instantly; at least, they occur in a time too short to measure. An explosion of dynamite or the neutralization of an acid with a base are examples of instantaneous reactions. Other reactions maintain a fair speed, such as the burning of wood or the solution of zinc in an acid. Some others are extremely slow, like the aging of wine or the ripening of fruit. In his efforts to control chemical action the physical chemist has measured the speed of many reactions under different conditions in order to speed them up or slow them down as practical conditions demand. In a manufacturing process he usually tries to increase the speed, but in the spoilage of food he hopes to slow it down.

Temperature is the most important factor in controlling the speed of a reaction. A chemical reaction about doubles its speed for each increase of ten degrees Celsius. The chemist constantly uses heat to accelerate reactions in both the laboratory and the factory and almost as often he uses ice or refrigeration to retard reactions. In addition to the familiar cold-storage warehouses and the kitchen refrigerator, there are manufacturing processes that must be carried out at a low temperature. And in the laboratory of the organic chemist, ice is often used to keep a reaction from running away, for the heat generated by some reactions may raise the temperature enough to boil away a reagent, decompose the substance the chemist is trying to make or cause an explosion.

CATALYSTS

Aside from temperature control a chemist may use a catalyst to change the speed of a reaction—usually to accelerate it, although there are some negative catalysts that retard reactions. Catalysts have been known for a long time; in fact, Berzelius invented the name. They are substances that change the rate of a reaction of other substances, but are not consumed in the process. If oxygen and hydrogen are put into the same vessel they seem to remain a simple mixture forever—such a mixture has been kept for many years. However, if a piece of platinum or palladium is dropped into the mixture, the gases combine rapidly to form water. Boil starch in water for hours and it is still starch, but add a little H^+ and the starch at once begins to react with the water to form glucose. Hundreds of examples are known in which a catalyst increases the speed of a reaction or gets one under way that does not get anywhere without it. They are essential in the manufacture of ammonia, sulfuric acid, gasoline and in the conversion of liquid oils, such as cottonseed, into solid fats for use as shortening or for the manufacture of margarine.

The industrial chemist is interested in what will catalyze what reaction, but the physical chemist wants to know how or why it does so. Just how a catalyst manages to accelerate a reaction without doing anything else to it is still something of a mystery. There are theories to explain how they work, but catalytic action cannot be predicted; catalysts are discovered by trial-and-error experiments and how and why they are effective may be different for each kind of substance. It is unlikely that a metal such as platinum or nickel works in the same manner as an enzyme such as pepsin. Many catalysts are specific; that is, they catalyze one reaction only. This is particularly true of the enzymes. The enzymes that digest protein have no effect on starch and vice versa. A strong acid, however, will accelerate the reaction of water with starch, protein, fats and several other substances. The metals show some versatility; for example, platinum encourages the reactions of SO_2 and O_2, the combination of CO and H_2, and the reaction of NH_3 and O_2 to make HNO_3. The last word has not been said on the how and the why of catalysis.

REVERSIBLE REACTIONS

A reaction that is common in student laboratories is the precipitation of calcium carbonate by adding a solution of sodium carbonate to one of calcium chloride:

$$Na_2CO_3 + CaCl_2 \longrightarrow CaCO_3 + 2\,NaCl$$

In 1798 Berthollet went with Napoleon to Egypt where he noticed deposits of sodium carbonate in salt lakes and decided that the deposits were produced by the reaction of the very concentrated salt solution with limestone or other calcium carbonate on the shore or bottom of the lake. The reaction would be the exact reverse of the one in the above equation. This is the first suggestion that a chemical reaction might be reversible. Berthollet's observation seems to have made little impression on chemists, for reversible reactions were neglected until 1863 when Pierre Eugène Marcelin Berthelot (1827–1907), a professor of chemistry at the Collège de France, showed that an equilibrium is reached when an ester is formed by a reaction between an alcohol and an acid.

The idea of an equilibrium in a chemical reaction is very simple. In order to react, two substances must come together, and the greater the concentration, that is, the more molecules there are in a given space, the more rapid the reaction will proceed. Suppose A and B react to give C and D and vice versa:

$$A+B \rightleftarrows C+D$$

If A and B are mixed they react and as they are used up the reaction slows down. Also, C and D begin to react slowly as soon as some of their molecules are formed and the speed of their reaction increases as their concentration becomes greater. Therefore, the reaction of A and B slows down as that of C and D increases, and so there comes a time when no more C and D seem to be produced because they are used up as rapidly as they are formed. Just where the point of equilibrium lies depends on the relative speeds of the two reactions. If A and B react much faster than C and D, the latter will predominate at equilibrium.

The reaction of alcohol with acetic acid is a reversible reaction that was among those studied by Berthelot:

$$C_2H_5OH + HC_2H_3O_2 \rightleftarrows C_2H_5C_2H_3O_2 + H_2O$$

Alcohol	Acetic acid	Ethyl acetate	Water
46	60	88	18

If 46 g (1 mole) of alcohol and 60 g (1 mole) of acetic acid are mixed they react very slowly, but a few drops of sulfuric acid speeds up the reaction. However, when 60 g of ethyl acetate and 12 g of water have formed, the reaction does not produce any more of either. If it went to completion there would be 88 g of ethyl acetate and 18 g of water. Furthermore, if we start with 88 g of ethyl acetate and 18 g of water and the same catalyst, we end up with the same equilibrium, namely, 60 g of the ester, 12 g of water, 15 g of alcohol and 20 g of acetic acid. These are the amounts of the various substances at equilibrium.

Another reversible reaction is the synthesis or decomposition of ammonia. Henri Louis Le Châtelier (1850–1936), with his many activities and honors in the course of his long life, first synthesized ammonia from its elements in 1901. At the time he was professor of chemistry at the Collège de France where he was doing research in thermodynamics and equilibrium. He discovered a law that says: *If a stress is put on a system in equilibrium, the equilibrium is displaced in the direction that tends to relieve the stress.* Applied to a chemical equilibrium the stress can be a pressure, temperature or concentration. The combination of nitrogen and hydrogen is exothermic and reversible as is indicated by the equation,

$$N_2 + 3\,H_2 \rightleftarrows 2\,NH_3 + 24 \text{ kcal}$$

All these substances are gases and so 1 volume, say 1 liter, of nitrogen combines with 3 volumes of hydrogen to make 2 volumes of ammonia. If molar volumes of 22.4 liters are used, the process gives off 24 kilocalories of heat and, since the reaction is reversible, 24 kilocalories will decompose 2 moles of ammonia. If we simply mix 1 volume of nitrogen with 3 volumes of hydrogen nothing happens; the mixture must be heated. Heat has two effects: the higher the temperature the faster the substances react; but this reaction is exothermic, and according to Le Châtelier's law, at a high temperature the ammonia will decompose to absorb the heat and relieve the stress. If the temperature is raised to 200° C and the pressure kept at atmospheric, 15.3 per cent of the gases will combine; at 500° C only 0.13 per cent combine. Now, how about the pressure?

If we apply the principle of Le Châtelier again, a high pressure should give more ammonia, because the nitrogen and hydrogen occupy 4 volumes and the ammonia only 2. That is, the ammonia occupies only half the volume of its constituent gases and since pressure decreases the volume of gases it should encourage the formation of whatever takes the least room. Experiment proves the argument correct, for at 1 atmosphere and 200° C only 15.3 per cent of the nitrogen and hydrogen combine, but at 200 atmospheres the yield is 86 per cent. Likewise, at 500° C combination increases from 0.13 per cent at 1 atmosphere to 17.6 per cent at 500 atmospheres. Other temperatures and pressures, of course, give other yields of ammonia. When several of them have been determined the chemist can select the best combination if he wishes to manufacture ammonia by the process. The more pressure the better, if the apparatus does not blow up, and the lower the temperature the better the yield of ammonia, but it takes longer to get it. It is obvious that he must compromise in a practical process.

The first commercial process was developed by Fritz Haber (1868–1934) in Germany, and production started in 1914. He used a pressure of 200 atmospheres, a temperature of 550° C and a specially treated iron as catalyst. The third stress, concentration, was relieved by dissolving the ammonia in water to remove it from the equilibrium. Since the First World War other chemists have devised ammonia manufacturing practices with other conditions, especially much higher pressures and other catalysts.

In general, physical chemistry is concerned with the behavior of matter rather than its composition. One of the big topics is the effect of light, or photochemistry. Two well-known applications of photochemistry are photography and photosynthesis of organic compounds by plants from carbon dioxide and water. Electromotive force, such as we mentioned in the discussion of the voltaic pile (p. 140), the quantum theory and a law called the phase rule are all among the main topics for consideration by the physical chemist, and an enterprising one can find still others.

Volumes could be written—in fact, they have been—on the activities of physical chemists. I have mentioned the highlights of the subject from the beginning of the nineteenth century in order to indicate the nature of the subject and its importance. A more profound treatment of the subject would require mathematics beyond arithmetic, algebra and peace of mind.

CHAPTER ELEVEN

The Atom Discloses Its Secrets

By THE END of the nineteenth century, physics and chemistry had reached a stage of completion. The physicists had thoroughly explored mechanics, heat, sound, light, magnetism and electricity—all the common forms of energy. The chemists felt that they understood the composition of matter down to the atom. If anyone wanted to know the composition of marble, coal, sand or salt all he had to do was visit the nearest library. If someone found a new material a chemist could soon tell its composition. Even organic substances had disclosed their secrets—sugar, alcohol, citric acid and hundreds of other natural substances were no longer mysteries. Some of the more complex organic substances were still of unknown structure, but every chemist felt that all that was needed was time—how to proceed was no longer a question. The atomic weights were all known, but, of course, all chemists realized that more precise work might yield another decimal place to any of them.

The manufacture of dyes and other chemicals was well under way before 1900, and the chemist began to make his presence felt in many nonchemical industries. He was now taking a hand in such matters as making steel, producing glass for special purposes, and in the preparation and processing of food. The physical chemists were busy trying to perfect their laws and theories of long standing. These were the comfortable years in the physical sciences. In less than a century and a quarter, chemistry had arrived.

In 1815 the French physicist, Jean Baptiste Biot (1774–1862) discovered that turpentine, lemon oil, solutions of sugar in water, camphor in alcohol and several other substances are optically active. These, and other substances that were discovered later, bothered the chemists for a generation because their chemical composition and reactions indicated the same structural formula for the two compounds that were the same in all but a single respect: one of them rotated polarized light to the right and the other to the left. If the structures were the same, why the difference in this one property?

OPTICAL ISOMERS

In the year 1874 two young chemists explained the enigma of the optical isomers in papers published independently. They were Jacobus Henricus van't Hoff (1852–1911), who was a twenty-two-year-old chemist in Holland, and Joseph Achille Le Bel (1847–1930) in Paris. Their hypothesis said that the four valence bonds of the carbon atoms have definite positions in space as though the carbon atom were the center of a tetrahedron and its valences at the four corners—a tetrahedron is a triangular-base pyramid with four faces and four corners. The two young chemists pointed out that any substance that showed the property of optical activity had four different groups attached to one of the carbon atoms. For example, the lactic acid of sour milk has the formula

$$CH_3 - \overset{\overset{\displaystyle H}{|}}{\underset{\underset{\displaystyle OH}{|}}{C}} - COOH$$

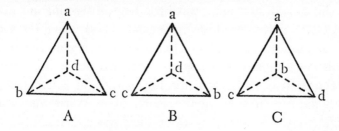

Figure B. In these tetrahedra the arrangement of the groups a, b, c, and d on B is different from that on A, but if C is turned so that a and b correspond with a and b on A then c and d will also have the same position. Therefore C is the same as A and any other arrangement will correspond to either A or B.

If the four groups CH_3, H, OH and COOH are placed at the corners of a tetrahedron there are two different arrangements possible and no more. This means that there can be two kinds of lactic acid with the structural formula shown above. If two of the groups are alike, say another H instead of the OH, then only one arrangement is possible. In this case the compound would be CH_3CH_2COOH, which is propionic acid, and it is not optically active. In order to distinguish between isomers on paper, the formulas are written as mirror images of each other, like the pictures of your two hands.

$$\begin{matrix} & H & \\ & | & \\ CH_3 - & C & - COOH \\ & | & \\ & OH & \end{matrix} \qquad \begin{matrix} & H & \\ & | & \\ HOOC - & C & - CH_3 \\ & | & \\ & OH & \end{matrix}$$

The hypothesis of van't Hoff and Le Bel explained all the problems of the organic chemist that involved optical activity and enabled him to predict which substances would be optically active and which would not, but it applied only to the carbon atoms and was little help in forming an opinion of the nature of atoms in general. These young theorists did not think that carbon atoms were triangular-face pyramids, but simply that the groups attached to the atom were in the relative positions of the four corners of a tetrahedron with the carbon atom in the center of it. What this atom might look like was no part of their speculations.

ELECTRONS

The Irish physicist, George Johnstone Stoney (1826–1911), professor of natural philosophy at Queen's University in Galway, attended a meeting of the British Association for the Advancement of Science in 1874. In the course of the meeting he suggested that electricity is composed of "atoms" of unit charge and proposed the name *electron* for the unit. The paper was not published until 1881 and, in the meantime, Helmholtz, of conservation of energy fame, made the same suggestion in a lecture he gave in London in 1877. Nobody seems to have paid much attention to Stoney's suggestion and in 1891 he brought the matter up again and further suggested that each atom of an element carries a definite number of these charges. Faraday's laws, which were published some forty years before Stoney first made his suggestion, clearly indicated that the atom carried a definite amount of electricity, but this fact did not seem to impress the chemists.

Early studies of the conduction of electricity showed that metals conduct a current very well and are not changed in the process. Solutions of acids, bases and salts also conduct readily but are decomposed by the current, while most liquids, gases and nonmetallic solids are very poor conductors —some of them do not conduct at all. An attempt to pass an electric current through a gas causes a violent spark like a small bolt of lightning. As early as 1709 an English scientist by the name of Francis Hauksbee described the pale glow of light in a glass tube after part of the air had been pumped out and the tube electrified, but the next hundred and fifty years added nothing to his discovery.

In 1821 Davy discovered, or rediscovered, that air is a better conductor of electricity if the pressure is reduced. Several other investigators undertook the study of this phenomenon and one of them, Heinrich Geissler (1814–1879), who was a mechanic and glass blower in Bonn, made a lot of tubes of various shapes and sizes for the purpose. The tubes were made of glass and had metal wires sealed through the glass at the ends. Each of them also had a side tube, for attachment to an air pump, which was sealed after the air had been exhausted. To study the effect of the pressure of a gas on its conductivity required a new tube for each pressure, or the seal had to be broken and resealed after the pressure was changed. At the beginning the research took more glass blowing than anything else. The principal discovery of these early investigators was that the current caused the gas to glow and the color of the light was different for each gas. Nearly a century later these researches led to the tubular colored lights now in use for signs and advertising.

In 1859 Professor Julius Plücker (1801–1868) of the University of Bonn discovered a new phenomenon in his study of gaseous conductivity. He used a straight glass tube with an electrode sealed into each end and found that as the gas pressure decreased the gas gave less light and that when the pressure fell below 0.1 mm of mercury the glass at the end of the tube opposite the negative electrode (cathode) began to glow with a pale green light (fluorescence) which increased in intensity as the pressure of the gas decreased.

This new color effect varies in hue with different kinds of glass but not with the gas in the tube. Plücker also discovered that the light spot could be moved about over the tube with a magnet. Ten years later Johann Wilhelm Hittorf (1824–1914), a former student of Plücker, discovered that a sheet of metal put into the tube cast its shadow in the fluorescent area.

Sir William Crookes (1832–1919), an English chemist with a large fortune and a private laboratory in London, investigated the conductivity of gases at great length. He devised a more suitable tube for the purpose, which still bears the name of *Crookes tube*. He was able to show that the rays, whatever they might be, came from the cathode, and so they soon became known as *cathode rays*. By 1879 Crookes reached the conclusion that these rays are charged particles striking the end of the tube like so many shots from a gun. Jean Baptiste Perrin (1870–1942), professor of physics at the University of Paris, found a negative charge on a piece of aluminum that had been in the path of the cathode rays, and then he supported the particle hypothesis of Crookes, but the German physicists thought that the rays were waves in the ether like rays of light, and so the controversy was on.

At this point a detour is indicated because of future developments in the career of the atom. In 1870 the Duke of Devonshire, who was chancellor at Trinity College, Cambridge, decided the college needed a building to house its physics department and offered to pay the cost of it. The offer was accepted and the building was completed in 1874. It was named the Cavendish Laboratory for Sir Henry Cavendish, the eccentric eighteenth-century chemist of hydrogen fame—the Duke was a member of the ancient Cavendish family. The first director of the laboratory was James Clerk Maxwell who established the wave theory of light.

J. J. THOMSON

Joseph John Thomson (1856–1940) was born in suburban Manchester in 1856 and at the age of fourteen entered Owens College in his home city. He finished there in 1876 and went to Trinity. There he remained until his death sixty-four years later. He studied mathemathics and physics and took his degree in 1880. Maxwell died in 1879 and Lord Rayleigh succeeded him as head of the Cavendish Laboratory. Thomson's research was then being directed by Rayleigh and he did so well that when Rayleigh resigned in 1884 Thomson was made head of the laboratory. His investigations were on the most popular topic of the day, the conductivity of electricity by gases. By 1897 Thomson had definitely established the fact that cathode rays are streams of particles of negative electricity, which he called *corpuscles*, but they soon became known as electrons, the name Stoney had proposed.

ROENTGEN AND X RAYS

In 1895 Wilhelm Konrad Roentgen (1845–1923), professor of physics at the University of Würzburg, discovered a strange property of cathode rays that nobody else had noticed. He was investigating a report that cathode rays would pass through a thin metallic window in the glass tube and cause fluorescence outside the tube. He covered a tube with heavy cardboard to see if the rays would go through that. He then darkened the room and turned on the current. To his amazement a fluorescent material over a yard away began to glow. He knew that cathode rays would not travel that far through air and decided that there must be some other kind of ray coming from his tube. He soon learned that his rays would pass through more than two yards of air and still cause the fluorescence. Since the rays passed through cardboard, how about other materials? Roentgen was soon able to announce that they passed through a book of one thousand pages, two packs of cards, and one sheet of tin foil, although several sheets stopped them. They also passed through a half-inch sheet of aluminum and thick sheets of hard rubber and glass; however, it did not take much flint glass, which contains lead, to stop them. He also found that water and several other liquids were transparent to his rays and he even tried his hand. Here he found a startling thing. The rays passed through the flesh much better than through the bones and so the bones cast a deep shadow on the fainter shadow of his hand. This discovery excited the physicians, for they at once saw its possibilities for the diagnosis of broken bones, foreign bodies and possibly other human ills. How right they were is now known to everybody.

Roentgen had first observed the fluorescence of barium platinocyanide, but he soon found that glass, calcite, rock salt and some other minerals glowed with the same pale light when exposed to the rays. Fluorescence was not the only property of Roentgen's rays, for they also affected a photographic plate, and that gave him a means of making a record of their effects. Like a good algebra student he named his rays simply X rays, for exactly what they were was unknown. They are still called X rays, although some call them Roentgen rays after the discoverer.

Roentgen determined most of the properties of the X rays, but he was a physicist and the fact that they cause serious burns escaped him. Physicists, of course, were off in full cry as soon as Roentgen announced his discovery; consequently, the source and nature of the rays were soon known. They turned out to be light of very short wave length, 0.01 to 0.3

nm (nm=nanometer or 10^{-9} m). Their penetration proved to depend on the density of the material; the denser the material the more quickly the rays were stopped. The density of aluminum is 2.4 g per cubic centimeter and that of lead is 10.3, and so a thin sheet of lead will stop the rays as effectively as several sheets of aluminum of the same thickness. Metals are denser than wood or paper and the bones are denser than the flesh, and that is why X rays will show a nail in a board or a broken bone in the body.

The discovery of X rays was to have far-reaching effects on chemistry, physics and medicine. Roentgen made his original discovery on November 8, 1895, and presented the first paper on the subject to the Physico-Medical Society of Würzburg on December 28. The paper was printed at once and reprints were sent to several prominent physicists and doctors. Almost at once the whole scientific world was agog with the new discovery, as were the newspapers and even the comic magazines. The transparency of bodies that had always been considered opaque caught the imagination.

BECQUEREL AND THE CURIES

The next episode in solving the mystery of the atom occurred at the University of Paris. Professor Antoine Henri Becquerel (1852–1908) had inherited a large number of minerals from his father, who was a chemist. Becquerel senior had studied the fluorescence of minerals and Henri was continuing these studies. When he read Roentgen's paper he concluded that since the X rays came from the fluorescent spot on the Crookes tube, they were caused by the fluorescence, and decided to test the idea. He had a piece of fluorescent potassium uranium sulfate among his minerals and so he wrapped a photographic plate well with black paper, placed the sulfate on it and exposed it to the sunlight to produce the fluorescence. Sure enough, when he developed the plate there was the image of the mineral. Here fate entered. He conducted his experiment in February 1896 and the sun shone only now and then. When he got a second plate ready for further experiment, the sun did not shine for several days and he put the plate with the mineral on it in his desk to wait for more sunshine. The sun was slow to appear and Becquerel decided to develop the plate anyway. (He didn't say why.) There was the image of the mineral, although both the plate and the mineral had been in the dark drawer of the desk all that time. Further experiments convinced Becquerel that the mineral itself, with no help from the sun, was emitting rays that behaved like the Roentgen rays, but Becquerel was busy with other problems and did not pursue the matter much further.

A Polish immigrant, Marie Sklodowska (1867–1934) had come to Paris in 1891 to study at the university. In 1894 she married Pierre Curie (1859–1906), but continued her work for the doctor's degree. By 1896 she was ready for a thesis topic and selected the strange radiations that Becquerel had discovered. Unfortunately, she had no place to work, but Pierre was chief of the laboratory at the School of Physics and Chemistry of the city of Paris. Marie had no official connection with the school, but they gave her an unheated shed in which she could work. Pierre was doing research in electricity, but soon turned his attention to radioactivity, as Marie now called the subject. Pierre's salary was so small that in 1900 he took a position as tutor in the physics department in the Sorbonne, which housed that department of the university. That same year Marie was hired to teach physics and chemistry in a girls' school in suburban Sèvres—a position she held for ten years. She received the doctor's degree from the University of Paris on June 25, 1903.

Aside from living expenses, the cost of the research was considerable, but in 1903 the Curies and Becquerel shared the Noble Prize in physics. In 1904 Pierre was appointed professor of physics at the University of Paris, but there was no laboratory attached to the job. Finally, he succeeded in having one built and equipped. By November 1904 his laboratory was completed and Marie was appointed chief of laboratory at a salary of 2400 francs (about $450) a year. It was her first official position that had any connection with her research. The family was now much better off in both laboratory facilities and finances. But their triumph did not last long, for Pierre was killed by a dray in a street accident early in 1906. On May 1 of that year Marie succeeded him as professor of physics at the university.

Although the Curies investigated the physical activity of the new form of energy, they are best known for their work in chemistry. (In 1911 Madame Curie received the Nobel Prize in chemistry—the first person to receive that honor twice.) Their research traced the radioactivity to the element uranium, and the activity was the same regardless of what elements the uranium might be combined with: the oxide was just as active as the sulfate. Madame Curie tested all the minerals in the available collections in Paris and found that only uranium and thorium compounds were radioactive. Some of the Curie experiments indicated there were other radioactive elements in some of their uranium samples, and they decided to hunt for them.

In Bohemia, which was then part of Austria, there were uranium mines from which the metal was obtained for use in making glass. The Curies wished to examine the natural ores to try to locate the unknown radioactive elements they thought might be mixed with the uranium. The Austrian government gave them a ton of the material after the uranium had been removed. The Curies undertook to find what metals remained in these tailings in their pathetic shed. Only a chemist can appreciate the size of the task. The rock had to be ground fine and soaked in acid to extract the metals and all the metals had to be recovered and identified. They had to supply the acid they used and also the vessels to hold the solutions, from their personal funds. In July 1898, after months of tedious and costly work, they found a new radio-active element and named it *polonium* after Marie's native country. But there seemed to be still another element present. By December 1898 they announced its discovery and, be-cause its salt glowed in the dark, they named it *radium*— it radiated light. Their sample was not pure radium, but after working four years they got 0.1 gram of pure radium chloride, $RaCl_2$, from a ton of the ore residues.

ERNEST RUTHERFORD

Pierre died in 1906 and Marie in 1934, but other chemists and physicists entered the field and within a few years radio-activity was no longer a mystery. Among the more active of these investigators was Ernest Rutherford (1871–1937), later Sir Ernest. Rutherford was a young man from New Zealand who came to Cambridge in 1895 to study physics with J. J. Thomson. He was Thomson's first student. He had al-ready graduated from the University of New Zealand, pub-lished several papers in physics and taught school before he came to Cambridge. He spent three years in the Cavendish Laboratory and there he began the study of radioactivity, the hottest topic of the day. In 1898, upon Thomson's recom-mendation, Rutherford went to McGill University in Mon-treal as professor of physics and remained there for nine years. In 1907 he returned to England as professor of physics at the University of Manchester, which was the former Owens College from which Thomson had graduated. In 1918 Thomson was made master of Trinity College and, at his invitation, Rutherford came back the next year to head the Cavendish Laboratory.

Becquerel had noticed that there was more than one kind of ray coming from the radioactive elements, and Rutherford, among others, undertook to unravel them. There turned out to be three kinds of rays, and they were named by the first three letters of the Greek alphabet: alpha, α; beta, β; and gamma, γ. Scientists frequently resort to Greek letters because there are so many letters in use for abbreviations and mathematical units that the Roman alphabet is about exhausted—everybody remembers pi, π, from his elementary arithmetic.

Each of the three rays from uranium has different properties. The gamma rays are the most penetrating and were found to be the same as the very short X rays, that is, light of extremely short wave length.

BETA RAYS

To return to the electron and Professor Thomson: it will be recalled that for over twenty years Stoney had insisted that there were particles of electricity and had even named them electrons although he had never found them experimentally. Several properties of these electrons were soon discovered, among them the fact that the electron has a charge of 1.6×10^{-19} coulomb and that it takes 1840 of them to weigh as much as a hydrogen atom. This is a very tiny bit of electricity. A *coulomb* is the amount of electricity produced by a current of 1 ampere flowing for 1 second. A 60-watt light bulb carries a current of about half an ampere and so in 1 second the light uses half a coulomb or 6.25×10^{18} electrons. A current of electricity consists of these electrons passing from atom to atom along a wire. Some atoms handle the electrons better than others and so some metals are better conductors than others—copper is better than iron, for example. Some atoms do a very poor job because of either their nature, or the way in which they are tied up with other atoms, or both. Such materials are called nonconductors, or insulators, and among them are glass, porcelain and rubber. Air is also a nonconductor; an electric spark is a multitude of electrons jumping through the air from one object to another. Benjamin Franklin in his famous kite experiment showed that lightning is simply a big electric spark. He was lucky that his kite string was not a very good conductor, so that a rather small number of electrons came down from the clouds to jump off on his knuckle.

It was not long after Thomson discovered electrons until the beta rays from radioactive metals were found to consist of a stream of electrons ejected by the metal.

The alpha rays were a more difficult problem. They were particles much heavier than electrons and they seemed to turn into helium. Then somebody found that uranium had lead mixed with it. By 1902 Professor Rutherford, at McGill University, offered an explanation of all these facts, which he and others had discovered. His explanation is known as the *theory of radioactive decay*. The historical steps in the development of the theory are somewhat intricate and cannot be given in further detail here, but the conclusions are of the utmost importance to a chemist, as we shall see from the following pages.

ATOMIC STRUCTURE

About 1900 J. J. Thomson proposed a structure for the atom. His atom consisted of a sphere of positive electricity with electrons embedded in it like raisins in a bun, but this atom explained very few of the many properties that atoms were known to have. Consequently, it made very little impression on the thought of chemists, but it is important as the first attempt to picture the nature of atoms in general.

In 1911 Rutherford proposed a better atomic structure, and with some improvements it still survives. It was designed to account for all the properties of substances that chemists and physicists had discovered over more than a century. The amended Rutherford atom is made up of three kinds of particles: the electron, the proton and the neutron. The proton was discovered by Rutherford in 1920 and is a particle that weighs as much as 1840 electrons and has a positive charge equal in size to the negative charge of the electron. The neutron was discovered in 1932 by a former student of Rutherford, James Chadwick (b. 1891), who later became professor of physics at the University of Liverpool. The neutron weighs about the same as the proton, but it has no electric charge. From these two discoveries and the experimental results of many physicists and chemists over a period of more than a generation, it is now possible to draw a fair picture of an atom.

The simplest atom is that of hydrogen, the lightest element. It consists of 1 proton as a nucleus and 1 electron rotating about this nucleus somewhat as a planet rotates around the sun. With a structure of this kind we must be specific when we speak of its size. To refer to the solar system, we might mention the diameter of the sun or of the orbit of the outermost planet. In the case of the atom the nucleus is very small, around 10^{-12} centimeter in diameter; the diameter of the space enclosed by the orbits of the electrons is 10^{-8} centimeter or about ten thousand times that of the nucleus. If the mathematics does not convey a clear picture, let us say that if the nucleus were the size of a dime the electron would be 250 feet away from it. The atom is far smaller than anything that can be seen with the best biological microscope.

The list of elements on page 157 has a column of atomic numbers. These numbers were established experimentally in 1913 by Henry Gwyn-Jeffreys Moseley (1887–1915) in Rutherford's laboratory at Manchester. They are whole numbers that run continuously from 1 to 92. They came from Moseley's work on X-ray spectra. The lines in an X-ray spectrum are not visible. They are too short for the range of the eye, but they can be recorded on a photographic plate. X rays are produced by the electrons from a cathode in an evacuated glass or quartz tube striking a metal anode at the opposite end of the tube instead of the glass as in the early tubes used by Roentgen. By using different metals for the anode Moseley discovered that the wave length of the lines are different for each metal and that the square root of these wave lengths gave an orderly series of whole numbers that increased with the atomic weight of the metal. From these data and the order of the elements in the periodic table, Moseley determined the atomic numbers of several of the elements. Then he joined the British Army and was killed at Gallipoli in 1915, but other physicists determined the atomic numbers of more of the elements.

Although the atomic numbers were determined from spectra they were at once connected with the structure of the atom. The atomic number is the number of protons in the nucleus of the atom. In the case of hydrogen the atomic number is 1 and so the nucleus of the lightest atom consists of just 1 proton. The electron rotating around the nucleus weighs so little that its weight is usually neglected and the weight of the atom is simply the weight of the proton. The atomic number 2 is that of the helium atom, which has the atomic weight 4. This means that the atom has 2 protons and 2 neutrons to complete the weight of the nucleus. The helium atom also has 2 electrons outside the nucleus, for the atom is neutral electrically and therefore must have 2 negative electrons to balance the 2 positive protons. Our picture of the helium atom, then, is 2 protons and 2 neutrons packed tightly together in a tiny nucleus with 2 electrons moving around in orbits some distance outside the nucleus. The helium nucleus without these electrons is the alpha particle from radioactive elements, a discovery that was made in Rutherford's laboratory. The alpha particle readily picks up electrons from its environment and becomes the helium that occurs with natural deposits of uranium.

We now have the pattern of the structure of atoms in general, and it is interesting to note that the components all descended from the Cavendish Laboratory. Thomson contributed the electron. His student, Rutherford, gave us the proton. And Rutherford's students (Thomson's grandstudents, so to speak) Moseley and Chadwick furnished the atomic number and the neutron, respectively. The atomic number of any atom is the number of protons and, of course, the number of outside electrons also. The atomic weight is the combined number of protons and neutrons, for they have practically the same weight. The diagrams on page 336 show these features in the structure of a few atoms.

There is a mystery here that has not yet been solved. Like charges of electricity repel each other. Why don't all the atoms heavier than hydrogen fly to pieces because of the repulsion of all these positive charges? The neutrons evidently exert some influence because every atom with 2 or more protons also has 2 or more neutrons—usually more neutrons than protons. A neutron appears to be a proton with an electron tightly bound to it. Perhaps these electrons manage

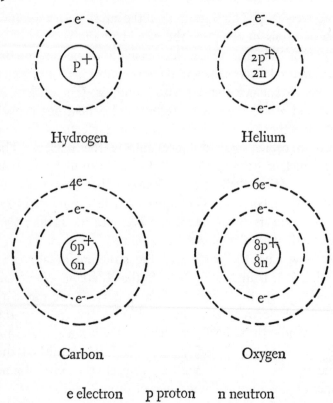

Hydrogen   Helium

Carbon   Oxygen

e electron   p proton   n neutron

to hold things together somehow; and then again perhaps they do not.

An atom of uranium has the atomic number 92 and the weight 238—it has in its nucleus 92 protons and 146 neutrons surrounded at a distance by a cloud of 92 electrons in several layers.

Inspection of the table of elements shows that the atomic numbers are continuous and whole numbers, but most of the atomic weights end in fractions and have gaps from one to the next. For example, the first five elements have the numbers 1, 2, 3, 4 and 5, but the atomic weights are 1.008, 4.003,

6.940, 9.02 and 10.82. This irregularity raises two questions: Why are the weights not whole numbers since there are no fractional protons or neutrons, and why are some weights missing?

ISOTOPES

The fractional atomic weights were explained by Frederick Soddy (1877–1956), who graduated from Oxford with a degree in chemistry in 1900 and then began a wandering career. He first went to McGill University in Montreal as a demonstrator in chemistry. There he met Rutherford and began research in radioactivity. He returned to England in 1903 and did research for a year at the University of London. Then he was appointed lecturer in physical chemistry at the University of Glasgow. He discovered that there are more radioactive elements than there are places for them in the periodic table, whereupon he invented the word *isotope* (Greek, "the same place") for those elements that have to share the same place in the periodic table. In 1914 Soddy transferred to the University of Aberdeen and in 1919 to Oxford. Conditions at Oxford did not suit him and, although he won the Nobel Prize for chemistry in 1921, he deserted the field, turned to economics and retired in 1936. Although his career in chemistry was short, his discovery of isotopes was a major contribution to the subject.

Soddy's work on isotopes was limited mainly to those of the radioactive elements. The more common elements were investigated by Francis William Aston (1877–1945), who was born at Birmingham and studied physics and chemistry at Mason College (later, the University of Birmingham) in that city. He was short of money and worked three years for a brewery. Then he received a scholarship and returned to the university to study physics. He published a few papers on the subject and, in 1907, inherited some money and took a trip around the world. In 1909 he went to Cambridge as an assistant to J. J. Thomson.

Aston had a mechanical turn of mind and great manual dexterity. He invented an instrument, which he called a *mass spectrograph* although it had nothing to do with light. It is an instrument that uses the effects of an electric field and a magnetic field to separate isotopes. He first used it to separate the isotopes of neon gas, which has the atomic weight 20.2. He found that the gas contains 90 per cent of an isotope of weight 20 and 10 per cent of another of weight 22. They have the same atomic number and the same chemical properties; therefore, they are both neon.

Aston was made a fellow of Trinity College in 1920 and was awarded the Nobel Prize for chemistry in 1922. He remained at Trinity for the rest of his life and determined the isotopic composition of nearly all the elements. In the course of his work he built three mass spectrographs, each somewhat bigger than its predecessor, but all of them were rather small laboratory instruments. The instrument has now been adapted for the determination of the molecular weights of organic compounds and recently the American government built one 40 feet long and 6 feet high; it weighs 25 tons and cost $381,000. As this is being written the government is looking for a place to build a bigger one, but it is doubtful whether these monstrosities will accomplish as much as Aston did with his more primitive instruments.

The natural element carbon has two isotopes. It is 98.892 per cent C^{12} and 1.108 per cent C^{13}. The isotope C^{12} is now the standard for atomic weights. In natural chlorine, with the atomic weight 35.457, there are two isotopes. It is about 75 per cent isotope 35 and 25 per cent 37. In order to avoid confusion the weights of the single isotopes are now called *mass numbers* to distinguish them from the weights of the natural mixtures which are still called atomic weights. The chemical properties of the atoms are caused by the electrons and not by the nucleus. Each isotope of chlorine has the atomic number 17. Therefore, each has 17 electrons arranged around the nucleus in the same manner and so one isotope reacts chemically just like the other. Each chlorine nucleus contains 17 protons, but the lighter one has only 18 neutrons while the heavier has 20. They are identical twins, but one of them has taken on a little extra weight.

The electrons of the atoms are in groups at different distances from the nucleus. The first two are at about the same distance and compose what has variously been called the first *shell*, the first *energy level* and the first *energy state*. The next electrons up to eight are farther out and form the second shell. The chemical properties depend mainly on the electrons in the outermost shell. It is these electrons that determine the similarities and differences that led Mendeleev to the construction of the periodic table. Sodium and potassium each have 1 electron in the outer shell, which accounts for the valence of 1 in these elements. Their atomic numbers are 11 and 19. This means that sodium has its valence electron in the third shell and potassium in the fourth. Consequently, the potassium electron is farther from the nucleus and so not attracted so strongly, which accounts for the fact that potassium is much more active chemically than sodium is. The arrangement of the electrons in the heavier elements is somewhat complicated and so for the present we shall confine our attention to the nucleus.

Even little hydrogen has three isotopes. The two principal ones are H^1 and H^2. The nucleus of the first one has just 1 proton, the second has 1 proton and 1 neutron; each has 1 electron. The hydrogen from water is about 99.98 per cent

H^1. When the second isotope of hydrogen was first discovered it was called *heavy hydrogen* and its oxide was heavy water. But later the heavy isotope was isolated in considerable quantity and studied separately. Consequently, it is the one isotope of a common element that has been given a name of its own. It is now called *deuterium* and the symbol is D. Heavy water is now deuterium oxide, D_2O. The isotopes of a natural element are very difficult to separate from each other, and, fortunately, there has not been much reason to separate them, except, of course, to satisfy the curiosity of chemists and physicists. However, deuterium and one of the isotopes of uranium have been found especially useful and have been separated from their counterparts with considerable success. The deuterium oxide is separated from water, and the difficulty is indicated by the cost of separation, which is now twenty dollars a pound.

I mentioned earlier that uranium forms helium and lead. This lead has the atomic weight 206, and was discovered before isotopes in general were known. Consequently, there was a heated controversy as to whether or not it was lead, because the atomic weight of lead was well known to be 207.2. We now know that natural lead consists of three isotopes, 24 per cent 206, 23 per cent 207 and 52 per cent 208.

The nuclear chemists are usually concerned with one atomic species only and not the natural mixture and they have devised a system to indicate the several isotopes. Thus $_1H^2$ means the hydrogen atom with mass number 2 and atomic number 1. The symbol $_8O^{17}$ indicates the oxygen atom that has the atomic number 8 and the mass number 17. The first number may seem superfluous because all the oxygen atoms have the atomic number 8. It is sometimes omitted, but it indicates the number of protons in the nucleus and it is sometimes convenient to have the number handy—chemists do not often remember all the atomic numbers.

In answer to the question above as to why the gaps in the atomic weights, there really are not many. When all the mass numbers of all the isotopes are considered, there are very few missing between 1 and 238, which is the complete span of the natural elements. However, some of the isotopes exist in very small amounts. In most cases the natural element consists mainly of one or two isotopes, sometimes three, and then perhaps others in very small amounts; but a few have several in good quantity. Osmium has ten isotopes of which six are present to the extent of more than 1.5 per cent of the total.

The discovery of isotopes raised a serious question in the minds of chemists. The chemist uses the atomic weights as a basis of many of his calculations. Suppose he were to get a sample of chlorine of weight 35 instead of the usual 35.457. His calculations would be wrong unless he first determined the atomic weight of the chlorine on hand, and an atomic weight determination is a major operation. The problem met with the obvious solution. Get samples of the element from hither and yon and see if the atomic weights differ. Get salt from a Louisiana mine, the salt wells of Michigan, the Great Salt Lake, the various oceans and anywhere else that comes to mind and determine the atomic weights of the chlorine or the isotopic composition. It took a lot of work, of course.

Water was widely collected. At least one physicist persuaded a sea captain to bring him a sample from the middle of the Atlantic Ocean. Reports soon began to appear that nature seems to have done a good mixing job because no variation was found, and once more all was serene. The lead found in uranium is an exception to the above statement; it has the weight 206 whereas all the other lead weighs 207.2. Later search turned up some other minor exceptions. Boron

from different sources has been found to have the weights
10.82 and 10.84, a variation of 0.2 per cent, which is too
small to be of consequence in most chemical work.

Some combinations of protons and neutrons are more
stable than others; at least, they occur in greater abundance.
In natural chlorine the 35 isotope with its 18 neutrons is
three times as abundant as the 37 isotope with 20 neutrons.
Likewise, of the different elements some are more abundant
than others as the table on page 180 shows. Chemists have
also estimated the relative abundance of the elements in the
entire universe and, although the nature of the problem casts
some doubt on the accuracy of the figures, they are probably
approximately correct. The results cannot be expressed as
percentage and so they are given as the number of atoms
relative to 10,000 atoms of silicon. The first twelve are:

Hydrogen	4×10^8	Nitrogen	66,000	Iron	6,000
Helium	3.1×10^7	Carbon	35,000	Sulfur	3,750
Oxygen	215,000	Silicon	10,000	Argon	1,500
Neon	86,000	Magnesium	9,100	Aluminum	950

It is estimated that hydrogen makes up about 93 per cent of
the atoms and 76 per cent of the weight of the universe.
Helium is next with 7 per cent of the atoms and 23 per cent
of the weight. All the first twelve elements are light; only iron
has an atomic weight above 40. The mass of the atomic
species is obviously one of the main factors in its stability,
but not the only one. Oxygen, for example, is heavier than
carbon, and iron has over twice the weight of aluminum, and
yet the heavier element is the more abundant in both cases.

One question that has been troublesome is that there are
no natural elements heavier than uranium with its 92 protons
and 146 neutrons. There may have been some at one time,
but they were unstable and have decomposed. Given an un-

limited number of building blocks there is a limit to how many one can pile up without having the whole pile come tumbling down. In the case of the atomic blocks, 83 protons and 126 neutrons are the most that have been found in any stable atom, that of bismuth.

DECOMPOSITION OF URANIUM

This idea brings us back to what is happening to uranium. It is unstable and the nuclei of its atoms are slowly falling apart. The 238 isotope constitutes 99.3 per cent of the natural element, the rest, 0.7 per cent, is uranium 235. The major isotope gives off alpha particles continuously. The alpha particle consists of 2 protons and 2 neutrons, which make a mass of 4; consequently, when an atom of U^{238} loses an alpha particle it leaves an atom of mass number 234, but since the alpha particle contains 2 protons, the atomic number is reduced from 92 to 90 and so the new element is thorium 234. The rate at which the alpha particles are emitted becomes slower as more of the atoms decompose. This change in rate makes it impossible to calculate how long it will take a piece of uranium to decompose completely. The usual practice is to determine the time necessary for half a sample to decompose, the *half-life*. The half-life of uranium 238 is 4.5×10^9, or 4,500,000,000 years.

The thorium atom 234 is also unstable and decomposes, forming various elements along the way, until it reaches lead 206, which is stable. The elements differ enormously in their stability. In fact, they vary so much that the half-life is reported in years, days, hours, minutes and seconds.

The elements formed by the decomposition of uranium 238 are thorium, protactinium, uranium 234, thorium 230, radium, radon, polonium 218, lead 214, bismuth 214, polonium 214, lead 210, bismuth 210, polonium 210 and lead 206. These steps in the decay of uranium and how each is brought about are shown in the following scheme:

$$_{92}U^{238} - He^{++} \xrightarrow{4.5 \times 10^9 \, y} {}_{90}Th^{234} - e^- \xrightarrow{24.1 \, d} {}_{91}Pa^{234}$$

$$- e^- \xrightarrow{1.14 \, m} {}_{92}U^{234} - He^{++} \xrightarrow{2.35 \times 10^5 \, y} {}_{90}Th^{230} - He^{++}$$

$$\xrightarrow{8 \times 10^4 \, y} {}_{88}Ra^{226} - He^{++} \xrightarrow{1.62 \times 10^3 \, y} {}_{86}Rn^{222} - He^{++} \xrightarrow{3.82 \, d}$$

$$_{84}Po^{218} - He^{++} \xrightarrow{3 \, m} {}_{82}Pb^{214} - e^- \xrightarrow{26.8 \, m} {}_{83}Bi^{214} - e^-$$

$$\xrightarrow{19.7 \, m} {}_{84}Po^{214} - He^{++} \xrightarrow{1.5 \times 10^{-4} \, s} {}_{82}Pb^{210} - e^- \xrightarrow{22 \, y}$$

$$_{83}Bi^{210} - e^- \xrightarrow{5 \, d} {}_{84}Po^{210} - He^{++} \xrightarrow{140 \, d} {}_{82}Pb^{206}$$

Thorium 232 and uranium 235 decay in a similar manner; thorium reaches stability with lead 208 and the uranium 235 with lead 207.

The emission of alpha particles by radioactive elements accounts for the alpha radiations discovered by Rutherford, but what about the beta radiations? These are streams of electrons that come from the nucleus. They are formed by the decomposition of neutrons into protons and electrons, for when they are emitted the atom does not change its mass number, but does contain one more proton and therefore has an atomic number one greater than that of the original atom. This charge is shown by the equation

$$n^0 - e^- = p^+$$

The neutron is electrically neutral and if it loses a negative electron, the weight does not change appreciably, but it acquires a positive charge. This change from neutron to proton occurs with enormous energy and always produces gamma rays, which are light of the wave length of X rays, as Becquerel suspected.

For twenty years after Becquerel discovered natural radioactivity, the decomposition of uranium and thorium, and the elements formed in the process, occupied the time of the nuclear physicists, or nuclear chemists—take your choice, or better still avoid the issue and call them nuclear scientists. Some people began to worry over the demise of the atom, which was supposed to be indivisible. No chemist ever lost any sleep over the matter because the atom is still the unit of all his reactions. A brick is still a brick and very useful even if some of them do crumble in course of time. A chemist is often slow in his work, but if he has half of his material left after 4.5 billion years, he is satisfied—after all he is not that slow. These radioactive elements are mostly metals and the final products of their decay are electrons, helium and lead. The intermediate products of decay between uranium and lead are all mixed together and must be separated for study. They are different elements and have different properties, which makes the separation much easier than the separation of isotopes of the same element. Not too easy, however—it took the Curies two years to separate radium from uranium and the other metals present. Of course, they did not know the properties of radium. Separation is a much shorter process now, but radium has continued to be scarce and expensive. In 1921, when Madame Curie visited this country, American women gave her a gram of radium, which cost $100,000. Later discovery of radium deposits in the Belgian Congo cut the price about in half and today its use in therapy has been to a considerable degree replaced by the cheaper X rays and radioactive cobalt.

NUCLEAR BOMBARDMENT

By the time the nuclear scientists got natural radioactivity in hand, some of them began to speculate on the possibility of decomposing the stable elements. How to go about it was the problem the alchemists never solved. Professor Rutherford thought of a possible method and put it into effect in 1919. He thought that if the nucleus of an atom could be bombarded with a high-speed missile of some kind, it might be possible to knock some protons or neutrons out of it and thus get an element of smaller mass number. The first problem was to find a missile. The nucleus of an atom is so small that it is not easy to hit it with anything. However, Rutherford selected the alpha particle from a radioactive element for his missile and what happened was not the result expected. The effect was more like rolling a marble into a group of closely packed marbles; some of the marbles fly off in various directions, but the one that caused the disturbance simply joins the group. Just exactly what happens depends on how many marbles are in the group, how they are arranged, how strong the impact and so on.

The first experiment in Rutherford's laboratory was the bombardment of nitrogen atoms by alpha particles with the result indicated in the following equation:

$$_7N^{14} + {}_2He^4 \longrightarrow {}_8O^{17} + {}_1H^1$$

When the helium nucleus, or alpha particle, struck the nitrogen nucleus it knocked out a proton and joined the others. That made a net increase of 2 neutrons and 1 proton which raises the mass number by 3 and the atomic number by 1. This is an atom of oxygen 17 and the freed proton soon picks up an electron from its surroundings and becomes an atom of free hydrogen. This equation must balance just like a chemical equation; the total mass on the left is 14 plus 4 and on the right is 17 plus 1. Some other elements were found to behave like nitrogen under alpha particle bombardment to form an atom of greater mass and a proton.

When beryllium was bombarded by alpha particles the result was unlike that of nitrogen:

$$_4Be^9 + _2He^4 \longrightarrow _6C^{12} + _0n^1$$

The mass increased by 3 as in the case of nitrogen but a neutron was emitted instead of a proton and so carbon was the only new atom.

Rutherford's experiments were repeated and extended by other physicists as the years went on and it soon became certain that the transmutation of several elements had been accomplished. The yield was small: enough oxygen and carbon had been produced to be identified with a spectroscope, but not enough to weigh or even see. The number of collisions was very small so that very few new atoms were produced. The process has been compared to shooting cherries off a tree with a rifle.

The two main difficulties encountered in the bombardment of atoms were the cloud of electrons that surrounds an atomic nucleus and the repulsion of positive missiles by the heavy positive charge on the nucleus. The attraction of the negative electrons slowed down the alpha particle and the nucleus repelled it. In the larger atoms these combined forces often stopped the missile completely before it reached the nucleus. The proton was a better missile than the alpha particle because its positive charge is only half as great. Then, in 1932, Professor Harold Clayton Urey (b. 1893) of Columbia University discovered deuterium, or heavy hydrogen, which earned him the Nobel Prize in chemistry in 1934. The deuterium nucleus, or *deuteron*, made a better missile than the proton because it is twice as heavy and has the same charge.

The year 1932 was an eventful one in the affairs of the atom, for also in that year James Chadwick, who was then in the Cavendish Laboratory, discovered the neutron, a discovery that brought him the Nobel Prize in physics in 1935. As a missile the neutron has an advantage over all three of the missiles just mentioned, for it is electrically neutral and is therefore not retarded by either the negative electrons or the positive nucleus. The problem now became where to get the neutrons. In the reaction of the alpha particles on beryllium a stream of neutrons is emitted at high speed. Radon is a radioactive element formed in the decay of uranium and a good source of alpha particles. This element and beryllium constituted the source of neutrons for many experiments. Then the physicists came up with their machines to increase the speed of particles; the best known of these machines was the cyclotron, which was invented by Professor E. O. Lawrence (1901–1958) of the University of California at Berkeley. The cyclotron increases the speed of all the positive particles—the proton, the deuteron and the alpha particle. The rays from radioactive substances ionize gases and so the proton and the deuteron can be obtained by exposing hydrogen or deuterium to these rays:

$$H_2 \longrightarrow 2\,H^+$$
$$D_2 \longrightarrow 2\,D^+$$

These ions H^+ and D^+ are the proton and the deuteron.

An illustration of the effects of the bombardment with these missiles is the reaction between the lithium atom and the proton. The proton is not ejected in the radioactive decay of any element and so it must be obtained from hydrogen and speeded up by the cyclotron or a similar machine. Its effect on an atom of lithium is shown by the equation,

$$_3\text{Li}^7 + _1\text{H}^1 \longrightarrow _2\text{He}^4 + _2\text{He}^4$$

The bombardment of lithium with deuterons, as one might expect, gives a somewhat different result; helium is formed but a neutron is ejected also:

$$_3\text{Li}^7 + _1\text{D}^2 \longrightarrow _2\text{He}^4 + _2\text{He}^4 + _0\text{n}^1$$

When neutrons are emitted they come off with great speed and enormous energy and so they can be used for bombardment.

$$_7\text{N}^{14} + _0\text{n}^1 \longrightarrow _5\text{B}^{11} + _2\text{He}^4$$

All the nuclear reactions that I have indicated are examples of the transmutation of the elements, and although they are extremely important as a triumph of theory, they may have no practical value because of the great expense and the small yield.

It was not long before a physicist without a cyclotron or an equivalent machine was like a man without an automobile, and as experiments became more widespread some new features naturally began to appear. The first novelty was the discovery that in some cases the new element was radioactive. The discovery of artificial radioactivity was made in 1933 by Madame Curie's daughter, Irène Curie (1897–1956), and her husband Frédéric Joliot (1900–1958). The Joliot-Curies produced nitrogen 13 from boron, phosphorus 30 from aluminum, and silicon 27 from magnesium by bombardment with alpha particles, and all three of these products were radioactive. For this discovery the Joliot-Curies received the Nobel Prize in chemistry for 1935.

Ordinary phosphorus is converted into radioactive phosphorus by bombardment with deuterons:

$$_{15}P^{31}+_1D^2 \longrightarrow _{15}P^{32}+_1H^1$$

The phosphorus 32 is radioactive and decays to sulfur with the loss of electrons:

$$_{15}P^{32} \longrightarrow _{16}S^{32}+e^-$$

The half-life of the phosphorus 32 is 14.3 days.

Large quantities of radioactive carbon are now prepared by the bombardment of nitrogen with neutrons:

$$_7N^{14}+_0n^1 \longrightarrow _6C^{14}+_1H^1$$

The carbon 14 decays with the emission of electrons:

$$_6C^{14} \longrightarrow _7N^{14}+e^-$$

The half-life of the carbon 14 is 5100 years. It is now widely used by chemists and biologists as a tracer element in the study of organic reactions and biological processes. It is easily detected because of its radioactivity and so it can be traced through the various changes its compounds undergo without destroying them.

THE "ARTIFICIAL" ELEMENTS

The various types of nuclear reactions have produced several new elements. There were four elements lighter than uranium that had never been found in nature. Some of them had been reported at one time or another, but the discovery had always proved to be a false alarm. These four elements have the atomic numbers 43, 61, 85 and 87. Although they have never been found in nature they have now been made artificially. Furthermore, ten elements with numbers above 92 have also been produced. All these man-made elements are radioactive and many of them have very short half-lives, which accounts for their absence in nature.

Element 43 was the first to be produced artificially. In 1937 Dr. Emilio Segré, now professor of physics at the University of California, made it in his laboratory in Palermo, Italy, by bombarding molybdenum with deuterons. He named the element *technetium*, Tc, which was derived from a Greek word that means "artificial." There are isotopes of mass numbers 95, 97 and 99. The half-life of technetium 99 is 212,000 years. By the first of the year 1961 technetium 99 could be bought for one hundred dollars a gram. Enough had already been produced to enable chemists to determine its physical and chemical properties. There are now other sources of technetium, from which physicists estimate that they can produce 1200 grams annually. It is a metal similar to manganese and was predicted from a blank in the periodic table.

Element 87 was the second of the four missing elements to appear. In 1939 Mlle Marguerite Perey, of the Curie Institute in Paris, discovered it as a product of radioactive decay of actinium. She named it *francium*, Fr, after her native France. It has since been produced by the bombardment of thorium with high-speed protons. There are several isotopes of francium; they vary in mass from 211 to 226. The most stable one is francium 223 with a half-life of 21 minutes. It is an alkali metal related to sodium and potassium.

Dr. Segré and others made element 85 in the Lawrence Radiation Laboratory of the University of California at Berkeley in 1940. They bombarded bismuth with alpha particles accelerated by a cyclotron:

$$_{83}Bi^{209} + _{2}He^{4} \longrightarrow _{85}At^{211} + 2 \, _{0}n^{1}$$

They named the element *astatine*, At, from a Greek word meaning "unstable." The 211 isotope is the most common of the more than twenty that have been identified—its half-life is 7.5 hours. Astatine belongs to the halogen family along with fluorine, chlorine, bromine and iodine.

Element 61 was a postwar product. It was made in an atomic pile (p. 359) at the Oak Ridge National Laboratory by three chemists, Lawrence E. Glendenin, J. A. Marinsky and Charles D. Coryell. They made it by bombarding neodymium 147 with neutrons, but it has since been found in quantity in the fission products of other elements. They named it *promethium*, Pm. It is one of the rare earths. The half-life of the most stable isotope, promethium 145, is 18 years. Although it can now be supplied at the rate of at least a pound annually it will probably not be found very useful because of its short life.

THE TRANSURANIUM ELEMENTS

More exciting than the discovery of the four elements that had been predicted by the periodic table was the production of elements with atomic numbers greater than 92 and mass numbers above 238, for no element had ever been found heavier than uranium and none predicted. The elements with atomic numbers above 92 are called *transuranium* elements, and most of them have been discovered at the University of California where Lawrence built the first cyclotron in 1929. Dr. Edwin M. McMillan and P. H. Abelson made the first transuranium element in 1940 and named it *neptunium*, Np. They bombarded uranium with deuterons:

$$_{92}U^{238} + {}_1D^2 \longrightarrow {}_{92}U^{239} + {}_1H^1$$

$$_{92}U^{239} \longrightarrow {}_{93}Np^{239} + e^-$$

The bombardment produces an isotope of uranium of mass number 239, which loses an electron from its nucleus and thus converts a neutron into a proton. This raises the atomic number to 93. Other isotopes of neptunium have been made; neptunium 237 is the most stable one, with a half-life of over 2,000,000 years. By the spring of 1962 the Atomic Energy Commission had about 200 grams of neptunium on hand and was willing to sell it for five hundred dollars a gram.

Soon after the discovery of neptunium Dr. McMillan left the Radiation Laboratory to do war work on radar and Dr. Glenn T. Seaborg continued the work on the new elements with the aid of several associates. The discoveries of these two men won them the Nobel Prize in chemistry in 1951.

Plutonium, Pu, was discovered by the Seaborg group shortly after neptunium. The first isotope found had the mass number 238, but the more important plutonium 239 has been made in considerable quantity because of its importance as a source of atomic energy. It is now made in what is known as an atomic pile and results from the following series of reactions:

$$_{92}U^{238} + {_0}n^1 \longrightarrow {_{92}}U^{239}$$
$$_{92}U^{239} \longrightarrow {_{93}}Np^{239} + e^-$$
$$_{93}Np^{239} \longrightarrow {_{94}}Pu^{239} + e^-$$

Plutonium 239 has a half-life of 24,360 years.

The next two transuranium elements emerged from the Radiation Laboratory in 1944 and were named *americium,* Am, and *curium,* Cm. Americium is made by bombardment of plutonium with neutrons.

$$_{94}Pu^{239} + 2\,{_0}n^1 \longrightarrow {_{94}}Pu^{241}$$
$$_{94}Pu^{241} \longrightarrow {_{95}}Am^{241} + e^-$$

Plutonium 241 has a half-life of 13.2 years, which seems a long time to wait for the americium, but it should be recalled that the reaction goes much faster at the beginning, so that one-tenth of the plutonium 241 decomposes in about a week. Americium decays to neptunium by the loss of an alpha particle; its half-life is 458 years. In 1962, 200 grams of americium were available at $1500 a gram.

Element 96 was named curium in honor of Pierre and Marie Curie. It was the first element to be named for a person. Laws and theories are usually named for the discoverer for very simple reasons. The law of constant composition and that of multiple proportions both have names descriptive of their meaning, but it would be difficult to find a good descriptive name for Boyle's law and for many others; consequently, the scientist who discovers a law or advances a theory usually publishes it without any name. But other scientists must have a name in order to talk or write about it and the name of the author is the simplest one to use; consequently, we have Avogadro's hypothesis, Charles's law and the Einstein theory. An element is an object and needs a name, so the discoverer gives it one, but every chemist to date has been too modest to name an element for himself. He invents a name and then some scientific society adopts it officially. The International Union of Pure and Applied Chemistry usually has the last word on chemical names.

Curium was first made by bombardment of plutonium with alpha particles, but it is now generally made from americium and neutrons:

$$_{95}\text{Am}^{241} + _0\text{n}^1 \longrightarrow _{95}\text{Am}^{242} \longrightarrow _{96}\text{Cm}^{242} + e^-$$

Curium 242 has a half-life of 163 days; consequently, no great amount of it has ever been made. However, isotopes of both americium and curium of longer half-life have been made recently.

In 1950 Seaborg and his group announced the discovery of elements 97 and 98 and named them *berkelium*, Bk, and *californium*, Cf. Berkelium was named for Berkeley, the city in which the Radiation Laboratory is located. It was made by bombarding americium with alpha particles, and californium was made from curium in the same way. Eight isotopes of berkelium from mass number 243 to 250 have been made; the longest half-life is that of berkelium 247, which is 7000 years. Of the eleven isotopes of californium from 244 to 254, the most stable is californium 251 with a half-life of 600 years. Neither element has been made in any great quantity.

Four other transuranium elements have joined the list. These are *einsteinium*, Es, of atomic number 99; *fermium*, Fm, number 100; *mendelevium*, Md, which is 101; and *nobelium*, No, number 102. These elements have been obtained only in traces.

Some of us wonder how much further the synthesis of new elements will go. At first glance it looks as if there were no end to the possibilities. However, the process is something like filling a basket with oranges. After the basket is level full, the tendency of any additional ones to fall off increases with each one added and there comes a time when not a single orange will stay on the pile. Most of the natural elements have at least one stable isotope, up to and including bismuth, which has 83 protons and 126 neutrons. Above atomic number 83 no element has a stable isotope. As the atomic and mass numbers increase from 84 up, the stability becomes less. At present it seems that einsteinium is the last of the elements of sufficient stability to be made in visible amounts. The chemical identification of mendelevium was made with one hundred atoms. Nobelium has not been so plentiful. Of course, new techniques may be developed; even now, heavier particles, such as $_6C^{12}$, are being tried as missiles, but the limiting factor will likely be the lifetime of the element. Nobelium has a half-life of 3 seconds. It looks as though the mine of new elements is about worked out.

FISSION

The radioactive decay that has been discussed in these pages has all been of an orderly kind. The atoms have changed by the loss of an alpha particle, a neutron, a proton or an electron at a fixed rate, which differs from a fraction of a second to millions of years. But there is another type of decomposition in which the atom suddenly splits into large chunks. This type of decomposition is called *fission*. The first hint of atomic fission was reported January 6, 1939, by the German physicists Otto Hahn and F. S. Strassmann, who found that there were lanthanum (57), cerium (58) and krypton (36) in uranium 92 that had been bombarded with neutrons. As the atomic numbers of these elements indicate, the uranium had split into several large pieces. This was such a striking idea that physicists in Denmark, the United States and elsewhere began to investigate the matter and by December 1939, when the first review of the subject was written, about a hundred papers had been published on the subject of atomic fission.

The work on fission led to the atomic bomb and, because of its military importance, much of the research on the subject was done in secret and not published. However, a number of papers were published before the research on the bomb began and a considerable amount of information has been released since the reaction has been adapted to the production of electricity.

Only a few elements undergo fission; plutonium 239, uranium 235 and uranium 232 are the most important. Uranium as it occurs in nature consists of 99.3 per cent uranium 238 and 0.7 per cent uranium 235. When a neutron strikes

U^{235} the atom splits into two large but unequal fragments; the larger fragment has a mass number between 127 and 154 and the smaller falls between 83 and 115. As an illustration we have:

$$_{92}U^{235}+_{0}n^{1}\longrightarrow{}_{92}U^{236}\longrightarrow{}_{38}Sr^{90}+_{54}Xe^{143}+3\,_{0}n^{1}$$

The strontium and xenon formed are both radioactive—the stable isotopes of strontium are 86, 87 and 88 and xenon has several from 128 to 136. Both decay by electron emission, which changes the atomic number but not the mass. Strontium 90 decays to $_{40}Zr^{90}$ with a half-life of 25 years and the xenon to $_{60}Nd^{143}$ with a half-life of half a second. Both zirconium 90 and neodymium 143 are stable isotopes. It is the radioactivity of the fission fragments that has given scientists some concern about the health hazards of atomic energy and the aftermath of atomic bombs. Strontium 90 in particular, with its half-life of 25 years, has been worrisome.

Atomic fission releases an enormous amount of energy and the question naturally arises, where does all the energy come from? The answer is simple, but somewhat astounding. It comes from the conversion of mass into energy. Throughout the earlier pages of this book I have frequently referred to the law of the conservation of mass and the law of the conservation of energy as fundamental to all chemistry and, of course, they still are. But in the field of neuclonics they must be considered as one law—the conservation of mass and energy. As early as 1905 Einstein had suggested that mass and energy are equivalent and proposed the formula, $E=mc^2$, in which E is kinetic energy, m is mass and c is the velocity of light. If we recall that the velocity of light is 186,000 miles, or 3×10^{10} centimeters, a second, it is apparent that a very small amount of mass is equivalent to a lot of energy. Suppose a kilogram (2.2 lb.) of matter were converted to energy. A kilogram is

1000 grams and the velocity of light is 3×10^{10} centimeters a second. If these figures are substituted for m and c in the Einstein formula and the calculation made, we have 9×10^{23} ergs, which is equivalent to 2.5 billion kilowatt-hours. The killowatt-hour is the unit you buy from the electric company. The 2.5 billion would supply the entire United States for over a month. If a kilogram of coal is burned it produces heat equivalent to 8.5 kilowatt-hours.

Einstein predicted that his formula would be verified by research in the field of radioactivity and by 1932 his prediction came true. Consider the reaction

$$_3Li^7 + {_1}H^1 \longrightarrow 2\ _2He^4$$

This equation balances with 4 protons and a total mass of 8 on each side. However, it balances because all the figures used are taken as the nearest whole number. The proton, $_1H^1$, actually has the mass 1.00758 and the lithium used has the mass 7.0165. The total mass then to the left of the arrow is 8.02408. Helium has the mass number 4.0028 and so the two helium atoms weigh 8.0056. Therefore, 8.02408 minus 8.0056 or 0.01848 units of mass have disappeared. The energy of the reaction measured experimentally and the result calculated from the formula agree very closely.

Thus, in atomic fission the mass of the fragments is less than that of the original element and the difference has been converted into energy. Atomic energy was first used for a bomb. Any explosion is a sudden release of energy, and so in an atomic bomb the fission must occur quickly. But physicists soon found methods for controlling the rate of fission, that is, slowing it down so it could be used to produce energy in the form of heat.

Conventional electric power plants have been of three types. In one type water from a high level has been led through a turbine connected to an electric generator. This simple arrangement transfers the energy of sunlight indirectly into electricity, for the sun raised the water to the higher level. Another type of plant burns coal, oil or gas to boil water to run a steam engine or turbine which is connected to the generator. The third type burns oil or gas in an internal combustion engine as a source of power. The atomic energy plant is like the second of these except that the heat to boil the water comes from fission and not from conventional fuel. The power plant project involved two major problems. The first was how to control the fission so as to get the energy as it was wanted and not in one big burst. The other was how to convert the atomic energy into electricity once the first problem was solved. The steam plant seemed to be the best solution to the second problem and was adopted.

PRODUCTION OF ATOMIC ENERGY

The first pile for the controlled production of atomic energy was built at the University of Chicago, and was first operated December 2, 1942. The production of atomic energy in large amounts depends on what a scientist calls a *chain reaction*, which operates like a chain letter. You receive one letter and send out two or some other number greater than one. The equation on page 357 shows that 1 neutron causes the fission of 1 atom of uranium and that 3 neutrons are emitted. These neutrons in turn strike other atoms of uranium, causing them to split and eject three more neutrons each. If each fission caused three others, the process would increase very rapidly, but some neutrons miss the nucleus of other atoms and some escape from the surface of the uranium into the environment. The principle used to control the energy rate is to control the speed of the neutrons and the number of effective collisions. A neutron is emitted by a fission at the enormous speed of 1.4×10^9 centimeters—about 900 miles—a second. Some of the effects of the neutrons depend on their speed. The high-speed neutrons are called *fast* neutrons and for some purposes are slowed down to 2.2×10^5 centimeters a second, or just over a mile a second. These slower travelers are called *thermal* neutrons. Both fast and thermal neutrons cause fission of uranium 235, but uranium 238, which constitutes over 99 per cent of the natural element, is split by neither of them, although thermal neutrons convert it into plutonium 239.

Several different problems are apparent. How to slow down the neutrons was the first one. The collision of alpha particles from uranium with certain atoms would supply the initial neutrons, but these are fast neutrons. Next, how large should the piece of uranium be? And what shape? If a thin sheet were used it has so much surface that most of the neutrons would escape. A sphere has the least surface of any solid form and so a somewhat flattened sphere was chosen for the first reactor. Unlike most experiments this one had to be approached cautiously lest it get out of control and eliminate everybody and everything for miles around. Many experiments were made just to get data and many calculations were made before the pile was built.

Neutrons are slowed down by what are now called *moderators*. A moderator consists of some material made up of atoms of low weight. If a tennis ball collides with some large, solid object like a post, it bounds off with little loss of speed, but if it hit the twig of a tree it would slow down by sharing its energy with the twig. This is the principle of neutron slowdown. The six lightest elements are hydrogen and its isotope deuterium, helium, lithium, beryllium, boron and carbon. Lithium and boron absorb neutrons and remove them from circulation. Helium is a gas and is also scarce and expensive.

Nuclear reactions are all independent of chemical combination and so water and deuterium oxide (heavy water) can be used as moderators. Beryllium is scarce but it has been used. Carbon in the form of graphite would seem to be the best selection and it has been widely used. Hydrocarbons are also effective as they are easily purified and contain only carbon and hydrogen.

The first atomic pile built contained 12,400 pounds of uranium metal lumps separated by layers of graphite bricks as moderators. It also contained some additional fuel in the form of lumps of uranium oxide, U_3O_8. This natural uranium fuel and graphite moderators were built up into a pile, which seemed to be as good a name for the contraption as anything.

After the composition of the pile was all settled the next question was how to turn it on and off. This was solved by the use of control rods. Several holes were left in the pile when it was built and rods of cadmium or one of its alloys were made to fit into these holes because cadmium catches and holds neutrons. When the rods were inserted into the pile they took enough neutrons out of circulation to lower the number to less than one a fission and so the chain was broken. Then as the rods were slowly withdrawn the reaction resumed and gained speed as there was less cadmium to absorb the neutrons. One of the rods was arranged to work automatically to control the speed, the others were operated manually in case of an emergency and in closing down the operation. Despite all the controls and precautions, the first pile was operated at half a watt of energy. The extent of this caution is apparent when we recall that a twenty-five-watt bulb is a small one. A few days later, however, the operation was increased to 200 watts. A news note of December 1958 announced plans for the construction of a plant in England for the production of 650,000 kilowatts an hour.

The first chain reaction for the fission of uranium was gotten under control in December 1942, but the problem of transforming the energy into electricity was not yet solved. Since then, atomic piles, or *reactors* as they are now generally called, of several types have been designed. These reactors usually contain uranium as a fuel, graphite as a moderator and cadmium control rods and they are designed so that a liquid can be circulated through the pile. This liquid helps out as a moderator, but its main duty is to carry away the heat. The pipes that carry the liquid go to coils inside a boiler to produce steam for the operation of a turbine, which is more efficient than a steam engine. Since the liquid keeps down the temperature of the pile it is called a *coolant*.

The selection of a liquid for use as a coolant is not easy. Several have been proposed, among them water, diphenyl, $C_{12}H_{10}$, molten sodium and potassium, a molten bismuth-lead alloy and the gases hydrogen, helium and carbon dioxide. The choice depends on several nuclear and chemical considerations. Chemical problems involve corrosion of the pipes. Hot water, either light or heavy, is very corrosive. Diphenyl slowly decomposes under the effect of the heat. If a pipe containing liquid sodium or potassium should spring a leak inside the boiler the reaction of the metal with the hot water would result in a major explosion. The escape of these hot metals into the air would also be a serious hazard.

One of the nuclear problems is the change of the atoms into radioactive isotopes by the radiation. Finally, deuterium oxide and helium are very expensive. However, a news note of December 1958 announced that there were forty companies in the United States that were willing to build a power plant with a helium coolant. The ideal coolant, if it exists, has not yet been found.

The fuel for a reactor may be any fissionable element. At present, the possibilities are the natural elements uranium and thorium and the separated isotopes uranium 238, uranium 235, plutonium and the other manufactured elements above 92 in atomic number. Each has its merit. The first International Symposium for discussion of the fuel elements was held at Columbia University in New York, January 28 and 29, 1959. The man-made elements and the separated isotopes are very expensive. Even natural uranium oxide cost $8.00 a pound in 1958, which brings the cost of the metal to $9.53 without the cost of smelting. There seems to be a popular notion that atomic fuel is everlasting and the long life of uranium seems to support that idea. But the 4.5 billion years is the time required for half a sample to decay naturally. In a reactor the process is fission and not decay; it goes at a controlled speed or in a flash if it is not controlled.

The oil-burning power plant has its smoke to dispose of, the coal burner has its smoke and its ashes and the atomic energy plant has its ashes. A pile of coal ashes may be unsightly, but the ashes from fission are dangerous because they are radioactive elements. Some of them and their half-lives are: iodine 131 (814 days), cesium 137 (37 years), krypton 88 (2.8 hours), xenon 133 (5 days), strontium 89 (54 days). After a time these elements accumulate in the uranium and interfere with the fission process. Then the fuel must be reprocessed; that is, the decomposition products must be removed and the uranium made back into suitable form for use. The renovation of the fuel is a chemical problem of considerable difficulty because of the dangerous radioactivity of the elements removed. Then comes the problem of what to do with the waste. The operator can always hope that somebody wants to buy some of his radioactive elements, but the market is not very great. Recently some wastes were embedded in concrete and dumped into the Gulf of Mexico at a depth of over a mile. Each plant has its own disposal problem.

Despite all the difficulties the use of atomic energy has increased enormously since 1942. There are now several electric power plants in operation or under construction, mainly in the United States, England and Russia, but there are other countries interested, especially those in which the usual fuels are scarce. Atomic energy is also used to power submarines and, recently, surface ships also. What do these plants cost? Plenty. But the economic picture at present is confused by government subsidies.

FUSION

Fission of the atom would seem to be the last word in the production of energy. Not so; there is still *fusion*. For example, the helium nucleus consists of 2 protons and 2 neutrons. The proton has the mass 1.007582 and the neutron 1.00893. These mass numbers should give the helium atom a mass of 4.033, but the mass of this atom is 4.0028. If 2 protons and 2 neutrons were combined to form a helium nucleus there would be a loss of 0.0302 units of mass. From the formula $E=mc^2$, the calculated energy equivalent of this mass is 1.62×10^{11} calories, or 190,000 kilowatt-hours for every 4.028 grams of helium produced—less than a cubic foot.

This is the characteristic reaction of the hydrogen bomb. It takes a high temperature to trigger hydrogen fusion and the temperature of the fission bomb is required to start it. Hydrogen fusion is also the source of the energy of the sun and stars.

The practical importance of the subject matter of this

chapter is mainly physics, for it concerns energy. However, the chemistry of the new elements and some of the effects of radiation are of interest to the chemist, particularly the biochemist. All changes in the composition of matter lie in the field of the chemist. Nuclear science is a good illustration of the fact that the division of science into the various fields is purely arbitrary and made for convenience in study, teaching and publication. The physicist must use matter in order to study energy, the chemist must take into account the energy effects of the changes in matter, and both, alas, must be good mathematicians.

CHAPTER TWELVE

What Now, What Next?

The NUCLEAR CHEMISTS have joined the nuclear physicists and gone off to found their own family, nuclear science, or nucleonics. This raises the question: What are the chemists who are left behind doing? There are over 100,000 of them in the United States and thousands more abroad. Their activities are of two general kinds. One group consists of those chemists working for the government or industry— doing research and analysis. The other works in universities, colleges, high schools and research foundations and they spend their time in teaching or research. This research is not planned for financial gain or for any other practical purpose. It is basic, or pure, research and simply aims to increase our understanding of the composition and behavior of matter.

Radioactivity, fission, fusion, atomic energy and the production of new elements are all activities that originate in the nucleus of the atom and so these subjects constitute the field of nucleonics. But the nucleus of each atom is surrounded by electrons and the atomic number tells how many there are in each atom. Hydrogen has 1, helium 2, lithium 3 and so on to nobelium with 102. The Rutherford atom had electrons rotating around the nucleus like the planets around the sun, and they are still referred to as planetary electrons. These are the electrons that occupy the attention of the chemist because they are responsible for all the physical and chemical properties of the atom except its weight. This idea poses an enormous field for research and speculation: How do these electrons cause all the properties of over one hundred elements? At first explanation seemed simple. Hydrogen has 1 electron. If it loses that electron it will have a charge of 1 positive and be the familiar H^+ ion. The valence could not be more than 1, of course, because the atom has only 1 electron and therefore cannot lose any more.

ELECTRON SHELLS

The other elements are not so simple. Helium has 2 electrons and it is a very inert element; it does not react with any of the others. All we can say about that is, 2 electrons evidently form a very stable combination and, come what may, an element with 2 or more electrons hangs on to the first 2 to the end. These 2 electrons move about at much the same distance from the nucleus and constitute the first shell, or the first energy level or the first stable state. There are six of these stable states, one for each of the six inert elements. The second one is the atomic number 10, which is the element neon. If we set aside 2 electrons for the first shell we have 8 for the second. Then comes argon with atomic number 18, which provides three shells with 2, 8 and 8 electrons. Krypton is next with the number 36, or 2, 8, 8 and 18. Xenon is number 54, or 2, 8, 8, 18 and 18. And finally comes radon with 2, 8, 8, 18, 18 and 32 to make up its total atomic number of 86. One fact that helps to support this electron distribution into shells is that these numbers 2, 8, 8, etc., correspond to the number of elements in the periods of the periodic table (p. 168). After these electron shells were established, the next observation was that an element tends most strongly to gain or lose enough electrons to bring its shells into the arrangement of the nearest stable element. For example, lithium has the atomic number 3, which means 2 electrons in the first shell and 1 in the second; therefore, when a lithium atom is brought near another atom it will hand over its 1 electron if the other atom will accept it and become Li^+. Its remaining electrons have the stable helium arrangement. In contrast to lithium, fluorine, number 9, has 2 electrons in the first shell and 7 in the second. When a fluorine atom approaches another it has no intention of giving up any of its 7 electrons, but gladly accepts 1 to raise the number in the outside shell to 8, the shell of neon. Furthermore, the fewer electrons to be transferred the more active the element. Sodium (11), potassium (19), rubidium (37) and cesium (55) have each just 1 electron above the nearest stable state and all are extremely active metals. For example, sodium reacts with water violently to set free hydrogen while magnesium (12) with 2 electrons to lose undergoes the same reaction only with hot water. Likewise, fluorine, chlorine, bromine and iodine, each with room to gain only 1 electron, are much more active than oxygen, sulfur, selenium and tellurium, each of which lacks 2.

It soon became possible to predict a lot of the properties of the elements merely by knowing the atomic number and the number of electrons in the stable groups. However, the idea was too good to last. For example, palladium (46) would have the arrangement 2, 8, 8, 18 and 10. The nearest stable state is 18 which would require it to pick up 8 electrons and form an ion 8 negative, but the element was not known to do anything of the sort. On the contrary, experiment had established that its valences are 2 and 3 positive. It is very much a metal and so it actually loses electrons. Palladium was by no means a lone exception; there were a lot of elements that did not fit the scheme, and so it was evident that the shell distribution needed some revision, although it worked fine for the first three periods and a few elements at the beginning and end of the others.

Scores of chemists worked at the distribution of electrons. They had two main sources of experimental information: the known experimental valences and flame spectra—the first appealed to the chemists and the latter to the physicists. The final result of the combined efforts of the many researchers was the establishment of subshells. The arrangement is a bit intricate but definite. One of the conclusions was that the outside subshell never can contain more than 8 electrons.

The subshells had no sooner been established than another tragedy occurred. In 1923 Louis Victor de Broglie, a French physicist, predicted that the electron would be found to have some of the properties of a wave. Right he was. In 1927 Clinton Joseph Davisson (1881–1958) and Lester Halbert Germer (b. 1896) of the Bell Telephone Laboratories, and quite independently Professor George Paget Thomson (b. 1892) of the University of Aberdeen, found by experiment that Broglie was right. Strangely enough, Thomson's father, J. J. Thomson of the Cavendish Laboratory, had proved the electron to be a particle. Nowadays the electron is a particle in some of its activities and a wave in others—the web of scientific theory becomes tangled at times.

Electron distribution is now considered well settled, but an atom no longer has electrons in orbits all their own, but each electron moves about like a bee outside a hive; and so the word *orbit* has been dropped and the word *orbital* substituted to describe the various places in which an electron may be found.

CHEMICAL BONDS

Today the theoretical chemists are mainly interested in bonding. There are two main types of chemical bonds, *electrovalent* and *covalent*. The idea of valence, introduced by Edward Frankland in 1852, meant simply the combining capacity of an element. The valence of oxygen was 2 because its atom combines with 2 atoms of hydrogen. But from the time of Berzelius chemists have been concerned about the nature of forces that hold atoms together. Why do some atoms combine while others do not? Berzelius thought the atomic attraction to be electrical: one atom positive and the other negative—the dualistic theory. In general, hydrogen and the metals were positive and all the others negative. Berzelius' idea prevailed for several years and then Dumas found that chlorine, which is strongly negative, could replace positive hydrogen in an organic compound and that the compound thus formed was not very different from the original one. Then, too, Avogadro came up with his diatomic molecules of elements such as H_2 and O_2. These two developments cast considerable doubt on Berzelius' theory and so the nature of chemical bonds remained unexplained for the next century.

After the electrical nature of the atom was established chemists again began to speculate on the nature of bonding between atoms. As early as 1902 Professor Gilbert Newton Lewis (1875–1946) of the University of California began to suggest to his students a connection between the electron and the bond that holds atoms together in the molecules. The first publication on the subject, however, did not appear until 1916. In that year Lewis published a theory of valency and in the same year Walter Kossel (1888–1956), professor of physics in the technical high school in Danzig, Germany, published much the same ideas. Here is another close race like those of Priestley and Scheele, Couper and Kekulé and van't Hoff and Le Bel. Kossel's paper was received by the editor of a German journal in December 1915 and Lewis sent his to an American journal in January 1916. Both explained ionic valence and Lewis also advanced the idea of covalence. Since the original papers were published many chemists have contributed to the details of the theory. In brief, Berzelius was right about the valence in some compounds, those that have ionic valence. These are mainly the acids, bases and salts, which are the substances with which Berzelius was mainly concerned. The explanation of ionic valence is very simple when we consider the structure of the atom. For example, when atoms of sodium are brought into contact with molecules of chlorine, they each give up 1 electron to an atom of chlorine.

$$2\,Na + Cl_2 \longrightarrow 2\,Na^+ + 2\,Cl^-$$

These oppositely charged ions attract each other very strongly and in a crystal of salt they alternate to form a cubical lattice that is very stable. When salt is melted the heat energy separates the ions and they are free to move about and carry an electric current. Likewise, when salt is dissolved in water, heat is absorbed and the temperature falls. Water is a nonconductor of electricity and keeps the ions apart so they are again free to carry an electric current.

Magnesium in contact with chlorine loses 2 electrons and becomes Mg^{++}, and aluminum loses 3 and becomes the aluminum ion Al^{+++}. According to the theory an atom always gains or loses enough electrons to bring its number to that of the nearest stable state. The atomic number of sodium is 11, magnesium 12, aluminum 13 and chlorine 17. The distribution of electrons is 2, 8, 1 for sodium; 2, 8, 2 for magnesium; 2, 8, 3 for aluminum; and 2, 8, 7 for chlorine. If an atom of sodium loses an electron its remaining electrons will have the 2, 8 arrangement of neon, but magnesium must lose 2 and aluminum 3 to reach this state. Chlorine needs to pick up only 1 electron to become 2, 8, 8, the configuration of argon.

Twentieth-century chemists were confused by difficulties that led to the downfall of Berzelius' dualistic theory. As the organic chemists made more and more compounds there was an increasing number of substances that did not conduct an electric current under any circumstances. Moreover, Dumas proved beyond doubt that negative chlorine and bromine could be substituted for positive hydrogen. And then there were the diatomic molecules of several gaseous elements. What could persuade an atom of hydrogen to hand over an electron to another hydrogen atom? Here was where Lewis made his most important contribution, the covalent bond. He suggested that the two hydrogen atoms in H_2 shared their electrons so that both electrons belonged equally to the two nuclei, and so each atom may be considered to have 2 electrons, which is the stable arrangement of helium. Nitrogen atoms have 7 electrons, which means 2 in the first shell and 5 in the outer shell; consequently when two atoms decide to share electrons they share 3 which gives each atom 8 in the second shell, the configuration of neon. To indicate these valences chemists use the old dash of Couper and write $H—H$ and $N≡N$ or the newer method of dots for the electrons and write H:H and :N:::N:, which show the 2 electrons for hydrogen and the 10 for nitrogen.

When two different atoms are bonded in a nonionic compound, electrons are also shared. Carbon has 6 electrons, 2 in the inner shell and 4 in the outer; consequently, all four must be shared to bring the number up to 8, which is the nearest stable structure. The electrons in the inner shells are ignored in valence matters as they play no part in chemical combination—they are mainly for physicists to play with. The simplest carbon compound is methane, with the formula

$$
\begin{array}{ccc}
\quad \text{H} & & \quad \text{H} \\
\quad | & & \quad \cdot\cdot \\
\text{H}-\text{C}-\text{H} \quad & \text{or} & \quad \text{H}:\text{C}:\text{H} \\
\quad | & & \quad \cdot\cdot \\
\quad \text{H} & & \quad \text{H}
\end{array}
$$

The second formula indicates the 2 electrons for hydrogen and 8 for carbon—each atom has reached its nearest stable state.

When two elements are bonded it is hardly to be expected that the electrons will be shared equally and, in fact, they seldom are. In the case of H : Cl for example, the electrons are shared, but they appear to be closer to the Cl than to the H so as to form a *polar* compound, that is, the chlorine is somewhat negative and the hydrogen slightly positive, like the two poles of a bar magnet. Neither gaseous HCl nor the pure liquid conducts an electric current, but when HCl dissolves in water the Cl gets the electron and we have H^+ and Cl^-, and the solution is a good conductor of electricity.

Covalence has led to three main lines of investigation: measurement of bond energies, bond lengths and bond angles and their respective effects on molecular and crystalline structure. Bond energy is the energy required to separate atoms that are combined. It is determined in the form of heat. To separate H_2 into its atoms requires 104 kcal per mole. That is, 104 kcal are required to separate 2 grams of hydrogen, or 6.023×10^{23} molecules of the gas into atoms. Some other bond energies are:

Br$_2$	46 kcal	HBr	87 kcal
Cl$_2$	59	HCl	103
O$_2$	119	NO	150
N$_2$	226	CO	250

When these substances react the atoms must separate before they can combine with others; therefore, the less the bond energy the more active the element. Chlorine is very reactive, nitrogen is not. Bond energies are very useful for calculating the heat effects of reactions that are difficult or impossible to determine experimentally.

Bond lengths are the distance between the nuclei of two atoms in combination and are measured in Angstrom units (10^{-8} cm), the favorite unit of the physicist. A few of these distances are:

H$_2$	0.70 A	CO	1.22 A
O$_2$	1.21	NO	1.15
Cl$_2$	1.99	HBr	1.42
Br$_2$	2.28	HCl	1.27

Single bonds between atoms of the same element seem to be the same length whatever other elements may be around. The bond between O and H in water, O — H, is 0.96 A and it is the same in hydrogen peroxide, H — O — O — H, and in methanol,

$$
\begin{array}{c}
\text{H} \\
| \\
\text{H} - \text{C} - \text{O} - \text{H} \\
| \\
\text{H}
\end{array}
$$

Likewise, the C — C bond has the same length in many compounds. However, if two elements are connected by a different number of bonds in different compounds the lengths are different; a single bond between carbon atoms, $C - C$, is 1.5 A in length, a $C = C$ is 1.34 A and a $C \equiv C$ is 1.20 A.

Chemists realized years ago that the atoms in molecules might have various positions in space relative to each other. In order to show how atoms are connected according to the structural theory of Couper and Kekulé the symbols were connected by dashes as Couper proposed and as I have done through Chapter Eight and in the illustrations in this chapter. For many purposes they are more convenient than the more literal dots. In order to get these graphic formulas on paper it is necessary to show all the atoms in one plane, that is, flat on the paper. The first departure from this practice was the proposed tetrahedral carbon atom of van't Hoff and Le Bel in 1874. Therefore, the organic chemists, who were the most concerned with structure, began to make diagrams or use models to show the relation of the atoms in space.

It had been known for centuries that crystals have a definite form characteristic of the substance, and these crystal forms have been the mainstay of the mineralogist for the identification of the natural minerals. In 1912 William Henry Bragg (1862–1942), then professor of chemistry at the University of Leeds, and his son William Lawrence Bragg (b. 1890) used the diffraction of X rays to show the relative position of the atoms in crystals. They studied several crystalline substances and then they and others extended the study to more and more complex substances. They measured the distances between the atoms and also the angles that the various bonds formed. Some twenty years after Bragg's original work, electrons were found to behave like waves and so chemists began to use electron diffraction instead of X rays and found that they could use the method to measure bond angles and distances in gases as well as in liquids and solids. As this work progressed some of the old theoretical ideas turned out to be true. In a simple molecule such as that of methane, CH_4, the angles formed between the bonds from the C to the H are 109.5 degrees, which is the size of the angle between lines drawn from the center to the corners of a tetrahedron. Also, benzene, C_6H_6, is a ring of six carbon atoms and the "straight" carbon chains are zigzag rows and not like so many beads on a string. If tetrahedra are connected in a row by their corners the chain will certainly be zigzag and not a geometrical straight line.

The bond angle of water is 104.5 degrees and so the structure of the molecule is

$$\begin{array}{c} H \searrow \\ \; O \quad \text{and not} \quad H-O-H \\ H \nearrow \end{array}$$

All these bond angles and distances raise the question: What would an atom look like if it were big enough to be seen? Rutherford's atom of 1911 and Bohr's of 1913 were easy to imagine—a small nucleus with electrons rotating about it, each in its own orbit like planets around the sun. In 1927, when Davisson and Germer showed that electrons sometimes behave like waves and are not always the pealike particles they had been thought to be, the picture of the atom began to get foggy. Next the shells became electron clouds because it seemed to the physicists that the electron just could not stay put, and we were soon advised not to try to imagine a picture of an atom, but just consider it to be a fuzzy bit of matter with a strong inclination to become a mathematical formula. But the little nucleus with its heavy protons and neutrons has been left to us and so have the valence electrons and their chemical consequences, even though the atom's total image is a bit fuzzy. In fact, the last word on the structure of the atom has not been said.

Some physical chemists are not particularly interested in bonds and they continue to do research in such old-fashioned subjects as thermodynamics, speed of reaction, catalysis and the position of equilibrium in incomplete reactions (of which there are thousands).

ORGANIC CHEMISTS

The organic chemists are busy with the steps by which their reactions occur and with the synthesis of new compounds. Syntheses, however, are not carried out with the abandon of the nineteenth century when a chemist made a new compound just to see if he could. Today, a synthesis generally has a purpose, which may be to prove the structure of some natural compound or to prepare a series of compounds in order to be able to compare the properties of compounds that are related structurally. One chemist has directed a research group that has synthesized several hundred compounds to try to locate the chemical structure that will cause skin cancer.

In 1965, Professor R. B. Woodward (b. 1917) of Harvard University won the Nobel Prize in chemistry for his synthesis of natural organic substances including chlorophyll and quinine. The chlorophyll required fifty-five separate steps, which is some indication of the complexity of the task. The prize was awarded for both his success in these difficult syntheses and the general manner in which he plans and carries out his work. Professor Woodward and other organic chemists are still in pursuit of the original purpose of chemistry: the determination of the composition of matter. Chemists feel that the composition of a substance is not known until the substance has been taken apart and put together again. Like watches, automobiles and other machines, chemical substances are more easily taken apart than put together. Quinine was known for a century and worked over by many chemists before its structure was finally determined in 1908. Then, nearly forty years and several chemists later, Professor Woodward succeeded in assembling the complex molecule from simpler substances. When a watch is assembled the same parts are used that were taken apart, but in an organic synthesis the parts from which the molecule is assembled are not always the ones that were obtained from the substance when its structure was determined by breaking it down. Therein lies the magic of the chemist, that is, his knowledge and his ingenuity.

BIOCHEMISTS

Closely related to the work of the organic chemist is that of the biochemist, who studies the composition of plants and animals and everything concerned with their growth and welfare. Van Helmont (p. 64), we recall, tried to find out what makes a tree grow, and Lavoisier discovered that animals get their energy from the use of the oxygen of the air. These are illustrations of the earliest work in biochemistry.

The biochemists of the nineteenth century gradually split into three divisions. Man gets all his food, directly or indirectly, from the vegetation and so one group undertook to find what makes plants grow to produce the fruits, grains, vegetables and forage upon which the animals depend. These biochemists became the agricultural chemists. They were often looked down upon by the theoretical chemists because they were not concerned directly with the composition of matter and the vagaries of the atom and used no mathematics beyond arithmetic. But their problems were much more difficult than those of their critics and of more immediate importance to their fellow men. Their first big problem was to find what there is in the soil that plants must have and whether more of it would produce more or better food. Every farmer knew that some soils were better than others. The practical possibilities of the work of the agricultural chemists had a strong appeal for the populace and agricultural chemistry was supported better than any other kind. The United States and other governments established experiment stations and financed their operation. By the end of the nineteenth century the main soil problems had been solved. Plants require several of the chemical elements and they must be in soluble form because the vegetation takes its nourishment by absorbing solutions of nutrients through its roots. Water, of course, is a requirement of plant growth as Van Helmont had established. The three essential elements most likely to be absent from the soil or present in insufficient amount are nitrogen, phosphorus and potassium. To supply these nutrients is the work of the industrial chemist.

Potassium compounds are all soluble and so do not occur in any great quantity on the surface of the earth, for the rain dissolves them and carries them into the ocean. For many years Europe and the United States were supplied with potassium salts from the mines at Stassfurt, Germany. When World War I broke out there was a wild scramble for potassium compounds outside of Germany. In this country, residues from the beet sugar factories were burned and seaweed was harvested off the West Coast and burned for the potassium carbonate in the ash. The salt lakes of our arid West were explored and several of them were worked for potassium chloride. One of them, Searles Lake in California, proved to be a good enough source to support the industry after the war. However, the brine from the bottom of this lake contains borax as well as potassium chloride, and the solid crust on the surface furnished common salt to help out with the economics of the process. In more recent years, wells in our western states and in Canada are our main sources of potassium chloride. For the present the agricultural needs for potassium are supplied, but the problem is sure to rise again as more and more land becomes exhausted of this element of fertility and the mines and wells run out of supplies. We can always resort to ocean water, which contains something less than a tenth of 1 per cent (about 0.035 per cent) potassium. One thing is certain: the biochemists are not going to be able to teach the plants to get along without it.

Phosphorus has not been a big problem for the industrial chemist. The mineral matter of bones is calcium phosphate, $Ca_3(PO_4)_2$, and the rock phosphate mined in Florida, the Carolina coast, Idaho, North Africa and elsewhere has the same composition as the mineral matter of bones. This calcium phosphate is insoluble and therefore useless to a plant, but treatment with sulfuric acid converts it into two kinds of phosphate that are soluble, $CaHPO_4$ and $Ca(H_2PO_4)_2$. Or the free phosphorus can be separated from the rock phosphate or bones, burned to the oxide, P_2O_5, which dissolves in water to form phosphoric acid, H_3PO_4. The acid can then be neutralized with lime or ammonia to get the soluble phosphate that plants can use. How soon phosphorus will become scarce is a question. The rate at which the rock is mined increases each year so that the fact that phosphorus has been in good supply for the past century is no indication of what the supply will be like a century hence.

Nitrogen was the real problem of both the agricultural and the industrial chemists. The air is 78 per cent free nitrogen, but only a few kinds of plants can use it. That mystery could not be solved until bacteriology became a science in the 1880s. Some of the plants that can use free nitrogen, N_2, are peas, beans, clover and alfalfa. As it turned out, these plants cannot use free nitrogen either, but their roots harbor a kind of bacteria that can. These bacteria make the free nitrogen into soluble compounds that the roots of the host plant use in return for the rent-free habitation the bacteria enjoy. The trees of the forest, fruit trees, grains and the root vegetables do not play landlord to these bacteria and they must get their nitrogen elsewhere. A primeval forest returns its elements of fertility to the soil in the form of decaying leaves and the bodies of fallen trees, but when crops are harvested the elements of fertility are removed and the soil depleted. They must be restored if more crops are to grow. The simpler compounds of nitrogen are all soluble and, like potassium compounds, are scarce on the surface of the earth. However, free nitrogen does not combine readily with other elements to form soluble compounds.

The nitrogen problem was realized long before the end of the nineteenth century. Black powder is made from charcoal, sulfur and saltpeter, KNO_3, and as early as 1500 Biringuccio was struggling with the manufacture of saltpeter (p. 59). Lavoisier made some improvements in Biringuccio's process and the method was in use up to the middle of the nineteenth century. About that time the sodium nitrate deposits in the desert country of western Chile and Peru became the world's source of nitrate. The sodium nitrate can be used as fertilizer just as it is and it was not difficult to make either nitric acid or potassium nitrate out of it; treatment with sulfuric acid gave the former and potassium chloride the latter. Of course, farmers have always used stable manure as a source of nitrogen, and in Japan sewage was also at one time collected for that purpose. The desperate need for nitrogen in the soil is indicated by the fact that farmers often use green manure—they raise a crop of clover, alfalfa or other legume to produce the nitrogen compounds from atmospheric nitrogen and then plow it under to raise a crop of wheat or corn. This involves an extra plowing and keeps the field out of production while the first crop is growing.

Chemists tried several methods of converting atmospheric nitrogen into soluble compounds. Equipment was devised for combining the gases of the air to form NO_2 in an electric arc. This oxide unites with water to form nitric acid, HNO_3, which reacts quickly with limestone, shells or marble to form soluble calcium nitrate:

$$CaCO_3 + 2\ HNO_3 \longrightarrow Ca(NO_3)_2 + CO_2 + H_2O$$

The drawbacks to the process were the cost of the electricity and the fact that very little NO_2 forms at the temperature of the electric arc, but the process was used for about twenty-five years at the beginning of this century.

German chemists invented another process for the fixation of nitrogen at the beginning of this century. They passed nitrogen over calcium carbide in an electric furnace to produce calcium cyanamide:

$$CaC_2 + N_2 \longrightarrow CaCN_2 + C$$

The cyanamide reacts slowly with water or quickly with steam to form ammonia and calcium carbonate, so that it could be used directly for fertilizer, or the ammonia neutralized with sulfuric acid to get soluble ammonium sulfate. The process was an expensive source of fertilizer because it involved three or four separate processes. Air had to be liquefied and distilled to get the nitrogen; the calcium carbide was made in an electric furnace from limestone and coke; the nitrogen was passed over the carbide in another electric furnace and then the ammonia was usually made in a fourth process.

$$CaCN_2 + 3 H_2O \longrightarrow 2 NH_3 + CaCO_3$$
$$2 NH_3 + H_2SO_4 \longrightarrow (NH_4)_2SO_4$$

The use of these two expensive methods to produce nitrogen compounds again indicates the desperate need for nitrates. Nitric acid is used to make smokeless powder, dynamite and other high explosives; consequently, if a country wants to start a war it had better first look to its supply of nitric acid— fertilizer and explosives are likely to be needed.

THE HABER PROCESS

Le Châtelier found a way to make nitrogen and hydrogen combine to form ammonia in 1901 but he was interested in basic research and not in the manufacture of ammonia so he did not try to commercialize the process. Fritz Haber (1868– 1934), professor of chemistry at Karlsruhe, was more interested in a practical process and by 1908 he had devised a small apparatus for the synthesis of ammonia on a laboratory scale. He used a pressure of 200 atmospheres and a temperature of 550° C and then began a search for a catalyst. His success is indicated by the fact that a full-scale industrial plant was in operation at Oppau by 1913. There was already a process for the oxidation of ammonia to nitric acid with air and platinum as a catalyst. Consequently, Germany was supplied with nitric acid for explosives and ammonium or calcium nitrate for fertilizer. World War I started the next year.

In 1914 Germany was still importing sodium nitrate from Chile, but after a couple of naval battles, that became impractical. The Allies were not in much better position because of the long distance from Chile to France and England and even to the United States. Everybody became interested in the Haber process. The principles involved were well known to all physical chemists from the work of Le Châtelier, and furthermore the process was patented. Under our law a patent must describe the process in sufficient detail for "one skilled in the art" to follow, but Haber had gotten his patent by describing the catalyst as a specially treated iron. Iron alone is not much of a catalyst and I suppose there are a million things one might do to iron and call it a special treatment. A frantic search for the catalyst began in several countries. The United States government established a special research laboratory with the primary duty of finding a good catalyst for the ammonia synthesis. Within a year or so the chemists were successful, and today the process manufactures thousands of tons of ammonia in most of the industrial countries of the world. The development of special steels has made it possible to use equipment at pressures up to 1000 atmospheres or more for better yields.

After the main elements of fertility were discovered the agricultural chemists also found that calcium, sulfur, copper, iron and several other elements are required in the merest traces for the growth of plants. Most soils contain enough of them, but some are added to fertilizer for crops that are known to have special requirements.

All this information about crop requirements is told in a few pages, but it took the combined work of hundreds of chemists a century to learn it. It may look to the layman as though the agricultural chemists have finished their task and can now retire, but pesticides to protect crops from insects and plant diseases and other problems remain and the really interesting problem has not even been attacked. Why do different plants, grown in the same soil and climate, produce such different things? They all make cellulose, starch and proteins. But some make pigments, acids or sugars and then there are the caffeine of tea and coffee, the nicotine of tobacco and the flavors of fruits, herbs and vegetables. Why does the oak tree produce tannin, the maple tree, sugar, and the rubber tree, rubber? Among them, the plants produce thousands of chemical substances. Why does the carrot produce carotene while the beet goes in for a nice red color and the turnip prefers a dash of purple on the top of its root? The question is not purely philosophical, for some of these products are drugs, vitamins or other substances that we humans yearn for.

The second group of biochemists undertook research related to agriculture but distinct from it—animal nutrition. What chemical substances does an animal need in its nutrition and where are they to be had? Of course, man was the main animal that got their attention although horses, cattle, sheep and hogs were not slighted, because their welfare is ours also. Think of all the labor, transportation, clothing and food they provide, not to mention the companionship of the dog and the family cat.

Scientists have been concerned with respiration and diet from the beginning of history and some of the ancient ones made studies that would now be classed as physiological research. Sanctorius (1561–1636), a teacher of medicine in Padua, was a very active experimenter and among other things he found that a person perspires a pound or more in the first four hours after a meal, two pounds from the fifth to the ninth hour and another pound from the ninth to the sixteenth. He also found that the perspiration rates are different when different foods are eaten. The loss in weight that Sanctorius found was loss of water through the skin and both water and carbon dioxide in the breath, but the explanation had to wait for two centuries for the science of chemistry to furnish it.

It is difficult to distinguish between physiologists and biochemists; for many years the biochemists were called physiological chemists. In general, the physiologist tries to find out what happens in the body and the biochemist tries to find out why it happens. That definition is a bit too simple and their activities are often the same—I shall make no attempt to distinguish between them in this brief discussion.

Lavoisier did the earliest work on the production of energy by animals. He and the mathematician and physicist Pierre Simon de Laplace (1749–1827) undertook to measure heat and invented a calorimeter for the purpose. They measured heat of combustion and other chemical reactions and then turned to animal heat. They used guinea pigs and sparrows as experimental animals and in 1780 reported that the heat and energy of animals comes from the conversion of oxygen to carbon dioxide just as it does in a burning candle. They gave the amount of heat produced for a given amount of carbon dioxide formed and showed that the nitrogen of the air had nothing to do with respiration, for the animals did just as well on an artificial atmosphere made by mixing oxygen and hydrogen. Fortunately, experimental animals do not smoke, for a spark or flame in that atmosphere would have ended both experiment and experimenters.

The last research that Lavoisier reported to the Academy of Sciences was on respiration. He and Armand Seguin (1765–1835) continued the respiration studies and Seguin himself was the experimental animal. They reported in 1789 that a man without food and in a room at 79° F uses 24 liters of oxygen an hour, but if the temperature is 54° F he uses 27 liters. Also, if he has just eaten he consumes 38 liters. With no food but hard work he uses 65 liters and with both food and work his consumption of oxygen is 91 liters an hour. Lavoisier's research ended in the early days of the Revolution and from then on his time was fully occupied with public service until his execution on May 8, 1794.

The Academy does not seem to have been satisfied with Lavoisier's work on animal heat for they offered a prize for the best paper on the subject. César Mansuète Despretz (1792–1863), professor of physics at the Sorbonne, and Dulong, who was both physicist and chemist, entered the contest and in 1824 Despretz won the prize. Neither of them added much to Lavoisier's conclusions forty years earlier, but their researches were notable for the number and variety of animals they used in their investigations. Despretz used ducks, chickens, pigeons, gulls, buzzards, owls, magpies, dogs, cats, rabbits and guinea pigs. Dulong studied the cat, dog, kestrel, capybara, rabbit and pigeon.

Research in nutrition in the early years was something of a French monopoly, for in addition to the five men just named there were Dumas, Magendie, Boussingault and Regnault.

Henri Victor Regnault (1810–1878), who was professor of chemistry at the University of Paris from 1840 to 1847 and then elsewhere, published an extensive paper on respiration in 1849. He had studied many animals including reptiles, frogs, beetles, silkworms, chrysalids, and earthworms and then mentions two regrettable omissions, fish and man. Then he explains that he knew Valenciennes was working on fish and that he did not have enough money for the necessary equipment to study human nutrition.

About the year 1840, papers on nutrition began to appear from chemists in Germany, England, the United States and other countries. Space does not permit us to follow the detailed study of nutrition from then to the present. The energy requirements of both man and animals have been thoroughly investigated and the conclusions are not a matter of theory but rest on hundreds of sound experiments scattered over the past two centuries.

The early experiments proved that the energy came from the conversion of oxygen to carbon dioxide and that the amount of energy produced depended on both the kind of food eaten and the amount of work done. The next question was where the carbon came from that formed the carbon dioxide. Again it took many experiments to settle the question. Natural foods are mixtures and the components that supply the carbon practically all belong to one of three kinds of organic compounds: carbohydrates, fats and proteins.

The usable carbohydrates are the starches and the sugars. Some animals can use cellulose and other carbohydrates that make up the structure of the plant, but man is not so versatile. He is limited to starch, the glucose of fruits, the lactose of milk and the sugar of the sugar bowl. Nearly all plants produce starch, generally stored in the seeds or the roots. Wheat, rye, barley, oats and rice store plenty of starch in their seeds. Potatoes, carrots, parsnips and the like lay up a good supply in their roots. The starches are insoluble in water, but the digestive system, beginning with the mouth, changes starch to glucose, $C_6H_{12}O_6$. The glucose is soluble and can pass through the intestinal walls into the blood stream. The sugars are soluble and do not have to stop to be digested, which is why they are quick sources of energy. Spinach and celery, like other leaves and stems on the food list, contain small amounts of starch and sugar.

Many fats are familiar in the grocery in pure form. These are olive oil, corn oil, cottonseed oil and lard and other shortenings. Then too, avocados, coconut, chocolate, nuts and meats all contain considerable fat along with their other components. The fats are all insoluble in water and so they are digested to glycerol and fatty acids before they are absorbed.

The carbohydrates and the fats are the main sources of carbon for the production of energy. The former supply 4 kcal per gram and the latter are more generous with 9. The diet of the average man (154 lb.) between the ages of thirty-five and fifty-five requires about 2600 kilocalories a day; women and older men require less.

THE PROTEINS

The muscles, nerves and even the bones all contain protein. In fact, the muscles are nearly all protein, and all living organisms, either plant or animal, contain some of it. Gelatin is the only pure protein carried by the grocer. The proteins average about 16 per cent nitrogen—the carbohydrates and fats contain only carbon, hydrogen and oxygen. Some proteins contain sulfur, and some, phosphorus; at least one contains iron. They are very complex in structure and have high molecular weights—anywhere from 30,000 to several million. The plants can all make protein from soluble compounds of nitrogen, even the simple ones such as ammonia, NH_3, and sodium nitrate, $NaNO_3$, but no animal can. Here is where man is absolutely dependent on plants. They are his only source of protein whether he eats the corn or eats the chicken that ate the corn.

Boiling with acid, or the action of enzymes such as the pepsin in the stomach and others in the digestive system, breaks the proteins down to amino acids. There are about twenty of these acids; all contain the amino group, $-NH_2$, and they all have rather low molecular weights. The simplest one is glycine and one of the two that contain sulfur is cystine.

$$H_2C-COOH$$
$$NH_2$$

$$S-CH_2-CH-COOH$$
$$S \qquad\qquad NH_2$$
$$S-CH_2-CH-COOH$$
$$NH_2$$

Glycine   Cystine

A protein molecule contains a lot of such acids joined together in a long chain. All twenty of these acids in the protein
chain are disconnected by digestion and are absorbed into the
blood, which distributes them throughout the body where
they are either oxidized to produce energy—4 kcal per gram—
or recombined to form the body proteins such as the hemoglobin of the blood, the keratin of the hair and nails and the
protein of the muscles.

The proteins differ from each other both in the relative
number of these acids and in the order in which they are
attached to each other. For example, gelatin contains about
25 per cent glycine and no cystine, while sheep's wool has
less than 1 per cent glycine and 7 per cent cystine. With so
many amino acids, millions of proteins are possible, and
when we consider how many plants and animals there are,
millions would seem to be required. The extent to which the
proteins of related species are alike has not been fully investigated, but the few that have been studied, such as those
of wheat, corn and barley, proved to be different.

All the vital tissues of the body are composed largely of
proteins, which the body can make from amino acids and
nothing else. The body, however, can convert some of the
amino acids into others so that only eight of the twenty
acids must be in the food eaten. Since the proteins of plants

or animals are our only sources of amino acids, the diet must contain protein. How much? Chemists have been trying to settle that question for the past century. The amount varies with age, sex, size, work and health. The recommendations vary from 40 grams a day for a child under three to 70 grams a day for a man.

Bones and teeth contain mineral matter, mostly calcium phosphate, and so both calcium and phosphorus must be present in the diet. But in what form and how much of them? Certainly not the free elements, for calcium is a metal and therefore hardly a food, and phosphorus is poisonous. Much investigation by numerous chemists have answered these questions. Soluble salts of calcium and soluble phosphates are satisfactory. Calcium compounds are present in fruits and vegetables, phosphates in eggs and meats and both in milk. Nutritionists consider the natural foods better sources of these elements than bottles of salts and the populace is inclined to agree with them. However, eggshells are calcium carbonate and are soluble in the hydrochloric acid of the gastric juice and so during World War II they were ground fine and added to the dried eggs of the military diet. Our average man requires 0.8 gram of calcium a day and growing children require more, but the composition of foods is such that if one gets enough protein and calcium he will also get enough phosphorus.

The red color of the blood is the color of the hemoglobin, which contains one atom of iron among its ten thousand atoms. There is iron in the body besides that in the blood, but the total requirement is so small that the nutritionists have decided that 10 to 15 milligrams a day is enough. Meats contain iron and so do the leaves and stalks of vegetables. The first idea was that the green pigment of plants was the source of the iron, and the idea dies hard because there are still many who believe it. Although there is iron in spinach it has no connection with the chlorophyll that provides the green color. The chlorophyll molecule contains one atom of magnesium, which has been known for half a century, and just recently gardeners and nurserymen have gotten around to using magnesium salts instead of iron to make their plants greener.

The human body contains 65 per cent oxygen, 18 per cent carbon, 10 per cent hydrogen, 3 per cent nitrogen, about 2 per cent calcium and 1 per cent phosphorus. Then there are small and decreasing quantities of potassium, sulfur, sodium, chlorine, magnesium, iron, manganese, copper, iodine, fluorine, cobalt, zinc and traces of others. Of these elements iodine is required by the thyroid gland, and in some sections of the world the soil and therefore the food and water contain little or no iodine. Sea foods are rich in this element and it is also now added to much of the salt from the grocer. Fluorine is a constituent of the enamel of the teeth, but is absent from most foods and from many soils. Consequently, many cities now add traces of fluorine to the water supply to prevent deficiency of this element in the diet of their citizens.

By the closing years of the nineteenth century many chemists thought that the nutrition problem had been solved. All an animal needed was enough carbohydrates and fats to supply him with energy; protein for growth of the young and maintenance of the tissues of the adult; and calcium, phosphorus and iron for the mineral requirement. To prove it the nutritionists began to feed animals "synthetic" diets. Purified casein from milk or gluten from wheat supplied the protein; starch or sugar took care of the carbohydrate; butter-fat, lard or vegetable oil gave him the fat; and a mixture of salts of calcium, phosphorus and iron supplied the minerals. Diets made by mixing these purified substances were fed to experimental animals, but they did not grow and bear young as well as they did on normal diets of natural foods. In fact, they were inclined to languish and die. The biochemists had not found all the answers to the problem of nutrition.

The artificial diets were all right as far as they went, but there remained at least two discoveries to be made, and the chemists began to look further for the dietary requirements.

Scurvy had been a dreaded disease for centuries, probably since the earliest days of man in northern climates. Soldiers, sailors and prisoners in particular were victims of the disease. Away back in 1564, Ronsseus, a Dutch doctor, recommended oranges for scorbutic sailors and, nearly a century later, an English doctor, John Woodall, recommended lemons as a cure for the disease. These remedies seemed to suggest that something sour was required in the diet, and by the end of another century a Scottish doctor, James Lind (1716–1794), decided to investigate the matter. He housed twelve sailors of the British Navy in the same sick bay and fed them in six groups of two each. One pair was fed the usual sailors' diet as a control, the diet on which they had acquired scurvy. Another group got a quart of cider a day added to the ration, a third pair was given 25 drops of sulfuric acid additional, a fourth received a teaspoonful of vinegar daily, the fifth had a pint of sea water, and the sixth had two oranges and a lemon. In 1753 Lind reported that of all the remedies in vogue at the time only the citrus fruit was effective. This is considered the first controlled experiment in medicine. Lind had no authority to put his findings into practice but, about fifty years later, Gilbert Blane, another Scottish physician, was the official physician of the British Navy and added citrus fruit to the sailors' ration.

In 1811 the United States Navy got around to adding lemon juice to the ration. The long sea voyages that began in the fifteenth century and continued to the middle of the nineteenth century were the greatest problem so far as scurvy was concerned, but northern cities were also stricken, especially in the winter and spring. As late as the California gold rush in 1849, scurvy was a mining camp problem. About 35 per cent of the miners had scurvy and 30 per cent of the patients died. Throughout the centuries thousands of men had died of scurvy and thousands more had been incapacitated.

Scurvy was not the only disease that seemed to be connected with diet. In 1836 Professor François Magendie (1783–1855) of the Collège de France, in his study of dogs on purified diets, noticed the appearance of an eye disease. It is even claimed that the ancient Greek physician, Hippocrates, recommended eating liver as a cure for night blindness.

The disease beriberi caused as much trouble in the Orient as scurvy did in the West and here again the worst trouble was soldiers, sailors and prisoners. About 1880 a Japanese naval vessel on a nine-month cruise around the Pacific had 169 cases of beriberi and 25 deaths in a crew of 276. Takaki, a naval doctor, got permission to send a similar vessel over the same route, but he cut down the amount of rice in the ration and added barley, meat, vegetables and condensed milk. Only 14 men developed beriberi and none of them had eaten his full ration of the new foods.

It is plain to us now that these experiences with food and disease indicate that there is something in some foods that the diet must contain, and it seems strange that the idea was not generally recognized sooner than it was. But there were two things that tended to prevent such recognition. From the beginning of time, I suppose, and up to the present, somebody has always been recommending his favorite food as a cure for something or other; most of the claims were and now are false. Doctors seldom paid any attention to such suggestions. The other factor was the rise in the science of bacteriology and the germ theory of disease. Pasteur's results were so sensational that doctors everywhere began looking for a germ to take the responsibility for any disease they encountered.

Now back to the purified diets. The break in the solution of the causes of dietary diseases came in 1906. Frederick Gowland Hopkins (1861–1947), professor of biochemistry at Cambridge University, was studying the effect of purified diets on animal nutrition and announced the conclusion that some natural foods contain an unidentified substance necessary for growth, and that the substance is soluble in water and alcohol.

By 1912, numerous laboratories in several countries were hot on the trail of the unidentified substance or substances. The last half-century has seen the announcement of remarkable results. The elusive substances were soon named *vitamins,* and since their chemical nature was unknown they were simply called vitamin A, B, C, etc., as they were discovered. At first there was just Fat Soluble A and Water Soluble B. That is, some foods contain very small amounts of something that is essential in the diet and that is soluble in fats, while other foods also contain an essential substance soluble in water. Most organic substances will dissolve in either fats or water, but very few will dissolve in both. Further investigation by scores of chemists disclosed that Fat Soluble A was a mixture of two vitamins, now called A and D, while Water Soluble B turned out to consist of about a dozen.

Nutritional research is generally undertaken by research groups usually directed by one man, in the universities, government laboratories, research foundations or the laboratories of industries connected with food or drugs. The names of the chemists who have contributed would fill several pages.

Among them they have found over a dozen vitamins and determined the part each plays in nutrition, which foods contain it, and its chemical formula, and in some cases they have synthesized it.

The cause of night blindness and the disease xerophthalmia that Magendie noticed is the absence of vitamin A, which is a complicated alcohol related to carotene, the yellow pigment of carrots and other plants. The vitamin itself, however, is colorless. Its formula and chemical name is rather complex and so it is just as well to call it vitamin A—everybody else does. It is abundant in cod liver oil, butter, eggs, milk and in the greens of the grocery counter including cabbage and cauliflower, which are not so green.

Beriberi results from the absence of vitamin B_1, or thiamine, with a structure more complicated than that of vitamin A. There is plenty of it in barley, wheat, oats and other grains and lesser amounts in fruits, vegetables and meats. Rice is one of the poorer cereal sources and, to make matters worse for the Orientals, in about the middle of the nineteenth century power mills were invented to polish the rice and the familiar white rice that they produce has no thiamine—neither has white flour unless it has been fortified with vitamins after it has been ground. The vitamin is in the outside layer of the grain and in the milling process the vitamin goes along with the bran. An amusing and confusing incident occurred in the laboratory of a Dutch doctor who was studying beriberi in a hospital in the East Indies (Indonesia) in the 1880s. He fed his chickens white rice from the kitchen of the hospital and they all got beriberi. Then the hospital manager decided that the doctor was too extravagant in feeding his chickens such luxurious food and the chickens had to eat a cheap unpolished rice. To the amazement of the doctor they all recovered from the beriberi.

Some twenty years later an American doctor had a similar experience with soldiers in the Philippines. They could not thrive on such luxurious food any better than the chickens.

Scurvy develops in the absence of vitamin C, which is ascorbic acid, a chemical relative of glucose but not derived from it. Its formula is $C_6H_6O_6$. The cause of scurvy in the earlier years is now clear: for practical reasons the food of sailors, for example, consisted of dried or salted meats, bread, dried beans and sometimes dried fruit—foods that would keep. Ascorbic acid is present in fresh foods and is easily destroyed in the processing. The best sources of it are citrus fruits, greens, tomatoes and other fruits. Smaller amounts are widely distributed in fresh foods of botanical source. It withstands cooking better in the foods that are acid and in the absence of air.

Other vitamins prevent other diseases, but all of them have a function in normal nutrition; the disease just appears as the last, or next to the last, effect of vitamin starvation. The biochemists are now primarily interested in how the vitamins operate and the chemical nature of all the other physiological processes.

Some pages back I said that there were two discoveries to be made. The vitamins were the first of these and the second was the discovery that of the twenty amino acids present in food some of them are essential parts of the diet, that is, some of the tissues require them and the body cannot make them from anything else.

Recently it appears that certain acids from fats are also essential, but the question has not been fully decided. Apparently, the complete requirements of the perfect diet are not settled yet, and the effect of diet on the common infectious diseases is almost totally unknown.

The third group of biochemists has worked with the specific effect of chemical substances on animals. These are the pharmacologists. The work began with that of the French physiologist François Magendie, whose work in nutrition we have just mentioned. Magendie studied the effects of such drugs as strychnine, morphine and bromides and introduced them into medicine. Claude Bernard (1813–1878), Magendie's student, who later became professor of physiology in the Collège de France, studied the favorite poison of mystery writers, curare (South American blowguns, arrowheads, etc.), and found that it affects the motor nerves. The big contribution of these two physiologists was the discovery of the fact that drugs affect some particular part of the animal's anatomy or physiology. Previously it had been thought that drugs and poisons affected the system generally, which made the search for remedies long and usually fruitless. Once the idea of specific action was introduced, studies could be made with animals to learn exactly what effect a drug has and what it affects.

A further boon to the pharmacologist was the germ theory of disease and the rise of the science of bacteriology in the latter half of the nineteenth century. Once the bacteriologist had found the germ of a disease the pharmacologist could look for a substance to kill that germ but not the patient. The discovery of the sulfa drugs, the antibiotics penicillin, streptomycin and others, the hormones, such as adrenalin and insulin, indicates the success of the pharmacological activities of the biochemists. However, like the millionaire who never has enough money, the biochemists never know enough to suit them and so their search for knowledge of the chemistry of the living organism goes on.

THE CHEMIST

These pages have contained very little about industrial, or applied, chemistry because I have been trying to explain what chemistry is and how it got to be that way. The glories of the science are already well known: its drugs and dyes, textiles and detergents, its fertilizers and pesticides, its synthetic rubber and plastics, its cosmetics and confections and its role in the processing of food. Chemistry as an art of making things to please the human race is older than history, and from the days of Boyle to the present the industry has exploited every major basic discovery for the benefit of somebody.

The chemist's ideal is a law or theory that would enable him to predict the chemical, physical and physiological properties of every substance under all conditions and also tell him how to make the substance. Mendeleev made a good start with the prediction of the physical and chemical properties of the unknown elements, but there it ended. With compounds, the best we can do is to predict the approximate chemical properties. Such physical properties as boiling and freezing points, color and density can only be guessed at. If a chemist wishes to know all the properties of a substance he must put on the white coat, go into the laboratory and determine them. Of course, he will first take a look around the library to see if someone has already done that.

Chemists are still trying to get to the bottom of things. In 1962 the journal *Chemical Abstracts* abstracted 166,749 articles from some eight thousand journals in fifty-two languages from one hundred countries. In the United States alone there are 125,000 chemists of whom about 23,000 are doing basic research. Of the papers published, 60 per cent come from universities and colleges, 30 per cent from industry, and the remainder from the government, research foundations and private laboratories. In addition to basic research the papers published include research on the problems of the industries, nutrition, medicine, waste disposal, air pollution, space travel and others.

Such is chemistry today.

Suggestions for Further Reading

The books in this list can be read by any layman who has read this book or who has had an elementary course in chemistry. Although most of the titles indicate the contents of the books, brief comments have been added for further information.

Farber, Eduard. *Great Chemists*. New York: Interscience Publishers, 1961. 1642 pp.

Biographies of chemists from Aristotle to some of the twentieth century. Many of the sketches were written by authors who knew the subject personally. Each sketch includes a portrait of the chemist and brief mention of his main contributions to chemistry.

Feinberg, J. G. *The Story of Atomic Theory and Atomic Energy*. New York: Dover Publications, 1960. 261 pp.

Dr. Feinberg traces the history of the atom from its invention by the ancient Greeks to the hydrogen bomb. He includes the effect of atomic energy on humanity.

Goran, Morris. *The Story of Fritz Haber*. Norman, Okla.: University of Oklahoma Press, 1967. 212 pp.

A detailed biography of the inventor of the ammonia synthesis, the head of the German chemical warfare service in World War I and the founder and director of the Kaiser Wilhelm Institute in Berlin.

Ihde, Aaron J. *The Development of Modern Chemistry*. New York: Harper and Row, 1964. 851 pp.

A comprehensive history of chemistry from the earliest times to the present. Profusely illustrated with portraits and with photographs and drawings of apparatus. It is a scholarly book, which chemists will appreciate, but the layman will also find it interesting and most of it understandable.

Lavoisier, Antoine. *Elements of Chemistry*. New York: Dover Publications, 1965. 511 pp.

This is a facsimile reprint of a translation that was made by Robert Kerr in 1790, of Lavoisier's *Traité élémentaire de chimie*. The present publisher has added an introduction by Dr. Douglas McKie, which gives a brief biography of Lavoisier and a short review of chemistry from the proposal of the phlogiston theory to the death of Lavoisier.

Leicester, Henry M. *Chymia No 11*. Philadelphia: University of Pennsylvania Press, 1966. 208 pp.

A miscellaneous collection of thirteen historical articles including a good account of Newlands' law of octaves.

Leicester, Henry M. *The Historical Background of Chemistry*. New York: John Wiley & Sons, 1956. 260 pp.

A brief history of the science from the earliest information to the later years of the nineteenth century. There are fourteen illustrations of apparatus of historical importance.

Levy, Martin. *Chemistry and Chemical Technology in Ancient Mesopotamia*. New York: American Elsevier Publishing Co., 1959. 242 pp.

Although this book was written for chemists, the layman will find it extremely interesting. It contains forty-six highly informative illustrations, mostly photographs of objects the archaeologists have unearthed.

Li Ch'iao P'ing. *The Chemical Arts of Old China*. Easton, Pa.: Journal of Chemical Education, 1948. 215 pp.

An excellent description of many common processes as they were carried out in ancient China, among them the smelting of iron, zinc and mercury and the production of salt, wine, vinegar and soy curd.

McKie, Douglas. *Antoine Lavoisier*. Philadelphia: J. B. Lippincott Co., 1935. 303 pp.

An account of the life and work of the father of chemistry.

Read, John. *Through Alchemy to Chemistry*. London: G. Bell and Sons, 1957. 206 pp.

A history of chemistry from the beginning of alchemy to the middle of the nineteenth century. Well illustrated with forty-nine photographs and drawings.

Seaborg, Glenn T. "Some Recollections of Early Nuclear Age of Chemistry," *Journal of Chemical Education* 45 (May 1968), 278–289.

An excellent account of the early work on nuclear fission and the production of new elements. Illustrated with several photographs of people and equipment involved. It will be easily understood by those who have read Chapter Eleven of this book.

Seaborg, Glenn T., and Valens, Evans G. *Elements of the Universe*. New York: E. P. Dutton & Co., 1958. 253 pp.

A beautifully illustrated treatment of the chemical elements written in simple language. About half of the book is devoted to the new elements and how they are made.

Smyth, Henry De Wolf. *Atomic Energy for Military Purposes.* Princeton, N.J.: Princeton University Press, 1945. 264 pp.

The official report of the development of the atomic bomb under the auspices of the United States government. The first chapter reviews radioactivity and atomic structure, the second states the problem to be solved and the others relate the administrative and scientific steps in the problem's solution. A fascinating account of this landmark in science.

Stillman, John Maxon. *The Story of Alchemy and Early Chemistry.* New York: Dover Publications, 1960. 566 pp.

A very readable continuous story of the progress of chemistry from ancient times to the end of the eighteenth century.

Thomson, George Paget. *J. J. Thomson and the Cavendish Laboratory of His Day.* New York: Doubleday & Company, Inc., 1965. 186 pp.

An account of the Cavendish Laboratory with emphasis on the life and works of its famous director and his associates. The book is illustrated effectively by twenty plates and twenty-five drawings. The author is the physicist son of J. J.

Index

Abelson, P. H., 352

Absolute (Kelvin) temperature scale, 278

Absorption spectra, 293, 294

Academy of Sciences, 99, 102, 103, 111, 125, 386

Acetic acid, 228

Acetylene series of hydrocarbons, 221–24

Acids: as chemical compounds, 190; characteristics and uses of principal, 191

Agricola (Georg Bauer), 60–62

Agricultural chemistry, 378–83, 384

Agricultural commodities, and analytical chemistry, 256–58, 259

Air: as one of Aristotle's four elements of matter, 21–22, 29, 42; composition of, 92, 94, 111–12, 135, 167, 180–82; liquefied, 181

Akkadians, 11

Albertus Magnus (Von Bollstädt), as thirteenth-century writer, 36

Alchemy, 21–41, 42, 57, 63, 87, 156–57, 346; origins of, 24–27; experimental objectives of, 27, 29; and fraud, 28; spread of, by Arabs, 28, 34; alchemistic theory, 28–30, 41; and philosopher's stone, 30, 33; symbols of, 30–31; and manuscripts of Zosimos, 31–32; and manuscripts of Jabir, 32–34; and writings of Avicenna, 34; and writers of thirteenth century, 35–38; decline of, 39–41, 42, 44; Paracelsus' writings on, 47

Alcohol: Paracelsus' use of, term for spirits of wine, 48; alcohol series of hydrocarbons, 225–28

Alcohol thermometer, 130

Alexandrian library and museum, 23–24, 28

Aliphatic acids, 228–29

Alkalies, 88, 192

Alkali metals, 167

Alkaline earths, 167

Alphabets, development of, 9

Alpha particles, 343, 344, 356, 360; as missiles in nuclear bombardment, 346, 347, 349, 351, 354, 355

Alpha rays, 331, 332, 344

American Association of Cereal Chemists, 85, 259

American Chemical Society, 85, 200, 217

American Indians: clay products of, 13; use of dyes and paints by, 19

American Oil Chemists Society, 259

American Pharmaceutical Association, 259

American Public Health Association, 259

Americium, 353–54, 355

Amines and amides, 231–33

Amino acids, and diet, 397

Ammonia, synthesis of, 317; Haber process, 383–84

Ampère, André Marie, 149, 203

Analytical chemistry, 122, 139, 241–71; two primary problems of, 241–42; in eighteenth and nineteenth centuries, 242; proximate analysis, 242, 250–55;

Calomel (mercurous chloride), 56

Calorie, 145, 295

Cannizzaro, Stanislao, 152–55, 177, 204, 239, 280

Carbon: crystalline and amorphous forms of, 100, 107–8, 112, 183–84; study of combustion of, 107, 112; use of, in metallurgy, 186–87

Carbonate of magnesium, 88

Carbon black, 183

Carbon compounds, chemistry of, 154

Carbon dioxide: discovery of, 64, 65, 83; research on, 88–90, 93, 95, 100; uses of, 190–91; and soft drinks, 284

Carbon monoxide, 92

Cartier, Jacques, 43

Castiglione, Baldassare, 44

Catalysts, 313–14

Cathode rays, 324, 325

Cavendish, Sir Henry, 90–94, 111, 112, 114, 167, 324; summary of scientific accomplishments of, 94

Cavendish Laboratory, Cambridge, England, 324, 325, 330, 331, 325, 348, 369

Celsius, Anders, 132

Centigrade scale, 132

Ceramic products: early manufacturing of, 13–15; work of Palissy in, 62

Cerium, 165

Cervantes, 43

Cesium, discovery of, 170

Chadwick, James, 333, 335, 348

Chain reaction in production of atomic energy, 359, 362

Chaptal, Jean Antoine Claude, 118

Charcoal, as amorphous form of carbon, 108, 112, 183

Charles, Jacques Alexandre, 146; law of, on constant expansion of gases with temperature, 146, 278–79, 280

Chaucer, and the alchemists, 39

Chemical Abstracts, 190, 399

Chemical action, and atomic theory, 137

Chemical balances, 104, 133

Chemical Beginner, The (Beguin), 50

Chemical bonds, 370–77; types of, 370; covalent, 370, 372–73; bond energy, 373–74; bond lengths, 374–75; bond angles, 375–76

Chemical combination, theory of, 176–77

Chemical compounds, 114; and atomic theory, 137; formulas of, 150–51; natural, 185; ores, 185–86; classes of, 190–94; synthesis, 196, 211, 377; optically active, 266

Chemical elements, 114–16, 122, 160–94, 241; definition of an element, 114, 161; and compounds, 114; Lavoisier's list of, 115, 160; as of today's list, 115; use of, in chemical nomenclature of substances, 116; symbols of, 141–43, 159, 274; determination of atomic weights of, 144–59; attempts to classify by weights, 161–62; classification of, and law of octaves, 162–63; periodic table of classification of, 164–68, 171; discovery of unknown elements, 166, 170, 350–56; predicting properties of unknown elements, 166–67; colors of gas and vapor of liquid or solid element, 168; concept of positive and negative, 176–77; valence, 178–79; relative abundance of, 180, 342; properties and uses of some common elements, 180–86; iso-

Fahrenheit, Gabriel Daniel, 130
Fahrenheit scale, 130–31
Faraday, Michael, 173–78, 197,
209, 222, 224, 322
Fat, determination of percentage
in mixture, by proximate anal-
ysis, 251–52
Father of chemistry, Lavoisier as,
117–18
Fatty oils, 52
Fermentation, study of gases
from, 93, 95, 112–13
Fermium, 355
Fertilizer industry, foreshadow-
ing of, 63
Fire, as one of Aristotle's four ele-
ments of matter, 21–22, 29, 42
Fire air (oxygen), 100
Firefly, as energy transformer, 297
Fission, atomic, 356–59
Fixed air, 88
Fluorescence, 323, 325, 326, 327
Food, Drug and Cosmetic Act
(1938), 258, 259
Food and Drug Administration
of federal government, 244
Food and Drugs Act (1906), 257
Food industries, and analytical
chemistry, 256–58, 259
Formic acid, 228
Formulas, chemical, 150–51, 159,
178–79, 242, 274–75; structural
or graphic, 207–10, 375
Fourcroy, Antoine François de,
116
Four elements of matter, of Aris-
totle, 21–23, 41, 42, 57, 160;
and the alchemists, 29, 47
France, geological and mineral-
ogical map of, 102
Francium, 351
Frankland, Edward, 178, 370
Franklin, Benjamin, 95, 104, 175,
297, 332
Freezing point of solutions, 304–6
Freezing point of water: Fahren-

heit scale, 131; centigrade
scale, 132
French Academy of Sciences, 84,
121, 143, 205
Frictional electricity, 175
Frobisher, Sir Martin, 43
Fusion: heat of, 298; atomic,
364–65

Galen, writings of, on medicine,
46, 50
Gallic acid, discovery of, 100
Gallium: discovery of, 166; char-
acteristics of, 194
Galvani, Luigi, 175
Galvanism, 171, 175
Gama, Vasco da, 43
Gamma rays, 331, 345
Gas: invention of word by Paracelsus, 48, 86; adopting of term
in general use, 117; liquefied,
288. See also Gases, study of
Gaseous conductivity, 323, 324,
325
Gaseous elements, 86, 177, 183;
atomic weights of, 146–49
Gases, study of, 83, 86–88, 133;
Hales' method of collecting, 87,
91, 96; carbon dioxide, 88–90;
hydrogen, 91–92; nitrogen, 92–
94; dephlogisticated air (ox-
ygen), 96–99
Gas silvestre, 64
Gay-Lussac, Joseph Louis, 135,
146–48, 197, 199, 201; and law
of combining gas volumes, 147,
153, 154, 158, 280
Geber. See Jabir ibn-Hayyan
Geber manuscripts, 38
Geissler, Heinrich, 323
Germanium, discovery of, 166
Germer, Lester Halbert, 369, 376
Germ theory of disease, 398
Gibbs, Oliver Wolcott, 264, 265
Glass: as early manufactured
product, 12–13; blowing, inven-